Water Production Using Nuclear Energy

# WATER PRODUCTION
# USING
# NUCLEAR ENERGY

*Edited by*
Roy G. Post and
Robert L. Seale

*Sponsored by*
Department of Nuclear Engineering,
The University of Arizona
Arizona Atomic Energy Commission
United States Atomic Energy Commission
American Nuclear Society

THE UNIVERSITY OF ARIZONA PRESS
TUCSON

# Preface

Under the direction of the Nuclear Engineering Department of The University of Arizona, a broad coverage of technical, legal, social and economic considerations of the use of nuclear energy in producing water, particularly by desalting, was incorporated into a comprehensive symposium in March, 1966.

We are most grateful for the sponsorship by the Arizona Atomic Energy Commission, the United States Atomic Energy Commission, and The University of Arizona student chapter of the American Nuclear Society. The latter represents the first sponsorship of an American Nuclear Society national topical meeting by a student chapter. We are particularly grateful to James T. Ramey, Commissioner, United States Atomic Energy Commission, Kenneth Holum, Assistant Secretary of the Interior, and John Cera, of the Division of Nuclear Education and Training of the United States Atomic Energy Commission, for their advice, encouragement, and assistance.

Without the much appreciated help of the session chairmen, Kenneth L. Geiser, Dr. Lawrence M Gould, Dr. Norman Hilberry, Dr. Donald H. White, Angelo Giambusso and Dr. Howard Coleman, the meeting could not have succeeded.

All papers were invited and the response of the authors, both in writing for such a diverse audience and in taking the time from busy schedules to present the papers and participate in the discussions, is gratefully acknowledged.

Roy G. Post
Robert L. Seale

# Foreword

The era in which it is our good fortune to live is characterized by dramatic advances in science and technology. We have begun to unravel the fundamental secrets of the life processes. We have learned to use rockets to explore space. And we are harnessing the energy of the atom for such peaceful purposes as the large-scale commercial production of electric power.

Scientific and technological achievements since the 1940's have made possible giant steps forward by industrial nations. These advances have also significantly enhanced the potential for improving the standards of living among the developing nations of the world, as well as conserving the resources of our planet for the use of future generations.

The population explosion and the marked increase in per capita water consumption are straining the water resources of industrial and industrializing nations. In the arid areas of the world, such as the rim of the Mediterranean, the Caribbean, and the Southwest of the North American continent, the dearth of water has become a limiting factor in the potential for the development of these regions. Thus, it has become important in many areas and most strata of economic and technological development to seek new sources of water or techniques of water utilization.

Among these sources, we are turning to the oceans of the world for fresh water. Desalting technology has made considerable progress since 1950, and is ready for scaling up for large-scale production of water from the seas. It is now time to coordinate our efforts, looking far beyond the present, in order to make possible the development of this technology to meet the demands of the future.

The use of nuclear energy to produce fresh water from the oceans represents the coupling of two emerging technologies -- nuclear energy and desalting. Putting these technologies to use is one of today's most fascinating concepts for development and one that holds great promise for answering the needs of an expanding civilization.

Successful development of nuclear desalting will not only significantly advance the peaceful utilization of the atom, but, as noted by Dr. Carillo-Flores of Mexico's National Commission for Nuclear Energy, it can substantially enhance the well-being and dignity of man. In the United States, we consider the expeditious development and scale-up of nuclear-desalting technology as an important national program. This program is being conducted as a joint effort by the Office of Saline Water, Department of the Interior, with full cooperation and participation by the Atomic Energy Commission. As President Johnson stated in his message to AEC of September 9, 1965:

> Our Government is proceeding with an aggressive program of nuclear desalting. We invite all countries to join with us in this effort. What we learn from this program will be shared with the world.

In this spirit of international cooperation we have joined with the International Atomic Energy Agency in conducting panels on the use of nuclear energy for desalting abroad, and in initiating a study of the feasibility of a large-scale nuclear desalting plant for the Mexico-Arizona-California area; and we have conducted joint studies into the needs and potential for nuclear desalting with Israel and the United Arab Republic.

This symposium on Water Production Using Nuclear Energy served an important and timely function in bringing together the latest ideas on nuclear desalting and in giving these ideas perspective by relating them to other important concepts in the broad field of water resource planning and development. The papers presented in these proceedings review not only the technical aspects of alternative approaches to water resource development, but also focus upon the significant economic, social, political and administrative issues which attend these approaches.

Compared to desalting, many of the alternate water resource development approaches described in the following papers have reached a relatively advanced stage of development. Only with concrete experience in the design, construction and operation of appropriate facilities can we hope to achieve a comparable level of confidence for nuclear desalting.

The success of this symposium is a tribute to the fine efforts of The University of Arizona, the American Nuclear Society and the Arizona Atomic Energy Commission. I highly recommend the excellent papers presented in this volume. Each of the eminently qualified participants is to be commended for his stimulating and cogent comments. From the diverse ideas, plans, studies, and active development projects discussed in these papers will evolve the technological basis for ensuring an abundant supply of fresh water for the future.

James T. Ramey
Commissioner
U. S. Atomic Energy Commission

# CONTENTS

## SECTION IV
## IMPACT OF NEW WATER SOURCES
### Donald H. White, Chairman

## SECTION V
## NUCLEAR REACTORS FOR WATER DESALTING
### Angelo Giambusso, Chairman

## SECTION VI

## SYSTEMS FOR WATER DESALTING
### Howard S. Coleman, Chairman

SECTION I

# WATER PROBLEMS
# OF NORTH AMERICA

Kenneth L. Geiser, Chairman
Arizona Atomic Energy Commission

# 1. The Atomic Energy Commission's Role
## In the Saline Water Program

James T. Ramey, Commissioner, U.S. Atomic Energy Commission

For several years now, different people have been setting forth
what they believe to be the proper role of the AEC and nuclear energy in the desalting program. The roles proposed have been
many and varied. Some of our friends, including those associated
with fossil fuels, have strongly suggested that the AEC might forget about desalting entirely, since the needs obviously could be
served by oil, coal and gas. In other words, they suggest the AEC
should simply be an observer of this rapidly developing technology.

Others have said that there is little if any role for nuclear energy until we have demonstrated specific requirements for intermediate and large-scale desalting plants. These individuals seem
to believe that the technology will be delivered to us by Aladdin's
genii when we need it. As many of you know, I have long con-
tended that the lead time for modern technology is such that we
simply cannot wait until requirements hit us. Of course, this situation is not unique to nuclear desalting -- the "Requirements
Merry-Go-Round" has plagued many undertakings in recent years.
All too often we are called upon for a "crash effort" to meet a requirement that had been swept under the rug as unjustifiable only
a few years previously. Many scientific advisors and budget people either have their heads in the sky or buried in the sand, and
then wonder why their vision is impaired.

At the other end of the spectrum, there have been some who
believe that the entire desalting program should have been assigned to the AEC. While this might appear to be a rather drastic
approach, the desalting efforts of the Soviet Union and the United
Kingdom are under their atomic energy programs. Just recently
in House Interior Committee hearings, it was mentioned -- perhaps in jest -- that the Office of Saline Water might well be assigned to the AEC and that Frank Di Luzio could then become one
of our Commissioners. While undoubtedly Frank could make an
outstanding contribution to any organization, and my associates
and I would welcome him, I am not sure that desalting -- in all of
its various aspects -- should be approached this way. Certainly
I have never favored this approach. Undoubtedly, the Department
of the Interior, which has long been recognized as our agency of
natural resources, could develop many good arguments against
such a proposal, especially in light of its fine work in water research and management.

1

Obviously there has to be some sort of organizational structure for the AEC and Interior to carry on this joint program. As many of you know, the AEC has, in some cases, worked out special arrangements with the user of a particular technology. In programs involving the Navy and the Space Agency, we have established joint offices with varying degrees of coordination and direction. I will have more to say later about how this concept might be applied to the desalting program.

### Our Concept of the AEC Role

What then is the role of the AEC and nuclear energy in the saline water program? I believe that our responsibility can best be broken down into two main areas. The first, as presented in the Report to the President on desalting in 1964, is to conduct a continuing program of reactor development to provide appropriate nuclear energy sources to meet the near-term and long-range energy needs for intermediate and large-scale desalting applications. In this effort, as in our other reactor developments, we must constantly bear in mind the matter of economics.

The second main area is the coupling of the desalting and nuclear energy technologies. This in itself necessitates a very close working arrangement to insure that interface approaches are mutually acceptable and that the two technologies are compatible. As you know, both nuclear energy and desalting are based in large part on common scientific disciplines and we believe that the knowledge that the AEC and the nuclear industry have acquired over the years can be valuable to the desalting effort. I believe our experience in the benefits of scale to achieve improved economics is of particular importance to desalting.

### BACKGROUND OF THE PROGRAM

### Early AEC Interest

Now, let me give you some brief history to show you how the AEC first got started in desalting work. For nearly two decades, the Commission, in cooperation with industry, has been developing nuclear energy systems for peaceful purposes. A considerable effort has been devoted to advancing reactor technology for the generation of electricity, but nuclear energy for process applications has not been overlooked.

In response to a request from Senator Anderson* for possible peaceful uses of nuclear energy in 1955, Dr. R. Philip Hammond

---

*At that time, Senator Anderson was Chairman, Joint Congressional Committee on Atomic Energy.

-- of Los Alamos Scientific Laboratory -- indicated that the economics of large-size reactors could help make desalting an attractive source of fresh water.  In 1959, plans were formulated by the
AEC and the Department of the Interior for a sea water distillation
plant using a small process heat reactor.  The reactor portion of
this project did not go forward because of siting difficulties,  but
Interior subsequently built its highly successful Point Loma demonstration plant.

In 1962, Dr. Hammond -- who by then had moved to Oak
Ridge -- recalculated some of his earlier work and published the
results in conjunction with the Oak Ridge National Laboratory.
This work attracted the attention of the Presidential Office of
Science and Technology and others, including Congressman
Aspinall, who is chairman of the House Committee on Interior and
Insular Affairs.  Dr. Wiesner, then the President's Science Ad-
visor, appointed an ad hoc task group to investigate the thesis that
energy costs from very large reactors would be low enough to
produce fresh water economically from sea water by distillation.
Two members of the Atomic Energy Commission -- the late Dr.
Robert E. Wilson and myself -- served on that task force.  There
was also representation from the Office of Saline Water, the Bureau of Reclamation, and the Federal Power Commission.  We
had meetings for more than a year, and issued our final report in
March 1964. [1]    This report, while less optimistic than Dr.
Hammond and the Oak Ridge Group essentially supported this position.

### Report to the President

After receiving the favorable report on the OST study, President Johnson in June 1964, requested the Department of the Interior, in close collaboration with the AEC, to develop a plan for an
aggressive and imaginative program to advance progress in large
scale desalting of sea water.  The requested program was prepared by the Department of the Interior and the Atomic Energy
Commission, working closely together, and was submitted to the
President in September 1964.

### THE AEC PROGRAM TODAY

The program that the AEC is currently undertaking in cooperation with the Office of Saline Water is an extension of the program recommended to the President.  This program was outlined
in detail in the paper Nuclear Energy -- Potential for Desalting
which my associates and I presented at the First International
Symposium on Desalination last October. [2]    Today, I would like
to discuss the progress we have made since that time.

## Specific Engineering Studies

As many of you recall our Florida Keys and Intermediate studies provided an assessment of dual purpose nuclear plants in sizes below those considered by the OST task force. [3,4]  We quickly recognized from the Florida Keys study that studies for specific applications to be of maximum value must involve the potential user, and subsequent studies of this nature have been conducted as cooperative ventures with the prospective users.

One of the major achievements during the past several months has been the completion of such a cooperative engineering study with the Metropolitan Water District of Southern California. [5]  Under the proposed arrangements between the local power utilities and MWD, water costs in the range of 22¢ per 1,000 gallons are estimated to be possible at the plant. Discussions are in progress which hopefully will lead to a large dual-purpose nuclear plant capable of producing 1,800 megawatts of electricity (gross) and 150 million gallons of water per day.

Another important cooperative engineering study involving the Government of Israel has also been completed since the Symposium. [6]  The results of this study are now being analyzed by the various Israeli groups concerned with that nation's water and power problems and it appears that a project of significant benefit may result from this study.

A third study has recently been started in cooperation with the International Atomic Energy Agency (IAEA) and our good neighbors to the south. While it is perhaps premature to speculate on the results of this study it appears that very large dual purpose nuclear plants on the Pacific coast or the Gulf of California may be particularly attractive for the vast arid region of Mexico and the southwestern United States. The water quantities from such plants to be studied may well be in the billion gallon per day range.

## General Technology Studies

Much of the AEC's program in desalting has been assigned to the ORNL for implementation. The long and effective experience of this laboratory in conducting technical programs in cooperation with industry is particularly helpful in our desalting effort.

The program which we have under way at Oak Ridge is directed at supporting the near-term and long-range application of nuclear power to desalting. For near term application, such as MWD and Israel, the program is primarily concerned with making a background of information available regarding the technical and economic characteristics of various coupling arrangements, and the control and operational flexibility of dual-purpose nuclear desalting plants. While these studies are at various stages of completion certain preliminary findings can be reported here.

Since the very large non-condensing turbines that are expected to be required for dual-purpose plants have not been built, there is no reliable price data available. A preliminary investigation of the costs of back pressure machines relative to condensing machines has indicated however, that large back pressure turbines should cost significantly less than comparably rated condensing turbines. A more detailed investigation of the cost of back pressure turbines is currently underway.

Several methods of achieving operating flexibility, that is the ability to produce varying amounts of water and power in dual-purpose plants, have been under consideration. One of the most promising techniques involves the ability to operate a given turbine over a range of back pressure steam conditions, depending on the amounts of water and power production desired. For example, it has been found that power and water production may be varied by as much as 25% through the flexibility inherent in back-pressure turbines. It appears this flexibility could be achieved with only modest increases in the turbine capital cost.

For long-range desalting applications such as those expected in the 1980's and 1990's, the ORNL program is primarily concerned with defining, developing and demonstrating those nuclear reactor concepts best suited for desalting applications consistent with advancements in desalting technology. Toward this end we have initiated a series of studies of the practicability of extrapolating the sodium cooled fast breeder reactor, the high temperature gas cooled reactor, the heavy water moderated organic cooled reactor and the boiling water reactor to 10,000 MWt single unit sizes. The contractor's studies of the HTGR and FBR have recently been completed and both conclude that 10,000 MWt single unit would be practicable. The results of these studies are currently being given detailed technical review by ORNL and the Commission staff.

An investigation of the siting problems associated with large dual-purpose systems is currently being conducted. Two possibilities for using the desalting plant evaporator volume to supplement reactor containment are being studied. In one of these methods, the evaporator is used as a pressure suppression system to reduce the pressure requirements of the reactor containment vessel. In the other method, the evaporator plant would be used to enclose the reactor vessel, thus providing multiple containment.

While not specifically part of our desalting effort, a study of off-shore siting of reactors has been initiated under our safety program. The particular concept being studied is a submerged caisson which may provide favorable safety features and be of strong interest to nuclear desalting installations.

ORNL for a number of years has been used by OSW in support of its research into the basic properties of water. More recently, the ORNL capabilities have been applied to the development and engineering of certain water desalting processes. This joint use of ORNL further strengthens coordination of the AEC-OSW efforts, especially in the large nuclear desalting plant area. ORNL also serves as a technical support group to our headquarters program offices. In addition to Dr. Hammond, Dr. Floyd Culler and others are contributing to the Oak Ridge work under the able direction of Dr. Alvin Weinberg.

## The AEC's Role in the International Desalting

As the recent International Symposium in Washington illustrated, desalting is an international field of endeavor. On the nuclear side we have looked to the International Atomic Energy Agency (IAEA) as a focal point for coordinating and disseminating the technology which the Agency and its member nations develop. The Agency has been very beneficial in this regard already, in convening several panels on the uses of nuclear energy for desalting. A special panel to review costing procedures for dual-purpose nuclear plants is scheduled to be held next month in Vienna and representatives from the AEC, ORNL and OSW will attend. Agency representatives have also served as observers in the Israel study which I mentioned earlier and have joined our technical personnel in visits to the UAR and Tunisia. Also, the U. S. - Mexico study is being conducted under the auspices of the International Atomic Energy Agency, and the Agency is providing the chairman and technical secretary for the study team.

Other activities in which we have been involved include our cooperative exchange agreement with the Soviet Union and discussions with representatives of Italy and the Government of Greece. Just last week, the AEC, along with the Department of State and Interior, met with Professor Delyannis of Greece and discussed arrangements whereby our experts would work with theirs in assessing various means (including nuclear desalting) for solving the water and power problems in Athens.

I could identify many other areas of international activities in which we have participated, but I believe it will suffice to say this morning that the world is looking to the U. S. for advancements in desalting and nuclear technology, and we have a commitment to work with our friends abroad in sharing our technology for the benefits of all mankind.

To implement this commitment, we have established within the Federal government an Interdepartmental Committee to weigh the role of desalting abroad and I am privileged to serve on this

committee as the AEC representative. As many of you also recall, President Johnson announced the "Water for Peace" program last October. This program is expected to provide technical assistance to all countries in solving their water problems and
to be beneficial to people throughout the world.

## JOINT OFFICE POSSIBILITIES

I mentioned earlier that in some AEC programs we have established joint offices. This approach probably provides one of
the better means for coordinating a major program in which more
than one agency is involved. While our experience with joint offices has been varied, we have had good success in such arrangements with the Navy and the Space Agency.

With respect to the desalting program, I am inclined to think
we will want to give careful consideration to establishment of a
joint office at some future time. At present, there is excellent
cooperation between the OSW and the AEC. But, as the program
moves into the hardware stage, there will be a heavy involvement
in money and manpower both by AEC and OSW, and at that point
we will need to reexamine the entire operation. Establishing a
joint office will involve careful consideration of timing, personal-
ities, and the general circumstances surrounding the program at
that point. I personally think the time is approaching when the
joint-office concept will warrant serious study.

## CONCLUSION

I hope these remarks will give you a better idea of the AEC's
role in the desalting program. It is a role of helping -- helping
to provide a more economical energy source by a program of
planned development . . . helping by sharing our technology, our
resources, and our experience. By these efforts, we can help
assure an ample supply of energy and water for future generations.

As President Johnson stated in his message to the Third International Conference on the Peaceful Uses of Atomic Energy in
1964:
> The time is coming when a single desalting plant, powered
> by nuclear energy, will produce hundreds of millions of gal-
> lons of fresh water -- and large amounts of electricity --
> every day.

Our government is proceeding with an aggressive program
on nuclear desalting. What we learn in this program will be
shared with other nations.

We in the Atomic Energy Commission believe that this time
is not too far away and that our efforts will hasten the day when

the world can enjoy an almost limitless supply of power and a virtually inexhaustible source of fresh water.

## NOTES

1   Office of Science and Technology, Executive Office of the President, "An Assessment of Large Nuclear Powered Sea Water Distillation Plants" (March 1964)

2   James T. Ramey, John A. Swartout, William A. Williams, Jr., "Nuclear Energy -- Potential for Desalting," U. S. Atomic Energy Commission, Washington, D. C. (October 1965)

3   Burns and Roe, Inc., "Feasibility Study of a Dual Purpose Nuclear Reactor Power Plant for the Florida Keys," NYO-10719, U. S. Department of the Interior and U. S. Atomic Energy Commission, Washington, D. C. (March 1964)

4   Catalytic Construction Company and Nuclear Utilities Services Inc., "A Study of Desalting Plants (15 to 150 MGD) and Nuclear Power Plants (200 to 1500 MWT) for Combined Water and Power Production," NYO-3316-1, U. S. Department of the Interior and U. S. Atomic Energy Commission, Washington, D. C. (September 1964)

5   Bechtel Corporation, "Engineering and Economic Feasibility Study for a Combination Nuclear Power and Desalting Plant," TID-22330 Volumes 1, 2, and 3, The Metropolitan Water District of Southern California, Los Angeles, California, U. S. Department of the Interior, U. S. Atomic Energy Commission, Washington, D. C. (December 1965)

6   Kaiser Engineers, "Engineering Feasibility and Economic Study for Dual-Purpose Electric Power-Water Desalting Plant for Israel," Report No. 66-1-RE, The Governments of Israel and the United States (The Department of the Interior and the Atomic Energy Commission) (January 1966)

## 2. Mexico's Hope for Nuclear Energy

Nabor Carillo Flores, Member, National Nuclear Energy Commission, Mexico

Twenty years ago when I was minding my own business in soil
mechanics in Mexico City, our representative on the security
council said we had to have somebody representing us in both the
political organization in New York and witnessing the atomic experiments in Bikini. It was by chance that our government picked
three men: one is now one of the commissioners, another is here,
my friend Carlos Graef Fernandez, and I was the third. Don't
ask me why they wanted me to do this but they did. In the last 20
years it has been part of my duties to try to help to bring the
benefits of atomic energy to my country; but if I may, I will tell
you one of my first experiences. In 1946 we were taken to Bikini
for the atomic experiments. When we returned to Mexico, we
started to try to see what we could do in this field. Sometimes in
my country things take longer. I was younger and with a sense of
impatience for the government to get started, but little happened.
Finally, ten years ago we started with a program that was basically intended to educate young people, to train, and to look for
our resources in a methodical way. In the last ten years, after
the start of this program, one of the important fruits of this program has been to have a continuing stream of young people of
Mexican nationale to train abroad. Now one hundred and thirty-
three have been trained, sixty in the United States, and many of
them have gotten their degree in various aspects of nuclear engineering; thirty-five in the United Kingdom, eleven in France, and
the rest in various countries. These one hundred and thirty-three
men who have been trained are the base on which to build in coming years. We have been exploring our resources also, and this
exploration has been increased in recent years. In just the last
two years we have discovered one-half of our resources. Of
these, the uranium resources are the most important. Up to the
month of December our resources were estimated as 2,400,000
tons of uranium ore of various types with an average proportion
of uranium of 0.07. Mexico has long been considered as a country that is rich in fossil fuel reserves and that has been one of the
motivations for trying to maintain a certain prudent pace in what
is considered to be much more complicated - nuclear power. Our
reserves are estimated as follows:

Oil

465 million cubic meters, which, if we are going to use it at
the rate which we used it in 1964, will last 23 years. Mexico is a
strange nation because in the last few years although the

consumption has increased, each year the 23-year reserve has
kept more or less constant.  Each year we find we have enough
oil field reserves for another quarter century.

### Natural gas

If we compare it as the equivalent of oil, will be 326 million
cubic meters, which is equivalent to 24 years of the amount that
we spent in 1964.

### Coal

We have recently found large reserves of coal, 17 times
larger than the reserves in oil; that is, 8,400,000,000 tons equivalent to oil.  This coal is equivalent to a 3,800 year amount of
coal we used in 1964.  This means that in 1964 we used practically no coal.  Our total output of energy comes as 62% from oil,
30% natural gas, 6% in coal, and only 2% from hydroelectric
plants.  This is the situation when we started to try to develop
our nuclear power plants.  Two years ago, we had not started
really into this game -- we had not even a research reactor.

Two years ago, we were trying to convince our government
that before we could go into further adventures we should have a
research laboratory; and we started a program for a nuclear
center that I would like to describe to you.  The reactor, that we
have purchased for our nuclear center is a Triga Mark-3 reactor
with a one-megawatt steady power level and is capable of pulsing
officially to 3000 MW and unofficially to 5000 MW.  That is, for a
fraction of a second, it can produce all of the power that Mexico
is using now.  We have the potential in Mexico for generation of
5000 MW of electrical power in the whole republic.  Our nuclear
center was chosen basically for psychological reasons.  In some
people there was the fear that perhaps a nuclear center might be
dangerous or subject to a dangerous accident, so it had to be taken
out of the Valley of Mexico, but not too far out.  We picked the site
for both technical and psychological reasons, but I would say primarily psychological.  Yet, it has the advantage that it is part of
the national park, so we can probably extend without much trouble
from speculators around us.  It is a lovely site.  It is 20 miles
west of Mexico City.  It has plenty of water, very good communi-
cations, a railroad nearby, and it is just outside of the Valley of
Mexico.  The only trouble with this nuclear center of ours is that
it is 10,000 feet high.  We will have plenty of cosmic radiation.  I
must say that we had very many problems two years ago, including problems with the people of the area.  There were some poor
villages around, very nice people but who were scared, and who
were using this land for grazing.  When it is wet, it is a very
beautiful sight.  It is a sight that is very difficult for some foreign
friends to imagine as being part of Mexico.  One of the things that
we have achieved is to help the people in that area, and many of
them are now working for us.  The ground-breaking ceremony

took place on July 3, 1964.  We expect to have the reactor building
finished by the end of the year or early 1967.  We have a tandem
Van de Graaff Machine 12 mev, and the two machines -- the accelerator and the Triga reactor -- are the two main laboratories that
we have for our nuclear center.  We expect to grow, but this is
what we have as of the first part of our program.  We expect our
nuclear center to be a laboratory that will be used not only for the
atomic mission, but also for the University of Mexico, for the
Polytechnical Institute, and for the various universities in our
country.  The reactor has three main purposes, and this is why
we picked the Triga.  I am very happy to hear Dr. Weaver telling
that we have picked a very good laboratory reactor that they have
had several years' experience with.  I was very happy to have his
support for our choice, since we had so much difficulty in deciding
at the time.  I would also like to acknowledge our gratitude to our
friend, Jim Ramey and members of the AEC who were most helpful when we needed them in trying to make the right choice as well
as getting the facilities from the AEC and from the export bank in
order to finance the program.  As I was saying, the Triga is going
to be used for training, for research, and for service isotope production.

The accelerator has two purposes -- one for basic research
into the nature of the nucleus of the atom.  The other for training.
We have a few young people who have done very distinguished
work, we are happy to report.  This will also be a laboratory to
produce experimental physicists that we are in bad need of in
Mexico.  So those are the five main purposes of the first step of
our nuclear center; and we have appointed as director of the nuclear center Dr. Carlos Graef Fernandez, who I have brought
with me today.

Now, outside of this nuclear center program we are highly
enthusiastic these days of the possibility for nuclear power associated with desalination.  Up to a few years ago, as you well
know, this nuclear desalination program was taken with a grain
of salt, but now in the last 18 months, I would like to say, progress has been really very important.  My government gave me
instructions, as you have heard, to sign October 7, 1965, what
might be a historical agreement for a joint study group under the
auspices of the United Nations, to try to help four states:  two
Mexican states and two American states.  The two Mexican states
are Sonora and Baja California, and the two American states are
Arizona and California.  This is, indeed, a most ambitious
project.  It may be the most ambitious in the world.  We are hop-
ing very much that this will prove to be a landmark in the progress of nuclear energy.

Ten years ago I remember when we went to Geneva, and we
listened to the late Professor Bhabha; he was highly optimistic in
those days of the possibility of fusion.  You might say that ten
years ago we were very optimistic about the possibility of burning

the oceans.  Now we are not so optimistic, but I think this is just
a delay.  My own personal opinion is that the problems will be
solved.  Even so, if we are not too optimistic about the possibility of burning the ocean, I think we are now very optimistic about
the possibility of drinking the oceans; and this might be a very
important consequence of the work that is now being sponsored.
So this idea of having a large plant on the Gulf of California to
help solve the problems of the two countries, in my opinion, is in
great hands.  By combining our interests and our efforts, I think
that the particular conditions in which we have a very rich neighbor to the north that can cooperate, for instance, is to our advantage in solving problems which with a little nation like Peru we
might not be able to solve.  If it can be mutually effective, then
we have the atom not only for peace but the atom for real friend-
ship.  And that is the great hope we share with our colleagues.

But we have another problem that I will just touch lightly because I don't want to steal the show from my friend, Dr. Graef,
who will discuss in more detail.  I will try to present this problem, but I would like for him to present to you the possibility of
solution.

It is the problem of Mexico City.  I always have my misgiv-
ings¯in doing this.  As I said before, my former training, if you
can call it that, was as a soil mechanic.  Now, I am having a love
affair with Nuclear Energy.  In Mexico City sometimes I feel that
what I am trying to do is to introduce my wife to my friend, and I
don't know if this is a good idea.  I do believe, however, that the
atom can be of extreme importance in trying to help us to solve
the dramatic problem in Mexico City.  I am going to talk on this
subject at Harvard University on April 21, 1966.  One of the suggested titles was "The Atom Versus the Sinking of Mexico City."
That doesn't sound very technical or scientific, and yet that is
exactly what is needed.  Figure 1 is a picture taken in 1910 in
Mexico City.  You can see in the first floor a curve that shows
you the sinking of the building when it was first built.  By comparing the vertical elevation, you can see that it sank about 6 feet
back in 1792.  This is a classical photo to show a unique soil in
the world.  The soil in Mexico City has seven parts of water per
volume, one part of solids; only one part of solids clay to seven
volumes of water.  So that all of the buildings that are not very
carefully designed sink a large amount as anybody who has been
there knows.  This soil is highly compressible, but, at the same
time, the pores for water are so minute that the water cannot
flow rapidly so that even though it does compress a lot for a certain length of time, it's rather slow process.  Just as a rule of
thumb, you must consider that buildings sink for about 20 years.
For the first five years the effects are serious, and then they decrease.  Here they carried the construction very slowly when
they realized that the building was sinking and curving.  You can
see that the roof is flat while the first floor is curved.  That was
the school of engineering in 1910 complete with 1910 transporta-

Figure 1.  Sinkage in Building
Indicated by Structural Curve

Figure 2.  Demolition by Sinkage
of Next Door Building

tion and styles.  Unfortunately, we don't have those carriages now;
I think that the style is also very commendable.

Figure 2 is an example that in the thirties was quite common.
In the thirties, there was a boom in the construction of high buildings.  Here you see they had a building eight stories high when it
sank and demolished the one next door.  This is a problem that
happens everyday in Mexico City.  Many engineers make their living, assisting one or the other.  In one case the man on the right
was trying to collect the whole cost of the building from the man
on the left, and the man on the left was trying to prove that the
man on the right had a very poor building.  Now this building was
next to my office at the time, and it was a very funny story.  The
man on the left, the owner, lost this case and he had to pay for
the whole building so he was scared and he ordered his engineer
to remove the upper three stories and leave only five.  He did that
when the building was more than five years old and couldn't do any
more harm.  He paid for the consulting and didn't use it.

There are wells near Mexico City in the old basin of Lake
Texcoco where we still have artesian water.  At the beginning of
the century we had artesian water below Mexico City; but about 30
years ago, in 1936 to be exact, we started to pump water because
the city started to explode.  Thirty years ago the population was
1-million people or thereabouts; now it is 6 1/2 million, so that
requirements for water for Mexico City and for industry in Mexico
have increased in an explosive way.  We have reduced the pressures under the city; and this loss of pressure, as you will read
from Dr. Graef in greater detail, is the reason why the city is
sinking at a rate of one foot a year.  You can imagine what the
effects of this sinking one foot per year can be.  It is estimated
that through the government of Mexico plus the city in one way or
another, we have paid, in the past twelve years, an average of
$240,000/day.  A contour line of the settlement through the central
part of Mexico City, taken in 1959, shows sinking of Alameda
Park, the cathedral, and the National Palace as 5 1/2 meters, 5
meters, and 6 meters, respectively.  There is a bending of all
colonial buildings in the area close to the palace.  That makes this
of tremendous importance to the government itself.  You can see
that the sinking is not uniform.  There are two reasons why the
sinking is not uniform.  One is that clay consolidated by a heavy
load by a precolonial Aztec pyramid or something is stronger than
the uncompacted clay.  Also, many of the buildings are on piles
that go through to a layer of strong materials.  Those piles do not
allow the clay to consolidate; and buildings on piles are coming up
and disturbing their neighbors.  An example from files which I
kept as a consultant will be of interest.  Riveted structures are
severely damaged by the level subsidence in Mexico City.  Figure
3 shows how rivets often look when we dismantle or repair a riveted structure.  Many buildings of riveted construction are completely destroyed or are in critical shape.  Figure 4 is another
example of the irregular sinking.  The building has piles up to this
point but no piles from here on.  So the part without piles follows
the sinking of the city, but the part on piles is starting to go up.
You see that the trees haven't had time to recover their vertical
attitude, since the movement is quite fast, one foot per year.
Subsidence can be prevented by consolidation.  An old Aztec temple, very near the national palace, has affected many of the buildings in this part of the city.  In the case of one monument structure which is on piles, we have had an interesting problem.  Where
the piles end, we had to change the concrete to asphalt to make the
transition more flexible.  The difference in elevation between
these parts is thirteen feet now.  This visible part is sinking
faster than the hidden part, which carries vertical load, which
means that the piles carried a greater load from the sinking of the
city than from the weight of the building itself.  In designing piles,
you can neglect the weight of the building, but you cannot neglect
the sinking.

This is a very quick presentation of a very dramatic problem.
If you can consider that the governments of Mexico are spending

Figure 3. Distorted Rivet    Figure 4. Sinkage Where No Piles

$240,000/day, it means that the water that we are pumping from
the soil in Mexico City is one of the most expensive water sources
in the world.  If ground rules are important for desalination economics, never are ground rules more important than in Mexico
City.  I will not discuss our hopes for solving our problems, but
I will just try to close by following the suggestion of Professor
Hilberry that introduced my talk.  It was to be called "Mexico's
Hope" not "Mexico's Probe for Nuclear Energy," so I will try to
say a few words in the line of Mexico's hope.  You know nuclear
science in the last 20 years has produced a very important change
in the philosophy of humanity.  There are, of course, still many
people who, if they could, would change the course of history, and
fission would never have been discovered.  Radiation, as you
know, is very often excessively condemned without any idea of
order of magnitude.  Before the war a certain amount of radiation
was considered a virtue in mineral water and now, of course,
anything radioactive is considered dangerous always.  This is
true for many people, even nuclear scientists.  Of course, this
fear is easy to understand, when one considers that if the first
application of electricity had been the electric chair, many people
would be reluctant to have their homes wired.  But for better or
for worse, thanks to science, the world has experienced a very
important change in philosophy and in attitude.  Now for the first
time in history perhaps, we see that mere material strength is
not the guarantee for survival because the hole in our armour
seems to be changing in a good direction.  The rules of the game
give more value not to desert earth but to survive on earth.  The
rules of the game.  As Professor Libby said may prove that the
most important peaceful use of the atom is not even desalination;
the most important peaceful use of the atom is peace itself.  This
might give background for a new philosophy for a new world which
is really our hope.  Thanks to science, there will be new rules
for the game, not among philosophers and priests, but among pol-
iticians in which the basis for playing will be respect for the dignity of the nations and dignity of the people.

# 3. North American Water Resources

H. E. Dregne, Professor of Soils, New Mexico State University

Increasing demands are being made upon our water supplies as the world's population expands and the standard of living rises. In nearly every part of the North American continent people face a water problem of some kind, either of quality, quantity, or both. This occurs despite the fact that annual precipitation and ground water supplies on the continent greatly exceed foreseeable water demands.

## PRECIPITATION AND SURFACE WATER

Air movement from the oceans to the land brings enough moisture each year to cover the continent to a depth of about 150 inches if it were all precipitated as rain.[1] Of this 150 inches, about 25 inches falls as rain or snow. A little more than 8 inches of the 25 appears as surface stream flow, the remainder returning to the atmosphere by evaporation and transpiration. These 8 inches represent the renewable water supply for the continent. Only about 50 per cent of the renewable supply, however, can be termed "disposable" water because of the need to maintain sufficient stream flow for sewage disposal, navigation, hydroelectric power generation, and fisheries.

Estimated annual precipitation and surface water supplies in North America are indicated, by countries, in Table I. It should be noted that the figures in the table [1,2,3] represent estimates based on fragmentary data that are subject to variable interpretation. Stream flow data are reasonably reliable for all but the unsettled area of Canada; the other data are no better than rough approximations. The settled area of Canada refers to a strip from east to west across southern Canada, where virtually the entire population is concentrated in one-third of the country.

Inspection of Table I makes it apparent that the relation of stream flow to precipitation varies from country to country, just as it does within countries. Canada's high stream flow percentage is typical of humid regions. In arid regions, such as southern Arizona, stream runoff usually amounts to less than 10 per cent of total precipitation. The 12 per cent figure for Mexico is lower than would be expected under an average annual precipitation of 28 inches.

The disposable water supply represents the amount of water

that can be considered to be available for continued use for the future if there is no significant increase due to desalination, weather modification, or runoff.  It includes discharge into streams of
ground water that comes to the surface.  Table II shows how much
disposable water there was for each person in the three countries
in 1963.  Canada was in by far the most favorable position, for
both the settled area and for the nation as a whole.  Mexico, with
a population of one-fifth that of the United States, has only one-
half as much water per person.

These figures are deceptive because of the uneven distribution of water supplies within each country.  Large Canadian cities
in the east already face the problem of obtaining adequate stream
flow for waste disposal.  Projections for 1990 point to a critical
situation by that time unless storage and distribution facilities are
increased greatly.  The same is even more true in the eastern
United States.  Mexico has pollution problems in its southeastern
humid area but the critical section is the semiarid Valley of Mexico, where Mexico City is located, and the northern states.

## GROUND WATER

Ground water supplies of North America are enormous, by
any estimates.  The figures in Table III are based on the calculation by Nace [4]  that the continents of the world are underlain,
within one-half mile of the land surface, by ground water equal to
a layer of water 105 feet deep (Table III).  As with surface water,
ground water is distributed unevenly.  Igneous rocks generally
contain small amounts; large amounts are more likely to be found
in sand, gravel, and limestone formations.  The figures given in
Table III include both saline and fresh water.  Fresh water, fortunately, frequently overlies saline water, but the reverse often
occurs, and fresh and saline water aquifers may be intermixed.
U. S. supplies probably are underestimated because of the very
large volume of saline water found under the coastal plain bordering the Atlantic Ocean and the Gulf of Mexico.  Data on ground
water supplies are incomplete, to say the least.  Primary emphasis has been placed thus far upon changes in ground water levels
rather than in total ground water resources.  If we are to make
the maximum use of ground water, we must know the interrela-
tions of ground water, surface water, and precipitation.  The hy-
drologic cycle involves all water, not just atmospheric and surface water.  Ground water is mined in the High Plains of Texas
and New Mexico, where the supply is finite; it is a renewable resource in the Rocky Mountains of North America and elsewhere in
the humid regions.

## WATER REQUIREMENTS

Total water resources in North America, including precipitation and stored ground water, exceed foreseeable water demands.

## TABLE I

### Precipitation and Surface Water Supplies of North America

| | Total annual precipitation acre feet | Average annual streamflow acre feet | Disposable water, acre feet | Stream flow as per cent of precipitation |
|---|---|---|---|---|
| | (millions of acre feet) | | | |
| Canada | | | | |
| Unsettled area | 3,300 | 1,600 | 800 | |
| Settled area | 1,600 | 770 | 385 | |
| Total | 4,900 | 2,370 | 1,185 | 48 |
| United States | 5,780 | 1,520 | 750 | 26 |
| Mexico | 1,230 | 147 | 75 | 12 |
| North America | 11,910 | 4,037 | 2,010 | 34 |

Estimated average annual precipitation:
Canada - 20 inches, United States - 30 inches, Mexico - 28 inches,
North America - 25 inches

## TABLE II

### Per Person Disposable Water Supply in in North America 1963

| | Acre feet/ year/person | Gallons/day/ person |
|---|---|---|
| Canada | | |
| Settled area | 190 | 171,000 |
| All Canada | 590 | 531,000 |
| United States | 4 | 3,600 |
| Mexico | 2 | 1,800 |

Estimated population:   Canada, 20,000,000;
United States, 190,000,000;
Mexico 40,000,000

## TABLE III

### Ground Water Supplies of North America

| | Within 2,640 feet of land surface, acre feet |
|---|---|
| Canada | 257,000,000,000 |
| United States | 246,000,000,000 |
| Mexico | 51,000,000,000 |
| Total | 554,000,000,000 |

Despite this, critical water shortages are prevalent or imminent
in many parts of the continent. Studies made by the U. S. Senate
Select Committee on National Water Resources have been instruc-
tive for not only the United States but also for Canada and Mexico.
These studies show that, for the United States, water use will double in the 20 years from 1960 to 1980 and almost double again by
the year 2000 (Table IV). [5]    By 1980 nearly all of the disposable
water supply of the nation (750 billion acre feet) will be utilized.
Further expansion in use will depend upon reuse of stream flow;
mining of stored ground water; desalination of ground and surface
waters; increase in precipitation (weather modification) reduction
in water losses by evapotranspiration; increase in runoff; and re-
distribution of continental water supplies. Mining of stored
ground water is an unacceptable long-range objective because it
leads to the inevitable death of whole communities. The Lubbock
irrigated area of Texas faces the sobering fact that annual recharge to the ground water supply upon which it is wholly dependent is only 4 per cent of the withdrawal. Sooner or later, the water will be gone, and the prosperous agricultural economy of that
section of the High Plains will go with it. Deeper and deeper
wells, along with desalination, will defer the day of reckoning,
but that day is certain to come unless some means are devised to
recharge the ground water supply or to bring surface water in
from distant regions. The same prospect faces many other areas
in Canada, the United States, and Mexico. Artificial ground water
recharge, which is being done in many areas of the U. S., is only
1. 5 per cent of withdrawals by wells. [5]

TABLE IV

Water Use in the United States, All Purposes

| Year | Total use, millions of acre feet | Municipal use per person, gallons/day |
|------|------|------|
| 1960 | 350 | 147 |
| 1980 | 700 | 185 |
| 2000 | 1,250 | 225 |

The total perspective of water use in the United States in 1960
is shown in Table V. [1]    Irrigation and industrial demands accounted for 92 per cent of the total; public and rural use (largely
domestic) accounted for only 8 per cent. By 1980 and 2000, industrial demand in the U. S. is expected to be about 65 per cent of
the total [5] and 85 per cent of the total for Canada [2] industrial
requirements probably will be less in Mexico. Nearly 20 per cent
of the water used in 1960 came from wells, and 65 per cent of that
was used for irrigation. Ground water use in the 17 western
states amounts to 90 per cent of total U. S. use, most of it for
irrigation.

Water demand data do not reflect the depletion of water supplies by different users.  Industry's principal need for water is for cooling and waste disposal, and only a small fraction of such water is actually lost to further use (Table VI). [5]   Domestic use largely is nonconsumptive except for losses incurred by evapotranspiration from lawns and parks.  An additional loss of unknown but sometimes considerable magnitude occurs in leaky city water distribution systems.  The greatest water consumer, by far, is irrigation agriculture, due to transpiration by plants and evaporation from soil surfaces, reservoirs, and canals.  An unknown amount of water diverted for irrigation is lost by seepage from canals and by deep percolation of excess water applied to fields.  This water, accounting for as much as 40 per cent of the total consumed, is not necessarily lost but may recharge ground water reservoirs and be stored for future use.  Ground water recharge by this means is an important factor in many valleys of the Southwest and in the High Plains.

TABLE V

Annual Use of Water in the United States, 1960
Excluding Waterpower

| Type of Use | Total withdrawn, acre feet/year | | Percent |
|---|---|---|---|
| Public supplies | 19,000,000 | | 7 |
| Rural use | 3,400,000 | | 1 |
| Irrigation | | | |
| Delivered to farms | 90,700,000 | 34 | |
| Lost from canals | 32,500,000 | 12 | |
| Total irrigation | 123,200,000 | | 46 |
| Self-supplied industrial | 123,200,000 | | 46 |
| Total | 268,800,000 | | |
| Total renewable supply | 1,520,000,000 | | |
| Total disposable supply | 750,000,000 | | |

TABLE VI

Water Consumption in the U.S.

| Use | Water Consumption | |
|---|---|---|
| | Per cent of total withdrawn | Annual acre feet |
| Domestic | 10 | 2,230,000 |
| Industrial | 2 | 2,450,000 |
| Irrigation | 75 | 92,000,000 |
| Total | | 96,680,000 |

## WATER QUALITY

Water quality problems are at least as great as water supply problems.  Irrigation is responsible for quality deterioration in the form of increasing amounts of dissolved salts as water is applied to fields and saline drainage water returns to the river or ground water reservoir.  An example of salinity changes throughout the course of a river is given in Table VII. [6]  The first major diversion of Rio Grande water in New Mexico occurs between Otowi Bridge and San Marcial in the Albuquerque area.  Other major diversions occur below Elephant Butte, Leasburg Dam and El Paso.  Each time there is a diversion for irrigation, the water supply is depleted and its quality deteriorates until at Fort Quitman the water is unusable for people, animals, or irrigation.

TABLE VII

Salinity of Rio Grande Water, 1963

| Station | Stream flow, acre feet | Salinity Conductivity ECx10° | Salinity Parts per million |
|---|---|---|---|
| Otowi Bridge, N. M. | 425,520 | 367 | 235 |
| San Marcial, N. M. | 266,641 | 705 | 477 |
| Elephant Butte, N. M. | 509,278 | 630 | 390 |
| Leasburg Dam, N. M. | 465,460 | 800 | 515 |
| El Paso, Texas | 263,711 | 1,322 | 875 |
| Fort Quitman, Texas | 23,361 | 5,815 | 4,000 |

Domestic use leads to sewage pollution, and the case of Chicago and Cleveland has been well publicized.  Industrial pollution introduces some of the most intractable water quality control problems in the form of stable organic and inorganic compounds.  They include chemical wastes, petrochemicals, salt brines, acids, sludges, and radioactive materials.  To make matters worse, about 400 new chemical substances are produced each year by industry in the U. S.  Many of these find their way into water supplies, and what to do about them is a perplexing problem.

For the continent as a whole, sediment pollution may well be the most costly problem we face.  Suspended soil fills stream channels, estuaries, and reservoirs, causes damage to power turbines and pumping equipment, plugs water filters, and reduces light for aquatic plants.  Sediment loads are estimated to be 700 times as much as sewage loads in U. S. streams. [5]  Siltation is as much of a problem for the Potomac River Basin in the humid region as it is for the Colorado River Basin in the arid region.  Figure 1 illustrates the sedimentation problem in an arid region [7]  Elephant Butte Reservoir on the Rio Grande has lost 20 per cent of its storage capacity in the 50 years since it was completed, and many smaller reservoirs in the Southwest have lost their entire capacity to store water.

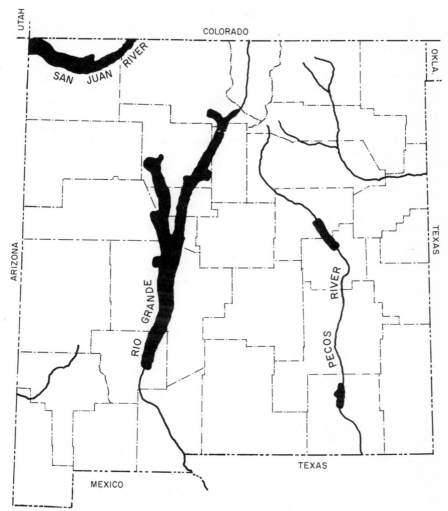

Figure 1.  Average suspended-sediment discharge in tons per year.
          Magnitude of discharge represented by width of bar (3
          mm. equals 10,000,000 tons)

Ground water pollution is a largely unknown condition but
there seems to be little doubt that we are contaminating these resources with biological and chemical pollutants that will be around
for a long time.  Cessation of pollution of surface waters usually,
in a matter of days or weeks, remedies the pollution problem as
the waters move downstream and into the oceans.  Ground water
pollution is much more serious because it may take ground water
reservoirs decades to recover, if they ever do, after pollution is
halted.

## WATER LOSSES

Excess water quality deterioration due to saline water en-
croachment, domestic and industrial waste disposal, and sediment
pollution may be considered as leading to water losses as long as
pollution control measures are uneconomic. With improved technology, such as that represented at this conference, polluted water will not be lost but will be used again and again. Direct and
irretrievable losses to the atmosphere result from the processes
of evaporation and transpiration. The magnitude of such losses in
the 17 western states from water surfaces and phreatophytes,
alone, is shown in Table VIII.[5, 9]  Evaporation causes a water
loss equal to 4 times the amount of water consumed for domestic
and industrial purposes in the entire U. S. in 1960. One estimate
of evaporation losses from Colorado River reservoirs predicts
that the advantage of having 50 million acre feet of proposed storage, as against the present 29 million acre feet, probably would
be offset by increased evaporation losses.[5]  It is no wonder that
the possibility of storing water underground, where evaporation
would not be a problem, is receiving widespread attention. Evaporation from low-value brush and desert lands in the arid regions
undoubtedly amounts to several hundreds of millions of acre feet
of water each year. Reduction in that water loss by sealing off the
soil surface and collecting the runoff could solve local water supply problems.

TABLE VIII

Annual Water Losses in the 17 Western States

| | |
|---|---|
| Evaporation from water surfaces | 21,000,000 acre feet |
| Evapotranspiration from phreatophytes | 25,000,000 acre feet |
| Total | 46,000,000 acre feet |

The water balance in the state of New Mexico is shown in
Table IX.[7] to indicate how water supplies are utilized in one
state. Four things stand out in the table: (1) the small part of the
precipitation that is recovered in streams, (2) the tremendous reserves of ground water, (3) the importance of ground water in the
water economy of the state, and (4) the great losses of water from
nonbeneficial evapotranspiration. Recovery of only 10 per cent of
the water lost by evapotranspiration from low-value rangelands
would more than double the surface water supply. Even if estimates of ground water supplies are high by a factor of 2, there
still is enough fresh water, alone, to provide for total 1964 state
demands for the next 800 years.

## FUTURE DEMANDS

Estimates of the ratio of surface water supply to water demand in the 17 western states for the years 1980 and 2000 are
presented in Table X.[8]  In these states both water demand and
water consumption are high, mainly due to irrigation require-

ments. A ratio of less than 1 indicates that water supplies are inadequate, within the region, to meet projected needs. The
favorable position of the Pacific Northwest and the critical position of the South Pacific region are evident. The Central Pacific
(central and northern California), Arkansas-Red Rivers, and
Western Gulf regions will about hold their own until 2000. The
others will be in varying degrees of trouble. Canadian regions
are expected to need from 5 per cent (Maritimes provinces) to 33
per cent (Prairie provinces) of their supply by 1990. [2]   Figures
for Mexico are not available.

TABLE IX

Water Balance for New Mexico, 1964
All Units are in Acre-Feet

| | | |
|---|---:|---:|
| Annual precipitation | | 90,000,000 |
| Precipitation recovered in streams | | 2,700,000 |
| Surface water consumed beneficially: | | |
| Irrigation | 868,000 | |
| Municipal and industrial | 20,000 | |
| Total | | 888,000 |
| Surface water consumed non-beneficially: | | |
| Evaporation from lakes and streams | 330,000 | |
| Use by phreatophytes, etc. | 830,000 | |
| Total | | 1,160,000 |
| Ground water supply: | | |
| Fresh water | 5,000,000,000 | |
| Saline water | 15,000,000,000 | |
| Total | | 20,000,000,000 |
| Ground water consumed beneficially: | | |
| Irrigation | 900,000 | |
| Municipal and industrial | 50,000 | |
| Rural | 16,000 | |
| Total | | 966,000 |
| Ground water recharge | | 700,000(?) |
| Surface and ground water consumed beneficially: | | 1,854,000 |
| Water consumed non-beneficially: | | |
| In waterways | 1,160,000 | |
| On rangelands | 42,300,000 | |
| Total | | 43,460,000 |

TABLE X

Projected Ratio of Surface Water Supply to
Demand, 17 Western States, 1980 and 2000

| Area | Water supply/water demand | |
|---|---|---|
| | 1980 | 2000 |
| Pacific Northwest | 4.7 | 3.8 |
| Central Pacific | 1.5 | 1.4 |
| South Pacific | 0.03 | 0.02 |
| Great Basin | 0.8 | 0.7 |
| Colorado | 0.5 | 0.5 |
| Upper Missouri | 0.8 | 0.7 |
| Arkansas-Red Rivers | 1.3 | 0.9 |
| Upper Rio Grande-Pecos River | 0.14 | 0.1 |
| Western Gulf | 1.4 | 0.9 |

Projections of this kind demonstrate why the southwestern states have cast envious eyes toward the Columbia River system. On January 27, 1966, the Colorado River Basin states of Colorado, Wyoming, Utah, New Mexico, Arizona, Nevada, and California finally agreed to stop fighting among themselves about water projects within the basin and, instead, to press for a study on ways to bring in additional water from the Columbia or Snake rivers. The eventual cost of importation of water may exceed $11 billion. The likelihood that Idaho, Oregon, and Washington will agree to diverting their water to the south, where it will be lost to them forever, appears remote, at present. Squabbles between the four upper basin states and the three lower basin states in the Colorado River Basin have been going on for years, with interminable lawsuits, after the original Colorado River compact was signed which shared the water equally between the upper and lower basins, with provision for supplying Mexico 1.5 million acre feet annually. The state of Colorado had problems enough to obtain agreement within the state for the Big Thompson project that takes Colorado River water through the continental divide and drops it into the Platte River, a tributary of the Missouri, in eastern Colorado. In view of U. S. troubles with river water allocation within and between states, persuading the Canadians to part with some of their excess water, as visioned in the imaginative North American Water and Power Alliance proposal, seems to be more than a modest challenge.

The discussion thus far in this paper has been centered on water resources and demands for broad areas. If we agree that total supplies are adequate, and we stop there, we are ignoring the reality that water resources are unevenly distributed in time and space. Unless action is taken to construct the necessary storage and distribution facilities, there is little consolation to Denver to know that 50 miles west of the city there is enough water in the Colorado River to meet its needs for decades. The Connecticut River at Hartford has an average flow of 17,000 cubic feet per second, but the dependable flow for 95 per cent of the year is only 3,160 cubic feet per second. [10]

## CONCLUSIONS

It has been said that our water problems would not be solved even if all the oceans were fresh water, because it still would be necessary to transport the water inland. In the heavily populated humid regions, pollution control and the construction of essentially local storage and distribution facilities must be accomplished to meet water demands. In the arid regions, pollution must be controlled and storage and distribution facilities must be constructed on a grand scale, as is shown in the California Water Plan to transport water hundreds of miles from the north to the south, if present supplies are to be utilized better. The only apparent alternatives to long-distance water transport are to (1) increase the proportion of atmospheric water that falls as precipitation, (2) improve pollution control, (3) increase and capture runoff from forest and range lands, (4) reduce nonbeneficial evapotranspiration, and (5) desalinize surface and ground waters. All of these alternatives offer great promise for the future but much remains to be done to bring them into realization. As of now, desalination and pollution control are the closest to success.

## NOTES

1.  Leopold, Luna B., and Walter B. Langbein, A Primer on Water, U. S. Government Printing Office, Washington, D. C., 1960

2.  Government of Canada, Resources for Tomorrow, Vol. I, Roger Duhamel, Ottawa, 1961

3.  Fernandez de Lara, Guillermo A., Rapport sur l'hydrologie et l'utilisation des ressources hydrauliques dans les regions arides et semiarides d'Amerique latine, L'Hydrologie de la Zone Aride, UNESCO, 1952

4.  Nace, R. L., Water management, agriculture, and groundwater supplies, U. S. Geol. Sur. Circ. 415, 1960

5.  U. S. Senate Select Committee on National Water Resources, Committee Prints 7, 9, 24, 30, U. S. Government Printing Office, 1960

6.  Wilcox, L. V., Discharge and salt burden of the Rio Grande above Fort Quitman, Texas and Salt-Balance Conditions of the Rio Grande Project for the year 1963, U. S. Salinity Laboratory Research Report No. 106, 1964

7.  Hale, W. E., L. J. Reiland, and J. P. Beverage, Water Supply in New Mexico, New Mexico State Engineer Technical Report 31, 1965

8.  Renne, Roland R., Conservation and efficient use of water on arid and semiarid agricultural areas, National Water Research Symposium, U. S. Government Printing Office, 1961

9.  Robinson, T. W., Phreatophytes, U. S. Geol. Sur. Water Supply Paper 1423, 1958

10. Wadleigh, C. H., Fitting modern agriculture to water supply, Research on Water, American Society Agronomy Publication No. 4, p. 8-14, 1964

# SOCIOLOGICAL PROBLEMS
# OF WATER PRODUCTION

Laurence M. Gould, Professor of Geology
The University of Arizona

# 4. North American Water and Power Alliance

Roland P. Kelly, Technical Program Director, The Ralph M. Parsons Company

You may wonder why a large-scale water transfer and power plan
is being presented at a Nuclear Desalting Symposium. Personally, I cannot think of a more opportune occasion than this to present the plan for consideration. The water problem, whether in
Canada, the United States, or Mexico, is one of water management. Its solution is not dependent upon the application of any one
technology. To assure adequate quantities of good, clean water
to all parts of our country for industry, agriculture, and municipalities, where needed, when needed, must be our objective. To
accomplish this we will have to use all means available to us to
obtain the water and then move it efficiently to where needed.
This means that we must practice pollution abatement, we must
economically employ desalting plants, we must provide adequate
storage, we must recycle our waste waters, we must control our
floods, and we must develop a large-scale integrated network in
much the same way that we have developed networks of electrical
energy interties.

Too often a plan, or a concept, is accepted as the panacea for
all problems. In our complex society of today, we have found
that this cannot be so. The same applies to our water crisis. We,
of the Ralph M. Parsons Company, do not view NAWAPA as a
solution to all our water problems; but taken in its right perspective and integrated into an overall water management plan, it can
provide the basis for solving our water problems.

Throughout the world, the chief problems are (1) too much
water, (2) too little water, (3) polluted water, and (4) the growth
of human demands for water beyond the perfectly normal and once
satisfactory supply. Of these, "too little water" is most in the
public eye in most parts of the North American Continent. Water,
where it is needed, when it is needed, that is pure enough to drink
and cheap enough to use in agriculture and industry, is one of the
world's most feverishly sought resources.

Droughts have been experienced in the last decade in Canada,
the United States, and Northern Mexico. Pollution is a serious
problem in Canada as well as in the United States. Large areas
of the United States and Northern Mexico are water deficient but
blessed with climate and fertile soil. Devastating floods are all
too common in Canada, the United States, and Mexico. The water
problem is not unique to the United States or to any one area of
the United States. This situation exists now, it is real, and it

will grow steadily worse.  Our advancing technology and expanding population will make it so.

Some predications indicate that the situation will reach
alarming proportions by the year 1980.  Others say 1990, and
still others indicate the year 2000 as being the critical year.  It is
significant that all predications indicate a critical period occurring; they disagree only on when.  Here again a curious situation
exists; the critical period falls within a thirty-year span, a small
period of time in developing a water supply project.  Historically,
water supply projects require twenty to thirty or even forty years
to develop.

Fresh water supplies can be increased through three means:
(1) reducing the need for water; (2) making more efficient use of
our present water supply, and (3) finding new sources of water.
The NAWAPA concept naturally falls into the last category.  The
requirement for such a plan is, we believe, dictated by the continental nature of the need which I have briefly touched on earlier.

This brings me once again to the NAWAPA concept for
NAWAPA is basically designed for the transfer of large amounts
of water and the generation of large amounts of power.

In presenting the NAWAPA concept, we fully recognize it
represents but part of the total water management problem - conservation and distribution, although in providing this element it
certainly affects many other elements such as flood control, recreation, reclamation, et cetera, quite substantially.

As I mentioned before, we realize the NAWAPA concept
poses many problems which must be solved before work can begin.  There are first and foremost the political problems.  Then,
of course, there are engineering problems, legal, sociological,
financial, et cetera.

We are making no attempt at this time to offer solutions to
these problems, but are merely presenting a concept for utilizing
surplus water now flowing unused into the sea.  We are trying to
solve one of the water-management problems - the problem of
proper distribution on this Continent.

Total drainage area involved in the primary NAWAPA collection region is approximately 1, 300, 000 square miles.  It has a
mean annual precipitation of between 15 to 60 inches.  Of an average annual runoff of 663, 000, 000 acre-feet of water, approximately 110, 000, 000 acre-feet, or less than 20 per cent of the total flows of the basins, would be utilized.  In addition, up to
48, 000, 000 acre-feet per year, as required, of the unused runoff
of the eastern slopes of the Rocky Mountains would be used for
development of the Canadian prairies and stabilization of the water level of the Great Lakes.

The primary sources of water collection, as shown on Fig. 1, are the Susitna, Copper, and Tanana Rivers in southeastern Alaska; the Yukon and Stewart Rivers in the Yukon Territory; and the Liard, Stewart, Stikine, Fraser, Peace, Kootenai, and Columbia Rivers in British Columbia. A series of dams and power stations would provide for pumping this water up to the Rocky Mountain Trench Reservoir at an elevation of 3,000 feet. From the Rocky Mountain Trench Reservoir, water would be pump-lifted to the Sawtooth Reservoir located in central Idaho. From here, water would flow southward by gravity passing the Sawtooth Mountain barrier through a tunnel.

Figure 1.  North American Water and Power Alliance, (conceptual plan)

NAWAPA water would be conveyed via canals and tunnels. The canals would be of trapezoidal cross section and concrete lined. The canals would be based upon a velocity varying from 2 to 3 feet per second and would have a slope of approximately 0.2 foot per mile (.04 foot per thousand feet). Tunnels would be concrete lined. Tunnel design would be based upon a velocity varying from 5 feet to 10 feet per second with a slope varying between 1.2 feet per mile (0.22 foot per thousand feet) to 0.76 foot per mile (0.144 foot per thousand feet). The NAWAPA system would include a total of 6,700 miles of water transfer canals and multi-purpose water transfer and navigational canals, and 1,800 miles of tunnels.

Lakes and reservoirs would be the primary delivery points for NAWAPA water. Secondary delivery points would be provided by turnouts on the canals connecting storage facilities. The location and size of turnouts would be dependent upon local requirements.

Total installed power generation capacity of the NAWAPA would be approximately 110,000,000 kilowatts based upon an overall efficiency of eighty-three (83) per cent. The total power generation would be 876,000,000,000 kilowatt-hours per year. Of this amount, approximately 613,200,000,000 kilowatt-hours per year would be available for marketing.

Total pumping plant capacity installed in the NAWAPA system would be 53,500,000 horsepower. Pumping requirements of the NAWAPA system would consume 262,800,000,000 kilowatt-hours per year of NAWAPA-generated power. Pumping plant capacity and power consumption are based upon an overall efficiency of eighty-three (83) per cent.

NAWAPA water would be surface waters collected over uninhabited, uncultivated catchment areas of sparse vegetation. The principal catchment areas will be above 2,000 feet and 3,000 feet, in glacial regions and areas subject to snow cover most of the year. NAWAPA water would contain about 50 p.p.m. of total dissolved solids, have a temperature range between 40 degrees F. and 55 degrees F., and in terms of the United States Public Health Service limits, have a color rating of approximately 2 units and a turbidity below 0.5 units.

Estimated construction costs based on 1964 prices and expressed in United States dollars are tabulated below.

| ITEM | COSTS IN BILLIONS OF UNITED STATES DOLLARS |
|------|-------------------------------------------|
| Land Acquisition and Relocation | 16.6 |
| Engineering | 8.9 |
| Construction | 64.5 |
| Contingencies | 10.0 |
| TOTAL | 100.0 |

NAWAPA would require about twenty (20) years to complete after resolution of political and international features. The Rocky Mountain Trench Reservoir, Sawtooth Lift, and Sawtooth Tunnel would be the first elements of the system to be constructed. Following completion of these elements, water deliveries could be made into Utah, Nevada, Arizona, California, New Mexico, Texas, and Colorado.

The NAWAPA concept envisions water deliveries into the Pacific Southwest Region about nine (9) years after initiation of the program and power deliveries about eight (8) years after go-ahead.

National benefits accruing to Canada, the United States, and Mexico through implementation of the North American Water and Power Alliance would be significant. The physical benefits would be readily manifest through the creation of scenic inland lakes and waterways.

While the physical results of the North American Water and Power Alliance would affect the three nations, directly and indirectly, the impact created by the economic benefits would influence all facets of their industry and society. The average annual increase in the gross national product of each nation would be increased many times and sustain economic development for generations. The impetus provided industrialization and economic growth would foster and encourage national developments consistent with the needs of ever-increasing populations.

The primary benefits accruing to the United States alone from NAWAPA water and power are:

1.  Water.

    (a) Delivery of approximately 69,000,000 acre-feet of water annually.

    (b) Delivery of approximately 11,000,000 acre-feet of water annually to the Great Lakes for municipal and industrial usage and diversions out of the Great Lakes system in the Chicago area for pollution abatement.

    (c) Delivery of approximately 37,000,000 acre-feet of water annually to the Great Lakes system for stabilization of lake levels.

2.  Power.

    (a) Make available 30,000,000 kilowatts of electric power.

    (b) Increase and stabilize power production of the Niagara hydroelectric complex.

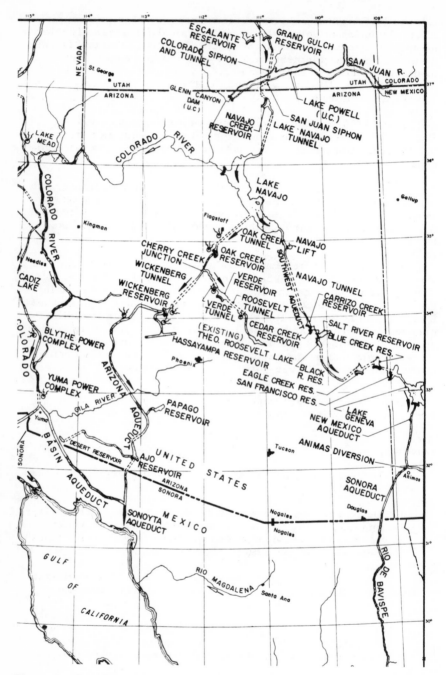

Figure 2.  NAWPA Construction for Arizona

As shown on Fig. 2, the North American Water and Power Alliance would entail extensive construction in the State of Arizona and result in the creation of numerous lakes, reservoirs, and a system of aqueducts crossing the state from north to south and east to west.

NAWAPA water would enter the State of Arizona via the Southwest Aqueduct in the northeast corner of the state. The aqueduct would be tunneled from the Utah state line into the Navajo Creek Reservoir. A combination of tunnels and open canals would provide gravity flow to a man-made lake, Lake Navajo, about 50 miles northeast of Flagstaff, Arizona.

The crest of the dam on the Little Colorado River forming Lake Navajo would be 4800 feet above sea level. Lake Navajo would have two outflows; one to southwestern Arizona and Sonora, designated the Arizona Aqueduct, and the second a continuation of the Southwest Aqueduct flowing south to serve southeastern Arizona, New Mexico, Texas, Sonora, Chihuahua, and other Mexican states.

The Arizona Aqueduct from Lake Navajo would divert water southwest toward Oak Creek Reservoir. Above and below Oak Creek, two power stations would generate a total of about 1000 megawatts of power.

Below Oak Creek Reservoir, a junction point called Cherry Creek Junction is planned. One flow toward Wickenberg Reservoir would pass through three power houses and generate about 770 megawatts of electric power. It would then pass on to southern and central Arizona reservoirs and Sonora, Mexico, for irrigation. The other course from Cherry Creek would be routed toward the Phoenix area and Theodore Roosevelt Lake. Power generation planned along this route is approximately 400 megawatts.

The Baja Aqueduct would split from the Colorado Basin Aqueduct north of Yuma, Arizona, and extend westward providing for irrigation of the lower Colorado delta region in Baja California and Sonora.

The NAWAPA system in the State of Arizona would include a total of 420 miles of water transfer canals and 280 miles of tunnels. Storage facilities of the NAWAPA system which are located in the State of Arizona are tabulated on the following page.

Potential benefits accruing to the State of Arizona from development of the North American Water and Power Alliance will be physical as well as economic. The benefits listed herein are indicative of the impact that the proposed project would have on the State of Arizona.

1.  Water.

    (a)  Deliver approximately 10, 000, 000 acre-feet of water
         annually into all major irrigable districts of Arizona.

2.  Power.

    (a)  Make available for distribution approximately 2, 000, 000
         kilowatts of electric power.

    (b)  Greatly increase hydroelectric power production in the
         Colorado power grid and throughout Arizona.

3.  Economic.

    (a)  Provide for an increase in agricultural income of approx-
         imately $510, 000, 000 annually.

    (b)  Provide permanent employment opportunities in con-
         struction, manufacturing, and agriculture.

4.  Population Growth.

    (a)  Provide for the support of an additional population of
         approximately 7, 000, 000.

5.  Recreation.

    (a)  Create a large lake on the Navajo Indian Reservation of
         great value to the Navajos and for fishing and recreation
         by visitors.

    (b)  Increase recreation and wildlife assets throughout Ari-
         zona.

The needs for importing water into the Pacific Southwest, as
well as other parts of the United States, are well  recognized.
Each day sees a more general acceptance of the fact that the solution of the water deficiency problem in the United States, as well
as Canada and Mexico, can only be solved by the importation of
water.  We are now publicly analyzing and evaluating various new
sources of water; desalting processes, methods for reclaiming
wastes, and large-scale long-distance transport of surface waters
to name a few.

The NAWAPA concept just presented you is one concept for
importing water sufficient to meet the needs of areas consistent
with anticipated growth and development.  It cannot be overem-
phasized that this concept is one way of accomplishing water deliveries.  In itself, it is not the answer to wise and prudent water

management.  Water management must include not only the importation of water to meet deficiencies, but also pollution abatement to clean our streams, reclamation of waste waters, adequate storage, and flood control.

| FACILITY | W.S. ELEVATION/FEET | STORAGE CAPACITY/AF |
|---|---|---|
| Lake Navajo | 4800 | 128,000,000 |
| Oak Creek Reservoir | 3700 | 500,000 |
| Wickenberg Reservoir | 3000 | 700,000 |
| Hassayampa Reservoir | 1800 | 170,000 |
| Papago Reservoir | 1150 | 350,000 |
| Ajo Reservoir | 1000 | 800,000 |
| Desert Reservoir | 600 | 200,000 |
| Verde Reservoir | 3000 | 2,400,000 |
| Carrizo Creek Reservoir | 5000 | 500,000 |
| Cedar Creek Reservoir | 5000 | 1,100,000 |
| Black River Reservoir | 4980 | 5,600,000 |
| Eagle Creek Reservoir | 4970 | 2,300,000 |
| Blue Creek Reservoir | 4960 | 1,100,000 |
| Navajo Creek Reservoir | 5000 | 400,000 |

It is well to note that some of the features of water management will be done with or without NAWAPA.  We must clean up
our rivers.  In order to maintain clean rivers, we will have to
clean our wastes.  Storage must be provided to take care of devastating floods.  All these will be done whether the NAWAPA concept is developed or not.  We, of The Ralph M. Parsons Company,
feel that the NAWAPA concept is one plan that will weld all features of intelligent water management into an integrated system
for obtaining maximum use of our waters.

In closing, I would like to reiterate a few salient points concerning NAWAPA.  NAWAPA is a concept.  The in-house funded
studies performed by The Ralph M. Parsons Company to date on
NAWAPA indicate that the water is there, the concept is technically feasible, and economically practical.  In the past, many
projects have been started without due consideration of the sociological, economical, and ecological impact.  These should, and
must, be considered in the early stages of the NAWAPA program.
In each country of this continent, population growth, industrialization, and an increasing economy are placing serious strains on
one of the most important natural resources - water - its supply,
distribution, and use.  Adequate planning is imperative to insure
that water resources are managed with foresight and vision.

## 5. Pouring New Water & Old Rights

Frank J. Trelease, Dean, College of Law, University of Wyoming

I wrote this somewhat in the dark, not knowing exactly what this
audience would like to know. I have assumed that somehow you
engineers and scientists have found, or think you are about to
find, a way to produce large supplies of potable water from sea
water and brackish supplies, and that you are wondering what to
do with it. I am assuming that your questions are these: who
should get it? What kind of water law do we need? What kind of
water rights should be given to the consumers? If these assumptions are not correct, I may have wasted my time and I may be
about to waste yours.

I may disappoint you by saying at the outset that despite the
newness of your contribution, I do not believe that you are going
to tax the inventiveness of the lawyers. We have lots of laws and
kinds of rights in our bag of tricks, and I think we can pull a couple of old ones out, dust them off, and put the combination to
work for you. Let us see what some of these are. There is no
need to make it hard or mysterious, and I will not read statutes
or rules to you, but will start out with a simple example.

Suppose you have a need for water. You have taken out the
glass, the ice cubes, a jigger, etc., and now you put the glass
under the faucet in the sink and turn on the tap. Nothing happens.
No water comes out. This is an intolerable situation. You immediately get on the telephone and call the man on the other end
of the pipe that leads into your kitchen. You explain, not in gen-
tle, dulcet tones, but in a loud shout, "Hey, you! I don't have any
water service, and I want water delivered right now." A calm
voice on the other end of the line then says, "I will see what we
can do for you." You say, "You'll see! You will darn well turn
my water on right now. I've got rights!" The calm voice says,
"Oh, have you? What rights?" This question should give you
some pause. In the first place, you will have to decide, what is a
right? Do you have some God-given or natural right to water?
Do you have a moral or ethical claim which the water supplier
ought to recognize? A moment's reflection will tell you that the
kind of right that we are talking about has to be a legal right, an
obligation or duty owed by some other person to you, one which
the law will enforce.

Suppose that you live in the eastern part of the United States
and you know that the basic water right doctrine there is that of
riparian rights. You are not quite sure what that is, but you say,

"Well, I think I've got a riparian right. " The man on the other
end of the line says, "Just a moment, and I will connect you with
the Judge. " The Judge comes on the line. He inquires, "Do you
own land that touches the bank of the river that is the source of
the water?" You may reply, "No, but I live next door to the guy
who does and I have a pipe to the river bank. " The Judge says,
"I'm afraid that is not enough. You have no riparian rights, even
though you have been using the water. You are a nonriparian, and
if riparian users need all of the water, you have no claim that I
can enforce. " But if you could answer the Judge's first question
affirmatively, and tell him that you do live on the river bank, but
that the river is now dry, the Judge will ask you what use you
were about to make of the water. He tells you that every riparian
owner may make a reasonable use of water that flows past or
through his land. You explain that you were about to build a high-
ball. The Judge says, "It sounds very reasonable to me, at first
hand. But reasonableness depends in part on a balancing of your
claims for water against the reasonable claims of other riparians,
and I will have to look into what are the uses of upstream riparians. If their uses are more reasonable than yours, I will have to
let them continue. If their uses are unreasonable compared to
yours, I can put a stop to them. If their uses and yours are on a
par, I will try to find some way to accommodate both of you. Why
don't you see your lawyer in the morning, and have him file a
lawsuit in which these things can be determined?"

But if you were located in the western United States, the conversation might go more like this: "I think I have an appropriative right. I have been putting water to this beneficial use for
quite a while. " The voice on the other end then says, "Hold on
while I connect you to the Water Commissioner. " The Water
Commissioner's first question is, "When did you begin this use of
the water?" You tell him. He might then say, "Okay, that gives
you an early priority. Those people who are using so much water
that you can't get any started their use only recently, and I will
shut them off and see that you get your water. " Or he might say,
"I'm sorry, but the river is very low this year and all of the water is being used by people who started before you did. They
have a better right to the water than you do, and I can't do a thing
for you. "

Or you might live in some places where the person receiving
your complaint would refer you to the Chief Bureaucrat of the
Water Bureau. That gentleman tells you coldly, "Sir, I am
charged by law with seeing that our water resources are put to
their highest and best use. My agency has discovered that you
are about to dilute bourbon with the water. We do not feel that
the dilution of bourbon is socially desirable, and we have therefore cut off your water and are now delivering it to Mrs. Jones,
who has just had her seventh child, and who uses her water to
wash babies and diapers with, which we feel is a higher use and
much more socially desirable than yours. "

If you live in some states and receive your water from your own private domestic well, you would find there was no one to talk to but the man next door.  Here the other end of the conversation might sound something like this, "So you don't have any water? That's tough.  I have all I want.  I have just dug some brand new, big, deep wells, and installed some big pumps.  They must be taking all the available recharge or must have lowered the water table beyond the depth of your well.  My lawyer tells me that whatever water I can find beneath my property belongs to me, if I can capture it.  I have captured it and if you don't like it, Buster, you can lump it. "

Still another possibility is that you have made private arrangements to buy water by a simple contract.  Perhaps you have a neighbor who has a big well that can supply more than his needs, and he has agreed to pipe water over to your house at so much a gallon.  When he answers the phone he says, "I am awfully sorry, old boy, but our arrangement was only for a year and the year is up.  Last month I sold my surplus water for next year to the neighbor on the other side who offered me more money than you were paying.  I asked my lawyer if I had to renew with you, and he says I can deal with anyone I want to, at any terms.  Sorry, but business is business. "

More likely than any of these is that you receive your water from the common type of public corporation franchised to serve a city's inhabitants.  In that case, you will find your call transferred to the Public Utilities Commission.  The first question you are asked is, "Have you paid your bill?"  If you give assurance that you have, the Commissioner will tell you, "All right, we will investigate this matter and quite probably issue an order requiring the company to resume service to you.  A public utility has an obligation to serve each member of the public within its service area, at reasonable rates, without discrimination, and at first blush it looks like you are being discriminated against if you are not getting water and your neighbors are. "  I might note here that a person receiving water from a municipally owned water system is owed much the same sort of duty by the city, although it is usually enforced by a court, not by the public utility commission.

There are other kinds of rights to water, but these illustrate the spectrum that the law can display.  The first four--riparian, appropriative, revocable permits, rule of capture--usually deal with the relationship of two users vis-a-vis each other.  The last two--private contract and public utility--deal with the relationship of a supplier to a consumer.  The first four types of rightholders usually get their water free, at least they pay no charge for diverting it from the source.  The last two, of course, pay a price for it.  But this is a spectrum and these can be infinitely varied, either by shading one color (or right) into another, or by mixing one with another.  Conceivably an appropriator or

riparian might be required to pay the state for each gallon or
acre foot he withdraws in the exercise of his priority, or of his
reasonable use.  Conceivably the public utility could recognize
either priority or most desirable use if it had to limit the amount
its customers could receive.  Conceivably a contract supplier
might agree to give a customer a priority, or the customer might
agree that under certain conditions others would receive the
water instead of himself.

So, if your question were, "What kind of water rights could
we give?" the answer is, "Any kind you want."  But I think your
question is rather, "What kind of water rights should we give?"
and that is a very hard question indeed.  In general, the law is a
human institution designed to enable men to live together in a
crowded and complex society.  The general goal of all law has
been stated by John Dewey, the philosopher, who describes the
law as ". . . a plan for organizing otherwise independent and potentially conflicting energies into a scheme which avoids waste,
a scheme allowing a maximum utilization of energy."  Roscoe
Pound, the great student of jurisprudence, expressed much the
same thought in this way:

> What we are seeking to do and must do in a civilized soci-
> ety is to adjust relations and order conduct in a world in
> which the goods of existence, the scope for free activity, and
> the objects on which to exercise free activity are limited,
> and the demands on these goods and these objects are infinite.
> To order the activities of men in their endeavor to satisfy
> their demands so as to enable satisfaction of as much of the
> whole scheme of demands with the least friction and waste
> has . . . been what law makers and tribunals and jurists
> have been striving for . . .

By and large, the law at any particular time and place represents the will of the majority for encouraging action deemed desirable by them and for discouraging or forbidding action thought
to be in conflict with the public interest.  By encouraging some
actions, but discouraging others, a state may use the actions of
individuals to reach its own desired goal.  There are few laws
that are self-executing in the sense that they control all conduct
and leave no choice of action to the individual.  Much law does
not literally regulate conduct in the sense of requiring or forbidding certain action, it instead provides an area of free choice,
setting outside limits within which a person may act as he chooses.
Many of these laws, such as those relating to property and contracts, unobtrusively form the basic frame work of our society.

The first choice to be made in selecting a rule of law that
will be the means of advancing these goals lies between the "public sector" and the "private sector."  Should the government itself build and operate your plant; or should it turn it over to private enterprise?  I think that substantial advantages lie with the

use of private capital, initiative and economic forces. Private enterprise--property, transactions, contracts--is not something apart from law, but is a mechanism established by law, a mechanism felt to be one of the most desirable methods of allocating resources, goods and services. To the extent that the laws of economics operate as an allocative and regulatory force, there is no necessity for law that minutely regulates the activities of the people. Decisions as to the most productive or wisest use of property can be made by private persons, relieving public bodies of the need to make them for the people at every turn. The maximization principle is generally believed to be achieved, or approached, by free men in a capitalistic society when they make decisions on where and how they will employ their labor and capital. Yet there may be need for government intervention. Some competition can be unhealthy and wasteful, and water distribution is one industry where this thinking has led to regulation. A consumer does not have two or three water mains in his alley from which he can choose to buy his water. The single water company that serves him has a franchise or a certificate of convenience and necessity, a legal monopoly. Its monopoly position puts him in a disadvantageous bargaining position, so its rates are regulated.

There may be need for more than government regulation. Some enterprises are too big to attract private capital, or the returns may be too distant or doubtful. The direct returns from the project may not show a profit, so that private capital cannot be attracted, but secondary and external benefits might make the project attractive to government. Yet even government should be efficient in the economic sense, and therefore the pricing arrangements I am about to suggest are applicable to either a governmental or a private enterprise. And even if the government were to lower its price in order to grant a subsidy to users, it should know what it is doing and whether its subsidy produces collateral benefits that justify the cost of the subsidy.

But let's hope for the best, and assume that your new water enterprise will be run by a private firm. I will next make the safe assumption that the plant will be an expensive one and that the process of producing water costs money. Next I will make the not unreasonable assumption that you will want to be paid for the water you deliver, so that you can recoup these costs. So we may eliminate the give-away element that exists in some of the types of rights we started with--this company would not be in a position of a state trying to develop its resources by encouraging people to use them to produce wealth. Even if the enterprise were run by a government agency, its product is not a natural resource, but is more in the nature of a service to particular citizens, to be paid for by those who receive the benefits, not (except to the extent that a subsidy is involved) by taxing the general populace. So whatever arrangement is made, it will include a price of some sort.

As we have seen, the law provides two principal methods of setting prices. In the first, the figure is reached by private contract, influenced by the presence of competition among sellers and bidding by buyers. The second is the price fixed by government--a "reasonable" price, one which gives the consumer the product at the lowest possible cost and gives the seller his costs and a "fair return on the fair value of his property." Traditionally this sort of price fixing is reserved for public utilities, usually performing some essential service or supplying some essential commodity, and often in a monopoly position. However, as you know, price fixing has been used by many governments for many purposes, usually to counterbalance some inequality in the relative bargaining strength of the seller and buyer.

Which system should be chosen may depend on many factors, but I am going to take only two. The first is whether you water suppliers will have a limited supply to sell or whether you can add to your plant to meet demands. The second is whether you will have a monopoly or be subject to competition. These again present a spectrum with many shadings and variations, but I am going to assume that they are polar positions. If a water supplier has an unlimited supply which can be increased at will, and if it is subject to competition, my belief is that the law should leave prices to be settled by the parties. An analog to this situation is the grocery store. Should you wife go to the home-owned store on the corner, or to the big chain store in the shopping center? Each of these enterprises will try to offer enough goods at competitive prices that enable it to capture a share of the market. The market will serve as an efficient regulator, and there is no need for government intervention. The market should similarly work for the new water factory if it is capable of indefinite expansion and if there is competition. The competition does not necessarily have to come from other water plants. The competition is more likely to come from existing sources. Although a valley's natural supply may be fully appropriated for agricultural, municipal and industrial uses, a new desalinization plant which adds to the natural supply will not have a monopoly that will enable it to set its own prices. Even if you don't build the plant, increases in municipal and industrial needs can be accommodated at the expense of a diminution in agriculture--the cities and manufacturers can buy the farmer's water rights. A city will not buy desalinated water at $100 an acre foot if it can buy natural supply from a farmer at $25. Indeed, the desalted supply must be cheap enough to compete with the marginal, lowest prices agricultural supply.

In the next case, you can still produce an unlimited supply but you have no competition. The analog to this is the electric utility. It might find that its profits would be maximized by selling a limited quantity at a high price. But public welfare might be maximized by a wider use of electricity. Typically, government will interfere here, and set a reasonable price, one that

might approach a simulated competitive price.  So if you decide
to make a garden out of Death Valley, or to supply water to a valley where the shortage is truly critical, you might expect similar
regulation.

The next combination is that of a limited supply in the presence of competition.  Here a useful analogy is the subdivision of a
farm on the outskirts of a growing city.  The subdivider has only
so many lots to sell, but his customers, the prospective home
builders, may choose his subdivision or a neighboring one.  His
price must be competitive and bear some relation to the prices of
lots elsewhere.  The market will be an efficient regulator, and
there is no need of laws for limiting or setting the price.  So, if
additions to the water plant are hard to come by, or if its source
is a limited source of brackish water, rather than the sea, and
there is competition from other sources, my inclination is again
to recommend that competition be the price regulator.

The last case is that of a limited supply plus a monopoly.
Here the analog is the lucky farmer who finds that the big city has
built an airport across the road and has located the main entrance
and passenger terminal building fronting his farm.  He has only
so much frontage land, and he has it all.  Ah ha, you say, a monopoly exists, and we should therefore regulate him to assure a
fair price and no discrimination.  Not at all.  Keep an eye on the
main goal--maximization of the use of the resource.  How can we
insure the best use of the land?  Should it be used for motels,
restaurants, or aircraft-related industries?  How can we find
out?  It's simple--put it up for bids.  The user who can make the
most out of the land will bid the highest for it.  So it should be
for water, if the demand is likely to exceed the supply.

Price, and how it is fixed, are not the only considerations.
In addition, we must ask what type of water right you will sell to
the consumer.  A person or firm with a need for water needs the
assurance that a continuing supply will be forthcoming.  Without
such assurance, entrepreneurs will not risk capital and labor in a
business doomed to failure in case the water supply is cut off.
Again, an important factor in choosing the type of law will be the
nature of the supply.  If the supply is unlimited, and if either
competition assures that that supply will grow to meet demand,
or a public utility commission will insure that all persons are
served at reasonable rates without discrimination, it is quite
likely that no more is needed.  If we have competition among suppliers, the consumer doesn't need a water right any more than he
needs a grocery right.  If the supplier is a public utility with a
legal duty to serve the public, this is enough of a water right.  It
is the right that most householders have, and who worries about
water rights, so long as water comes when he turns the tap?  He
pays for what he gets, and perhaps if he lives here in Tucson, he
will put in a "lawn" of crushed green stone so that he doesn't have
to water the grass.  Price may thus be a limit, but if he has the

price, he knows he will get the water.

But if supplies are limited, and the consumer suspects that demand will outgrow the supply, he begins to worry. He wants some sort of a permanent right, and he should get it. The maximization principle, I believe, would be furthered by this. We do not want to deter water users by discouraging investment in water using enterprises. We can avoid loss of capital sunk in permanent investment and facilities that cannot be transferred to other uses by giving a water right that will last for a sufficient length of time to permit the investor to recapture his investment through amortization. But the fear of loss of "sunk costs" is not the only deterrent to development. Time is invested as well as money, and the object of most enterprises is the founding of a going concern, and that going concern, the expectancy of the realization of opportunities, is the entrepreneur's most valuable asset. The giving of security of expectations of this sort requires the grant of a right which will last for the life of the enterprise. If the water is to be used in connection with an activity of limited duration such as the mining of a body of ore, the right should last as long as the expected life of the ore body. If it is to be used in connection with the sustained yield cropping of timber for paper production, the water use should be in perpetuity, since the supposition is that the forest and the plant (with replacements) will last forever. If it is to be used to irrigate a farm, the water right will be the major element of the value of the farm. The title to the farmer's water right ought to run as does the title to his land-- "to him and his heirs forever."

But there is one more consideration, flexibility of water use. No system of water rights should result in a rigidity that will hamper future generations, nor impose upon those generations a water use pattern suitable only for a bygone age. A water use law should be flexible enough so that today's lack of omniscience or prescience will not prevent the correction of mistakes. It must grow with the times. The water rights it creates must be flexible enough to enable shifts of water from use to use. While it may be permissible to assume that the use to which water is first put is the most desirable and economic at the time, it is fallacious to presume that such a use would be the best for all time. While we may wish to encourage water resource development today for its immediate benefits, getting the best use possible under present conditions, in years to come we may find that new and different uses promise greater benefits.

Going back to one of the many "ifs" and assumptions we have already made, of an unlimited supply, we find that if this exists we do not need to worry. Anyone who discovers or invents a new use or wishes to expand an old one can simply buy water for it at the going rate. Anyone who no longer needs water, or finds he cannot continue to pay its price simply stops using it. Nothing could be more flexible.

But if the supply is fixed, and it is all taken up by present uses, how can flexibility be achieved? If water is being used by farmers for irrigation but a manufacturing company can create greater wealth with the water, the maximization principle requires that the use should shift and the water go to the manufacturer. How should we do this? Should we borrow the old riparian idea and settle this in court on the basis of the most reasonable use? Or should we call in our old friend, the Chief Bureaucrat, and have him reallocate the water to its highest, best and most socially desirable use by cancelling the permit of the farmer and issuing a new permit to the manufacturer? If we choose one of these plastic, flexible rights, we have destroyed security, which we have just decided was desirable. The way out of this dilemma seems a paradox: make the rights even more secure, make them true property rights; not only secure but also transferrable. Again, let me use my analogy to land. Suppose today a farm on the outskirts of the city could be better used as a factory site. Do we run the farmer off the land, on the grounds that he is making an inefficient and wasteful use of a natural resource? Not at all. The industrialist simply offers to buy the land, tendering enough money to make it attractive to the farmer to leave. This same process holds true for transfers of western appropriative water rights currently held by irrigators, when industrial uses are more valuable. If the industrialist cannot pay the price, then by definition the transfer of the water to him would not produce greater benefits. If in fact it will produce greater benefits, the value to the purchaser is greater than the value to the seller, and the transfer can be made as in the case of the purchase of land. There is no reason to take the water without compensation, and impoverish the farmer, by destroying his investment and his expectation built on the farm as a going concern.

Let me make one clarification. I do not mean to say that the purchase of a permanent right would be a one-shot proposition, with one capital payment at the beginning. It is possible to distinguish between a right to receive water and the actual water received, and to set different prices for each. Thus, in my last example, the farmer with a permanent right to receive water, at a price would sell his right to receive to the industry, which would thereafter receive the water and pay for it. This is a common arrangement for the distribution of stored water in western states.

To conclude: A water law for desalinized water should look very much like one of the forms of water law we have today. Water can be sold as a commodity on the open market, water can be distributed to the public by a utility or a public district, or water consumers can be given water rights. The choice will be determined by the circumstances, but in any and all cases, the law chosen should be one that will provide maximum benefits from the use of the new resource. This end should be reached by laws designed to give enough security to the water user to encourage development, and enough flexibility to enable economic forces to transfer water from one use to a better one.   Public operation is needed only when private capital cannot do the job, and public regulation should be employed only when the public interest needs protection because the persons affected by decisions or operations are not in a position to influence the form they take.

# 6. The Economics of Water Production Using Nuclear Energy

J. W. Milliman, Director, Professor,
Institute for Applied Urban Economics, Indiana University

In October 1965, delegates attending the First International Symposium on Desalination heard President Johnson say that "only water can give future generations a chance to escape wholesale misery and wholesale starvation."[1] He charged scientists with the task of unlocking "the door to an unlimited supply of pure and drinkable water."

To this end, President Johnson announced a Water for Peace program as part of a massive cooperative international effort to find solutions for man's water problems. An important cornerstone in the new program is a five-year $200 million program of research and development to lower the cost of desalting water. In addition, the President promised to propose to Congress plans for constructing practical prototype desalting plants to produce 10 million gallons of fresh water a day by 1968 and 100 million gallons a day by 1970. The President said, "I earnestly believe that desalting is the greatest and most helpful promise we have for the future."[2]

Also in the news recently, statements have appeared to the effect that large plants will be able to desalt water at the rate of a billion gallons per day at a cost of $30-40 an acre-foot by 1975. Headlines have also featured conclusions from the recent study conducted by the Bechtel Corporation of a nuclear desalting plan for Southern California. We are told that water costs from such a plan would be about 22 cents per thousand gallons or $71 an acre-foot. Earlier studies of desalting costs had been in the range of 50 to 80 cents per thousand gallons or more. The Bechtel Study concludes that a nuclear desalting plant producing 150 million gallons per day for Southern California is not only practicable, but economically feasible.

In summary, there seems to be a underspread feeling that:

(1) a dramatic scientific breakthrough is near at hand which will drastically cut the cost of fresh water so that the age-long hope of mankind for unlimited supplies of cheap water for all uses and for all peoples is an attainable goal, and,

(2) that the major research pay-off is likely to be found in desalting ocean water with the use of nuclear power.

I hope that my remarks today provide some perspective on both questions.

## THE HOPE FOR UNLIMITED WATER

I suspect that the case for a scientific breakthrough which will sharply cut water costs has been overstated. But more importantly, it seems unwise to me to encourage people and nations to think that cheap or almost free water is just around the corner and that soon the laws of water supply and water demand will be reconstituted or repealed. The fact of the matter is that there is competition for the use of water resources and this competition will increase in the future. In general, we must expect the threshold of water costs to rise even with advances in technology. This means that we will have increased need for allocating water resources wisely between alternative uses, and it follows necessarily that higher valued uses should receive priority over lower-valued uses.

Moreover, it is quite clear that all known and prospective processes for increasing our supply of water at a given time and place are capital-intensive in nature. That is to say, the capital requirements of existing and proposed processes for water production are large. This means that the returns from water use must be compared with the benefits from other uses of capital or investment resources. And it is difficult to think of worthwhile activities in coming decades which also do not need large amounts of capital, such as space exploration, new transport systems, colleges and schools, and rebuilding our cities. This means that, even in an affluent society, we will have to make difficult economic choices between alternative employments or uses of capital. Of course, the less-developed nations will face the same sort of problem in even a greater degree.

I think it is reasonable to assume that important scientific advances in the technology of water production using nuclear energy will be made. Perhaps, the costs of desalted water will eventually reach levels of 50 dollars an acre-foot. But it is important to realize that such costs are not cheap and that the processes involved will be capital intensive in terms of resources, equipment, and trained man-power. Even under these conditions, therefore, water supplies will not be unlimited or available to all uses. This means that the economics of water use and the economics of investment in new supplies must be allowed to play an important role in shaping water policy if we truly intend to promote the good of mankind and to raise standards of living throughout the world.

## WATER RESOURCE ECONOMICS

The economic principles for the use and development of water resources can conveniently be divided into two categories:

1) The economics of utilization of existing supplies,

2) The economics of investment in additional water supplies.

I want to comment briefly on each of these two categories.

It is common for most analysts, when faced with the problem of a water shortage, to think first about the technology and engineering aspects of obtaining new water supplies. This type of thinking is unfortunate because it tends to neglect the economic principles of resource allocation. We, too often, forget that development of new supplies should not take place until existing supplies are well utilized. That is to say, existing supplies should be allocated and re-allocated to higher-valued uses until the marginal product of water, in all of its various uses, is equalized. New supplies should not be developed until marginal values in use are equalized and they should exceed the expected long-run marginal costs of the expansion of water supply facilities.

I believe that some of the current emphasis on the use of technology to solve our water problems by huge engineering projects for developing additional water supplies is premature because it can be shown that existing supplies in many areas are not being used efficiently. A well-known case in point exists in some of our Southwestern states where large percentages of existing water supplies are being used for relatively low-valued irrigation purposes while nearby urban areas, capable of using the water in greatly more productive uses, are short in supply. [3]

In fact, it can be argued that the "water crisis" in the United States is largely not one of water shortages at all but mainly a "managerial crisis." We have failed to develop a system of water law and a system of political institutions which might permit water allocations to take place and also which might provide efficient management of our river basins. [4] For example, it is easier and apparently more politically palatable to talk about building a nuclear desalting plant for New York City than it is to install meters, stop leaks, and make more efficient use of existing supplies. For polluted river basins, political leaders are considering banning waste disposal or instituting large construction programs instead of establishing basin management procedures for balancing benefits and costs from alternative uses of rivers among upstream and down-stream users. *

---

* The need to develop regional systems of water management is probably best argued by Allen Kneese. [5] He argues effectively that regional authorities should internalize the major offsite costs of water pollution. Legislation now before Congress may help provide some of the needed institutional framework.

## Principles for Use of Existing Supplies

The essence of economic principles to be followed in the allocation of water resources can be summarized in two rules:

1) The total value or product of water can be maximized by equalizing the marginal values in use for alternative uses of water. In other words, if the marginal products of alternative uses of water are equal, no amount of water can be transferred to a higher valued use. That is to say, returns from irrigation at the margin should not be less than the marginal value in use of water in a nearby city.

2) Water prices (explicit or implicit) should be made equal to marginal costs. If marginal costs differ among various uses, then prices should differ in corresponding fashion. Failure to correctly assess marginal costs has led to premature investment in new facilities and also failure to make better use of existing supplies. It would be inefficient, for example, to charge users prices which are less than the extra costs.

## Principles for Investment in New Supplies

For investment in new water supplies, there is general agreement that water investment should be accorded no special status in relation to other social investment. Without going into all of the theoretical and practical details, an investment is justified when the benefits can be shown to exceed the costs. The central problem in evaluation of investment is that the benefits and costs must be adjusted to a common time period through the device of discounting. We must determine the present value of future benefits and costs. The proper discount rate is one which reflects the rate of return on alternative investments sacrificed. [6]   If the present value of an investment, discounted or the rate of return of alternatives foregone, falls short of costs it should not be undertaken. *

Notice, that the correct rate of return for discounting may be higher than the capital costs of a subsidized loan if the rate of return on alternative investments foregone exceeds the loan rate. In less-developed countries, for example, rates charged on loans

---

*A common formulation of the present value rule is:

$$V_0 = -c_0 + \frac{s_1}{(1+i)} \quad \frac{s_2}{(1+i)^2} + - - - + \frac{s_n}{(1+i)^n}$$

Where $C_0$ is the immediate outlay; $V_0$ the net present value; $s_t = (b_t - c_t)$ are net returns in year $t$; and $i$ is the discount or interest rate per annum.

from international lending agencies may be substantially below correct discount rates which should reflect the general shortage of capital and rates of return at the margin.

Although these two sets of economic principles are well understood, scientific and public discussions of water resource problems are often carried on with little recognition of them. I am saying that the economic feasibility of new supply cannot be established without a study of the use of existing supplies and without a clear determination that an economic demand exists. Should we expect less when large capital investments are involved? When the level of water prices in a region is substantially below the costs of a new supply there is usually reason to suspect that the economic feasibility of new supply is doubtful or premature. These considerations may not make dramatic headlines but they are basic to wise use of all of our resources.

## GENERAL CONSIDERATIONS AFFECTING ECONOMIC DEMANDS FOR DESALTED WATER

It seems quite possible that research and development in desalting will bring the costs of water down to a point where they may be competitive in some parts of the world with transporting natural waters over long distances by conventional means. We have seen the cost of desalted water fall much below the old target of one dollar per thousand gallons (326 dollars per acre-foot). It now appears that costs of 70-80 cents per thousand gallons are reasonable for plants of 5-10 MGD and perhaps costs will soon fall to 30 cents per thousand gallons for plants producing 200 MGD.

Nevertheless, it is clear that achievement of these cost levels will not revolutionize the life of mankind nor cause the "deserts to bloom." Thirty cents per thousand gallons is almost 100 dollars per acre-foot. This is high-cost water (and will be high-cost water for many years), particularly when it does not include conveyance and distribution costs. Moreover, as I shall comment upon later, such costs are conditioned by the parallel need for large-scale markets for electric power produced in dual-purpose plants and also by the necessity of using a low rate of fixed charges (or a very low rate of discount in the present value formulation) on the large amount of capital invested in the nuclear power and desalting plants. As we shall see, some of the figures quoted for low-cost water from nuclear dual-purpose power plants have been reached by the use of fixed charges for capital substantially below the costs of capital available for such purposes here or abroad.

A second general consideration affecting the demand for desalted water is the comparison of the trend of desalting costs with the cost of conveyance of natural waters through aqueducts and pipelines.  On a general basis some comparison needs to be made between the economies of scale in the case of desalting with the costs as a function of capacity for water "production" via aqueduct.  It is clear that a great deal of research on the cost functions of the various water production alternatives needs to be carried out.  Moreover, there are a great many variables which need to be considered.  This means that generalizations are very difficult to make.  I suspect that comparisons will be most meaningful when related to particular or specific alternatives which reduce speculation about such things as impoundment, waste disposal, treatment, and load curves.

Two important studies are available which seem to shed light on this general question, one by Louis Koenig and the other by the Department of Sanitary Engineering and Water Resources at John Hopkins University. [8]   There seems to be close agreement that the economies of large size production are potentially greater for the production and conveyance of natural waters by conventional means than for saline water conversion.  Apparently, fresh water-conveyance costs decline sharply with size, approaching the square root of capacity.  Whereas, the costs of large capacity for nuclear desalting plants fall much more slowly. *  Both the Koenig and Johns Hopkins studies show that the net economic distance for competition to take place between saline and fresh waters is inversely a function of size.  For example, in the Johns Hopkins study, four major items of cost were analyzed in 2520 combinations.  It was found that the production and transportation of fresh water in the amount of only 100 MGD could be extended almost 750 miles before reaching a cost of 50 cents per thousand gallons.  Clearly, economic distances or break-even points for massive volumes, such as one BGD, become very large. **

Unless these studies are shown to be in error, the conclusion seems to be evident that desalting plants will generally be more feasible in small and modest sizes ranging from one MGD perhaps up to as large as 200 to 300 MGD.  At present, very large size demands seem to favor fresh water alternatives.  On the other hand, it may be entirely proper for a growing area to turn to nuclear desalting as a short run or interim supply until demand

---

*Crever[9] indicates that the scaling low for nuclear desalting plants goes as the -0.2 power.

** The capacity of the present Colorado River Aqueduct operated by the Metropolitan Water District is approximately one billion gallons per day or 1.2 million acre-feet per year.  At a consumption rate of 180 gallons per person per day, this is enough water to supply the industrial, commercial, and domestic needs of an urban population of 6 million.  The Feather River Aqueduct now under construction will be able to bring approximately 2 million acre-feet of water per year to the Southern California area.

builds up to a level (and until future uncertainties are reduced) to justify building a large-scale, long-mileage pipeline or an aqueduct. Future research in nuclear desalting perhaps can make its contribution in two ways: one is to continue to lower the costs of small and medium-sized plants, and two, to seek methods to increase the slope of capacity-cost curve.

A third general consideration affecting the future demand for desalting is the possibility that the development of large plants for reclamation of waste waters may be practical in many urban areas as an alternative to the development of new supplies. It seems highly probable that research on waste water reclamation will make it possible to upgrade these waters to make them reusable for a wide variety of uses. It is well-established that a community's waste waters constitute a disposal problem. Yet, it is seldom pointed out that these waste waters may be of a higher quality and potentially more easily treated than saline water.

Despite its unconventionality, the reclamation of waste waters has long been discussed in Southern California water circles. [10] Apparently, reliable estimates have been presented that it would be feasible to reclaim approximately 350,000 acre-feet per year (approximately 300 MGD) at costs of about 25 dollars an acre-foot. As a rough rule of thumb perhaps 25 per cent of the water use in Southern California can be reclaimed at these moderate costs and a somewhat larger fraction, up to 50 per cent, could be made available at costs under $50 an acre-foot or about 15 cents per thousand gallons. [11]

Although it has been claimed that a well-designed reclamation plant can produce a well oxidized and sterilized effluent of good chemical and biological quality, [12] most authorities feel it prudent to limit use of these waters to certain agricultural and industrial uses and to recharge of groundwater basins. Recharge would provide extra filtering as well as blending with other supplies.

Recent reports, however, of research underway show promise that some of the remaining hurdles to wider use of reclaimed waste waters may be amenable to treatment. The problem of removal of disease-causing viruses is currently being studied by a number of researchers. Professor Albert F. Bush of UCLA's School of Engineering is having good results in removing viruses with a method that combines agglomeration with bacteria, settling and filtration. Bush contends that up to one-half of the 600 MGD which Los Angeles alone puts into the ocean through expensive outfalls can be treated and reused for many purposes. [13]

Professor Rolf Eliassen of Stanford University recently reported that a tertiary reclamation process of diatomaceous-earth

filtration, followed by anion exchange, can be accomplished at
about 21 cents per thousand gallons, including all plant costs for
operation, maintenance and capital recovery.  This reclaimed
water is apparently suitable for most purposes including surface
storage. [14]  Previously, the principal difficulty of surface storage of reclaimed municipal waste waters was that nutrient elements in the waters stimulated the growth of algae.  The Stanford
research concentrated, therefore, upon the removal of phosphates
and nitrates.

Increasing urbanization will require increased waste disposal
facilities whether the waters are reclaimed or not.  This may
mean that extra costs of extra water treatment for reclamation
may be very low when the alternative may be to construct expensive ocean outfall lines, in addition to providing standard secondary treatment.  This is an important consideration for cities located along sea coasts.  Water conveyed to the ocean by outfall is
not available to a down-stream user as in the case of a river outfall.  The economics of the situation would seem to call for a balancing of the extra costs of reclamation of waste waters with the
extra costs of new supplies.  It would seem important that funds
be made available to study promising methods of waste water reclamation.  It is fair to say that research on conversion of saline
water seems to receive more political and scientific support.
Perhaps the apparent public distaste against use of reclaimed
waste waters is more of a political and psychological barrier to
this alternative than seems to be warranted by scientific research.

## THE ECONOMICS OF DESALTING

There are a number of technically workable ways of producing potable water from brackish and saline waters.  All of the
methods which show promise are now under study by private and
governmental organizations.  Plants now in operation range from
small shipboard units to plants of 1.4 MGD at Guantanamo, Cuba
to approximately 3 MGD at Aruba.  A plant producing 2.5 million
gallons will be constructed for the Florida Keys.  Egypt is considering a plant in the 5-10 million range; plants of the size of
100-150 MGD are being studied for Israel, Mexico, and Southern
California; and speculation has taken place that plants can be
built to produce one to two BGD.

Essentially there are four types of choices to be made in the
selection of desalting processes:  a) method of desalting, b) size
of plant, c) single or dual-purpose operation, and d) type of fuel
to use.  Actually, all of these choices are interdependent.  In
addition, the choices are conditioned by such matters as the size
of prospective markets for water and power, the physical geog-
raphy of the area, the cost of fuels, safety requirements, and the
cost of capital.

## Choice of Desalting Process

At the present time, five alternative desalting processes appear technically feasible; multistage flash distillation, multiple effect distillation, vapor compression distillation, electrodialysis, and freezing. Other processes under study include solar distillation, reverse osmosis, ion exchange, direct contact distillation and solvent extraction. None of these latter processes, however, appear sufficiently developed to warrant commercial application at this time.

There seems to be general agreement among experts that water supplies in quantities above one million gallons per day are best served by the multistage flash distillation process. This is a relatively simple process which has been proven in a number of plants throughout the world. The plants at Kuwait, Malta, Aruba, and Freeport, Texas, on the other hand, use the multiple effect distillation process. Current opinion seems to be that this process is not as economical as the multistage flash process. Brackish waters, containing only 1,500 to 10,000 parts per million of dissolved salts compared to 34,000 parts per million for sea water, seem best treated by electrodialysis or vapor compression processes. All of the studies for proposed large scale plants now underway involve the employment of the multistage flash process. Apparently, a good deal of research needs to be done on the mechanics of flashing brine and on materials to improve heat and mass transfer of vapor, but it seems agreed that:

Desalting techniques, other than distillation, are not expected to be available for large scale use for many years. Moreover, early development of other distillation techniques with significantly lower product costs is not considered likely. [15]

## Fossil versus Nuclear Fuels

Next is the question of the source of energy for the desalting plant. Distillation plants require large amounts of heat as steam energy to heat the raw sea water under pressure to about 250° F. Then heated brine is conveyed to evaporators where it starts a series of flashings. The desalting process also uses a considerable amount of electrical energy to operate the pumps bringing in the sea water as well as the pumping required for collecting and conveyance of product waters. The desalting plant design is not greatly affected by the source of energy.

The major sources of energy are gas, oil, coal, and nuclear. The cost of steam is the primary factor in considering whether the source of heat should be from fossil fuels or from nuclear fuels. The major factors conditioning this statement are that nuclear steam supplies have the possible disadvantage of some

radioactive contamination of the fresh water and they may create
some location problems in terms of recommended nuclear site
safety analysis. Exclusion areas, population densities, seismol-
ogy, radioactive waste disposal and other factors must be considered to assure low risk of public exposure and to reduce the possibility of a nuclear accident. On the other hand, the burning of
fossil fuels may add to smog and air-pollution difficulties in some
urban areas.

For comparison of the choice of fuels, the cost of steam is
influenced by two primary factors: the capital costs of the respective steam systems and the costs of the fuels themselves over
the period of the life of desalting plant (approximately a 30-year
period). Most authorities seem agreed that nuclear plants require considerably more initial capital investment, but that the
fuel costs per million Btu's are considerably lower. Moreover,
the trade-off between the two types of plants is influenced by the
scale of operation and the total amount of energy required. In
larger sizes, nuclear energy becomes increasingly competitive
because fuel cycle costs are lower for nuclear reactor plants than
for fossil fuel plants. Thus, the larger capital costs of nuclear
plants, on a unit basis, becomes less important.

Prices for fuel vary a great deal in various sections of the
world. They are also influenced by the optimism of the investiga-
tor with regard to future trends. Proponents of nuclear power
tend to use planning assumptions that fossil fuels will cost between 35 cents to 50 cents per million Btu compared with nuclear
fuel costs for slightly enriched uranium dioxide ranging from 10
to 15 cents per million Btu. When interest rates are low, these
figures clearly swing the decision to use of nuclear power. Representatives from the fossil fuel industries claim that nuclear
fuel costs as well as interest rates tend to be underestimated and
are influenced by specific governmental price and loan policies
designed to make nuclear power attractive. Both groups of proponents tend to point toward alleged future scarcities of fuel reserves and the likelihood of increases in fuel costs in the future.
Future fuel prices depend upon the supply of reserves both of uranium and of fossil fuels, and on the conversion ratios. Clearly,
the possibility of a significant reduction of low-cost reserves is a
matter which deserves serious study in the choice of fuels.

## Single Purpose Versus Dual Purpose Plants

Ocean water can be desalted in a single purpose plant or in an
operation which produces two products, electricity and desalted
water. The economic choice between methods of operation depends upon the possibilities of cost savings from joint operation,
the scale of operation necessary to achieve cost savings and the
markets for both power and water.

The evidence seems clear-cut that dual purpose operation can achieve cost savings because of economics of scale in the production of steam. These savings increase with the size of the operation. 16 However, realization of these savings depends upon the ability of the power and water markets to absorb large blocks of both products. More importantly, the costs of operation of the dual-purpose plant are apparently very sensitive to instability of the production ratio and to continuous versus discontinuous operation. In other words, low costs of dual operation are dependent upon achieving a stable ratio of output for both products and the plant should be base-loaded for both power and water. These requirements may raise problems if the power and water systems which receive these two products do not have other means of handling seasonal and peak demands which are characteristic of most water and power use.

Perhaps some comment is needed on the reasons why dual purpose operation may be more efficient and less costly than a single purpose desalting plant. From the standpoint of thermodynamics, there is no benefit to a power plant to combine power production with desalting. There seems to be a notion that the heat from the power plant that is used to distill the sea water would, otherwise, be wasted. Crever points out that, "the most economical heat rejection temperature for power-generation and distillation may not be substantially different." 17 If this is true, then extra water is obtained only at the sacrifice of extra power. Apparently, power plants are able to convert heat to electricity over the full range from high steam temperatures down to some heat sink. The waste heat from a power cycle cannot be used to desalt water anymore than it can be used to produce power.

The advantage of dual operation came from economies of scale in the production of steam. One large energy plant can supply steam more cheaply than two plants. More directly, all steam generators whether fossil fueled or nuclear, can produce steam at high temperatures and pressures for very little higher costs than low temperature steam and pressure. This factor is important when considered in conjunction with the fact that distillation processes have not been developed which can operate at high temperatures and pressures because of serious scaling and corrosion problems. Even with pretreatment of sea waters with sulfuric acid, current sea water distillation plants cannot employ steam above 250º F. This means that it is possible to generate electricity with high-pressure, high-temperature steam and set a heat rejection rate for power at a level which then can be used to operate the distillation plant. Thus, the steam temperatures and pressures above the top temperature of a desalting plant can be used to produce power.

Of course, the advantage of this sort of dual purpose operation depends upon the saleability of both products. Clearly, large scales of operation which reduce steam costs will necessarily produce large blocks of both water and power. Huge desalting plants might achieve low costs of water, but this feasibility is also conditioned by the need to market a large block of power on a continuous basis. It might be thought that power could be generated at the expense of water at some times and that the product mix could be reversed when peak or seasonal demands favored water. This type of flexibility in product mix, however, can be brought only at a penalty in terms of efficient plant design. Present experience on questions of this kind is very limited, but the size of the capital investment involved would seem to dictate a policy of operating with a high load factor for both products. Water can be stored while electricity cannot. On the other hand, storage costs of water in or near urban areas would not be small. As a last point it might be said that dual purpose operation may also allow the elimination of certain items of equipment such as condensers and secondary water systems. It has also been claimed that certain economies may accrue by virtue of operating both plants under a common management. However, this latter economy may not always be realized if power is produced and sold under one set of general rules and water under a different set of standards. In this case joint operation might create administrative diseconomies.

## The Allocation of Joint Costs

It is clear that the economic feasibility and the level of costs for water and power produced in a dual purpose plant are very sensitive, not just to interest rates and to fixed capital changes, but also they depend to an important extent on how costs of the joint facility are allocated between water and power. It can be shown, for example, that the cost allocation method commonly employed in nuclear desalting feasibility studies attributes all of the economic advantages of joint operation to water, thereby minimizing water costs at the expense of power. There is no necessary or logical reason for not doing the reverse unless the analyst deliberately wants to present a case favorable to water costs or unless desalted water is viewed as a by-product.

The question of the allocation of costs in multipurpose projects has long been discussed in the economic literature. Many attempts, both theoretical and practical, have been made to resolve the question of how to allocate costs which are joint between several products or classes of service.[18]   In all of the methods proposed, the costs which are clearly separable, in the sense that they are incurred solely for the benefit of a single product or class of users, are assigned to the particular purpose. The remaining costs are joint or inseparable and can be assigned in a wide variety of ways, all of which have some logical difficulties and widely differing economic consequences.

When the costs are truly joint and not separable or

incremental, McKean says:

> Inability to allocate all costs meaningfully among joint prod-
> ucts is often a fact of life, not a sign of disgrace or laziness.
> The extra cost of adding on a function or feature can be cal-
> culated--but not a meaningful total cost for one feature when
> undertaken jointly with others. [19]

Hirshleifer, DeHaven and Milliman argue that costs should be
allocated on the basis of which costs are incremental to the decision compared with the alternative.  For example, if the decision
is whether or not to add power features to a proposed dam (or the
desalting facility), no part of the common costs of the dam (or the
desalting facility) should be weighed as an offset against power
benefits in making the decision: "For this decision, there is a
correctly unique 'allocation' to power--precisely zero. "[20]

On the other hand, if the dam (or power plant) is being built
to produce power, then the same sort of reasoning would apply to
the consideration of the adding of extra facilities for water production.  In this case, water facilities should not be credited with
any portion of the joint costs but only with the incremental costs
of water production, i. e. , the total cost for any one purpose
would simply be the sum of the incremental costs assigned.

If we take this line of reasoning, the investment decision
would involve three questions:

1) Do total benefits exceed total costs (in present value
terms ?

2) Do the separable benefits of each purpose exceed the separable costs of each purpose?

3) Which purpose in a multiproduct project is incremental to
the project?

Although I believe these three questions to be technically correct, it is clear that the last question may be a matter of judgment or of stated policy.  This, of course, is not the fault of the
analysis but rather the need for being extremely precise on what
questions we are attempting to ask and answer.  To put it bluntly,
if our goal really is to provide extra water supplies rather than to
build extra power facilities, then it would seem logical and correct that power be credited only with the incremental costs of the
extra facilities needed to produce the extra power, with all of the
common costs being assignable to water.  The exact opposite procedure has been used in economic feasibility studies of dual purpose operation to date which seems to imply either that power
production is the primary purpose or else that attempts are being
made (deliberately) to minimize the "costs" of desalted water.

What does one do when neither power nor water can be considered "primary" and the other a secondary or incremental product? I suppose the correct thing to do in this case is not to attempt to allocate joint costs. For the investment feasibility decision, all that is required is a showing that total benefits exceed total costs and that separable benefits cover separable costs. For pricing decisions, once the facilities are built, the economically relevant cost is the marginal cost. In principle, this should not be difficult to determine because it involves finding the increase in the total costs, due to a unit increase in one product or type of service.

If one persists in trying to allocate joint costs in spite of the reasoning here, he can have his choice of allocating costs "proportional to benefits," "proportional to use of facilities," "proportional to separable costs," proportional to single purpose costs," "proportional to separable costs minus remaining benefits," or some other formula. Each of these "solutions" involves certain difficulties, each has some merit.

Joseph Barnea has recently advocated allocating the total costs (not just the joint costs) of a dual purpose plant according to the ratio of the costs of two single purpose plants having the same net marketable output of water and power. While this method does not require a determination of which purpose is "primary" and thus apparently does not "load" the costs in favor of one product or the other, it has no logical superiority over many of the other methods which might distribute joint costs in other ways, e. g. , why not allocate costs "proportional to benefits" instead of proportional to single purpose total costs.[21] , [22]

Most dual purpose studies to date have had as their specific aim the establishment of the lowest cost of water. This means that cost allocation has tended to favor water at the expense of power. This is usually done in the following manner:

1) Develop the total cost of dual purpose plant producing power and exhaust steam for desalting.

2) Deduct from this the cost of operating a single-purpose generating plant that produces no exhaust steam but generates the same amount of power at the same site with the same load factor.

3) The remaining cost is assigned to the production of water.[23]

Under this method, all of the economic advantages of large scale steam production derived from the dual purpose plant have been assigned or used to reduce the cost of water. The larger the plant, the greater the credit that is automatically given to water in the form of lower steam costs. Because steam costs are a large proportion of total water costs, the overall effect can be quite substantial.[24]

### DESALTED WATER FOR SOUTHERN CALIFORNIA:
### THE BECHTEL STUDY

Perhaps the most complete feasibility study to date of a large scale nuclear power and desalting plant has recently been completed by the Bechtel Corporation.   The study was jointly sponsored by the Metropolitan Water District of Southern California, The Office of Saline Water in the Department of Interior, and Atomic Energy Commission at a reported cost of $873, 000.   Copies of the three-volume report are available to interested scholars who will find that the pages and exhibits, comprising eight and one-half pounds of printed materials, contain a wealth of information on technology and operation of a large-scale dual purpose plant. 25   This report should probably be required reading for all specialists in the field.   It clearly exhibits the strengths and weaknesses of methods now employed to determine the engineering and economic feasibility of nuclear power and desalting plants.

I will limit my observations today to some of the economic aspects of the study.   I will say at the outset that I am not competent to judge the study from a technical or engineering point of view.   In fact, given the limited time I have had to digest the report, I should warn you that my comments are mainly preliminary in nature.   Nevertheless, it would be my observation that the engineering aspects of the study received a good deal more attention than did the economic features.   For example, the text and the appendices give every indication that independent advice was sought on questions of plant design, site location, oceanographic factors, meteorological conditions and the like.   Yet, curiously enough important economic questions, for example those relating to markets for power and water, the prices at which these products might be sold, and the uses to which they might be put, were given very sketchy treatment.   Perhaps these and similar economic matters might be appropriate for a study of this scope, magnitude and importance.

The Bechtel report states that "the feasibility of designing and constructing a large combination nuclear power and desalting plant to produce 150 million gallons per day (mgd) of desalted water is confirmed. "26   The water costs from such a plant are estimated to be 22 cents per thousand gallons ($71. 00 per acre-foot) and the product water could be delivered to a distribution plant at an additional 5 cents per thousand gallons, for a total 27 cents per thousand gallons ($88. 00 per acre-foot).   The plant would be built on a man-made 43 acre island located 3500 feet offshore from Orange County, California.

The report was based upon a plant with two 3 million thermal kilowatt, light water-cooled and moderated reactors; three turbine generator units with a gross capacity of 1. 8 million electrical kw; and a multistage flash type of distillation plant.   Net power output from the facility would be 1. 6 million kw, enough power for a city of approximately 2 million people, an amount twenty five per cent greater than the electric power generated at Hoover Dam. Water production of 150 MGD is equivalent to approximately 150,000 acre-feet a year or an amount sufficient to support a population of 750,000 at a consumption rate of 180 gallons per person per day.

The total investment is estimated to be $390,900,000. The share attributable to power is $213 million and the cost of the water plant is $144,000,000 plus $33,500,000 for a conveyance line to the distribution plant. A group of electric utility companies[27] are assumed to finance the power investment and the MWD is responsible for the water investment.

Perhaps three major kinds of issues to be raised in appraising the economic feasibility aspects of the Bechtel report: the cost of capital, the market for power, and the market for water. On each of these three issues serious questions can be raised or at least healthy skepticism can be expressed.

The ground-rules in force throughout the three-volume feasibility study stipulated that the cost of capital should be 3.5 per cent per annum. Presumably, this might be the borrowing rate at which the Metropolitan Water District might be able to sell long-term bonds to finance expansion of its facilities. This rate is a very favorable one because District bonds carry the tax-exemption privilege. In addition, the bonds are backed by the taxing power of the District which can levy property taxes upon total assessed property values in Southern California in excess of 17 billion dollars. For example, in the 1963-64 year the District collected over $29 million in tax revenues with a basic rate of 14 cents per $100 of assessed valuation. In the same year District revenues from the sale of water were approximately $23 million.[28]   It is clear that this interest rate is a very favorable one when one considers that the current yields (1966) on long-term Treasury bonds issued by the Federal government generally exceed 4.7 per cent.

More important, is the fact that the 3.5 per cent interest rate was used in calculating the capital costs of the entire combination power and water plant - not just the water features. Perhaps this device made the cost calculations easier to compute because it would have been a bit more complicated to use one interest rate on the power facilities and another rate for the water portion. Yet, it is clearly stated in the report that the Electrical Utilities Group would finance the power features of the project. It is fair to say that few power firms, public or private, can legitimately cost capital at a 3.5 per cent rate of interest.

Notice, that a low interest rate may serve to bias the whole study of a large-scale capital intensive operation. Even if we were to use higher interest rates on the power investment alone this would also affect the cost of water by raising the cost of

exhaust steam to the distillation plant. For example, the energy
cost to the proposed desalting plant is calculated at 2.5 mills per
kwh. [29]   Rates at this level are difficult to conceive at more
realistic rates of interest for nuclear power investment. The
Bechtel report used a 30-year life for the nuclear power and desalting plant facilities. On the basis of a sinking fund deprecia-
tion of 1.94 per cent, total fixed capital charges were computed
at a rate of 5.44 per cent (3.50 plus 1.94). I suspect that this is
the lowest rate of fixed charges ever used in a feasibility study
for a nuclear desalting plant. Earlier assessments of the possible feasibility of distillation plants from the Office of Science and
Technology have used alternatives rates of 7 and 14 per cent for
fixed charges. [30]   I have not been able to perform sensitivity
analysis of unit costs with regard to alternative rates of interest
(other than 3.5 per cent). This important kind of sensitivity analysis would seem to be basic material for inclusion in an economic
feasibility study of a large capital intensive operation producing
both power and water.

With regard to the market for the 1,600,000 kw of net electric power to be produced by the combination plant, the Bechtel
report is completely silent. Perhaps this omission is under-
standable and entirely proper because the sponsors of the study
were primarily interested in the water to be produced. Also it
could reasonably be assumed that the Electric Utilities Group
would be entirely knowledgeable about the power market and prob-.
ably would be doing their own market analysis. Undoubtedly, the
real test of this point will come when it comes time to proceed to
put the plan into effect and to actually sign contracts. I merely
want to stress that much of the economic feasibility of the project,
and the estimated costs of desalted water, depends upon the ability of the power market to absorb this large block of energy, and
probably to absorb this block as a base load. When power units
of this size are considered, it may well be that the normal practice of having spinning reserves equal to the largest single generating unit may have to be modified.

Probably the most important consideration for present discussion is the market for water. Should the Metropolitan Water
District purchase an extra supply of 150,000 acre-feet a year to
be available at best in 1971, when in 1972 or so it will have access to Northern California water in an amount approaching 2
million acre-feet per year? What are the costs of desalted water
in relation to current prices governing water use and in relation
to costs of alternative supplies? Does the MWD need 150,000
acre-feet of water per year at $88 per acre-feet (assuming that
these costs are correctly measured)?

Again on the question of water markets, just as in the case of
the power market, the Bechtel report is not very informative.
Perhaps we might say again that this problem was not within the
scope of the Bechtel study. It could be that this matter was

properly thought to be the concern of the Metropolitan Water District who was responsible for one-third the cost of the study.  If this is the case then the real economic feasibility study of nuclear desalted water for Southern California is yet to be presented.

On the other hand, one can find passages in the Bechtel report that appear to suggest that Bechtel believes the combination plant to be economically justified; e. g. ,

> The proposed desalting facility will produce and deliver distilled water at a unit cost comparable with future sources of imported water for Southern California.  The importation of water from more distant sources, such as the Columbia River, will require large capital expenditures and it appears unlikely that water will be provided at significantly lower unit costs than those calculated for the dual-purpose nuclear power-desalting plant. [31]

> A timely decision on the desirability of desalting as compared to the future importation of water from distant sources is necessary.  Construction and operation of the desalting plant offers the District an opportunity to demonstrate the costs of producing desalted water.  Such demonstration is highly desirable to the proper planning of water resources. The investment required for this desalting project is small compared to the costs to the facilities for the importation of water from distant sources.  Moreover, plant operation will provide invaluable operating experience and economic data. [32]

These two passages are quoted to show the extent and type of economic justification used in the Bechtel report.  The claim is made that desalted water for Southern California is cheaper than importation of water from the Columbia River and, second, that the plant would be a valuable demonstration exercise.  I shall comment more upon the cost of alternative water sources below. It is probably correct to say that desalted water is cheaper than going to the Columbia River, but the real question to be asked is: Are there any cheaper alternatives than either desalted water or Columbia River water ?  And when are alternative sources needed, assuming the aqueduct from Northern California can probably supply needs now foreseen until 1990 ?

The point about the value of the demonstration exercise and the technical knowledge to be gained is undoubtedly valid.  Here we might ask:  does the demonstration need to be on this scale? [33] To whom will the benefits accrue; and who is likely to pay the costs ?  From the standpoint of the Metropolitan Water District, it is difficult to see how it should go ahead on its own to advance the frontiers of knowledge without substantial outside subsidies, presumably from the Federal government. The plant then would be justified on a different basis than one designed to economically supply water to Southern California in the near future.

Three other reasons why the Metropolitan Water District might be interested in desalination were advanced last year by Robert A. Skinner, General Manager and Chief Engineer of the District:[34]

1) Northern California water will not be available to Southern California until 1972. Until that time, the water supply in Southern California might become "critical" in the sense that the ground water replenishment program would have to be curtailed even though the District could meet municipal and industrial demands.

2) Aqueducts now supplying Southern California cross earthquake fault lines. The desalted water could serve as an emergency supply if service were interrupted by an earthquake.

3) The desalted water could be used to improve the quality of District water supplies through blending and eliminate the need for capital expenditures for softening.

Upon examination these reasons for a District desalting plant at this time do not appear entirely convincing. At best the combination nuclear desalting plant cannot be placed into operation until 1971, even on the basis of a tight construction schedule. In 1972, massive water supplies will be available from the North. There is no convincing evidence that curtailment of ground water recharge would be a serious problem even if it persisted for several years. Actually, ground water reserves should be relied on for temporary emergencies of this kind, including service disruptions caused by earthquakes.

The recharge program in Southern California has been underway for a number of years and is beginning to yield outstanding results. In Orange County, for example, the static ground water level in the basin was 24.1 feet above sea level on November 1, 1965. This was 39 feet higher in the intake area than it was five years earlier and the highest average elevation since calculations have been made starting in 1931.[35] In addition, surface aqueduct storage in Southern California is sufficient to last a month. This might allow time to repair an aqueduct break or institute a program of limited waste water reclamation. Certainly, if these measures just suggested were not effective, it is doubtful if a supply of 150 million gallons a day could really act as a major emergency supply to an area as large as Southern California.

The question of blending to improve water quality is an interesting one because it has not been widely acknowledged that distilled water (perhaps containing only 5 parts per million of dissolved solids) would be highly corrosive in a conventional water distribution system of ferrous pipes. Special enamel-coated steel pipes are usually recommended for the conveyance of distilled water. This means that distilled water must be treated with chemicals to render it non-corrosive or it must be blended with

other waters.   The amount of distilled water blended into a conventional municipal system should probably be increased very
gradually over time to avoid a loosening of layers of matter which
tend to coat the insides of old distribution pipes.   For example, in
San Diego it was found that distilled water from the Point Loma
distillation plant tended to soften asbestos-cement pipes.   Treatment with calcium carbonate and minimum blend ratio of 3:1 was
used to protect pipes and mortar linings. [36]   Blending or post-
treatment is also necessary to give the distilled water a taste.

For the Metropolitan Water District, the Bechtel report calculated that distilled water could be blended with waters to save a
nominal softening charge on these other waters of $1,800,000 a
year.   If we credit these savings to the distilled water it would reduce desalted water costs from 27 cents per thousand gallons ($88
per acre-foot) to 23.4 cents per thousand gallons ($76 per acre-
foot). [37]   While these savings are important, it is clear that they
do not greatly lower the cost of distilled water, even if we neglect
the point that the distilled water would probably have to be blended
in any event.

In the final analysis it is probably fair to say that the level of
water costs set forth in the Bechtel report, is the product of a
number of assumptions, which if revised, could substantially
raise the level of costs above the level of 27 cents per thousand
gallons.   Interest rate charges were computed at 3.5 per cent;
operating factors for the water and power plants were assumed to
be 90 per cent; the Metropolitan Water District is not subject to
property or income taxes, the cost of right-of-way for a 25-mile
conveyance line was not estimated, power costs to the District
were estimated at 2.5 mills; and finally an amount of "exchange
power" in the amount of 100 megawatts was credited at 4 mills to
reduce the cost of water.   It is not clear that an exchange of power between the District and the Electric Utility Group should be
considered as anything other than a power transaction.   Yet, this
power credit was used to reduce the "cost" of water from 33.4
cents per thousand gallons ($108.9 an acre-foot) to the 27-cent
figure.

It can also be pointed out that even 27 cents per thousand gallons ($88 an acre-foot) is expensive water.   The District, itself,
has calculated the cost of present supplies from the Colorado
River at 10 cents per thousand gallons; the water from Northern
California for the District will cost about 20 cents per thousand
gallons ($65 an acre-foot).   However, in both cases, these costs
include the cost of a large distribution system serving a 4,500
square mile area. [38]   Full use of the water from Northern California is not anticipated until 1990 when demands are expected to
reach two million acre-feet a year.   Even in 1980 only half this
amount, or one million acre-feet of use is projected by District
officials. [39]

An additional perspective on the cost of desalted water can be seen from the fact that the City of Los Angeles is adding a second barrel to its own Owens River Aqueduct. This will increase the supply of water to the City by 150,000 acre-feet a year, the same capacity as the proposed District desalting plant, at an estimated cost of only $24-30 an acre-foot or less than 10 cents per thousand gallons.[40] In 1963-64, Los Angeles purchased only 77,977 acre-feet from the District or about 15 per cent of its total supply. When the second barrel is completed in 1968, Los Angeles purchases of District water will sharply decline.

Finally, it should be noted that District prices for softened water delivered at wholesale rates to member organizations are scheduled to rise on July 1, 1966 from $37 an acre-foot to $40 an acre-foot or less than 13 cents per thousand gallons. If District prices were raised to reflect the extra costs of the desalted water, as calculated by the Bechtel Report, they would have to be doubled. Of course, prices charged by the District will have to rise a great deal if they are to reflect the cost of Northern California water. It would be important to know the possible effects on the demand for water when prices at the wholesale level begin to reflect costs of this magnitude. The Metropolitan Water District has already assumed about three-fourths of the total cost of the Feather River Project from Northern California which is now estimated to cost in excess of 2 1/2 billion dollars. District payments to the State of California over the life of the contract will probably approach $6 billion.

It is true that none of these perspectives are conclusive. I have not studied the market for water for Southern California carefully; I do not know whether desalted water is economically feasible for Southern California. Yet, one cannot say either that this feasibility is clearly demonstrated in the Bechtel study. These matters of economic supply and demand, these principles of economic feasibility, are questions which deserve long and serious study. I hope that my brief analysis of the Bechtel report has demonstrated that a study of technical feasibility of desalting is not enough and that cost figures stemming from such studies must be carefully analyzed.

## CONCLUSION

The market for desalted water will grow in the future. Nuclear power will be often used as the fuel to supply exhaust steam in the distillation process. Yet, it seems apparent that the age-long hope for unlimited supplies of cheap water will not come about in the foreseeable future. No processes for the production of water which are inexpensive in terms of capital, equipment and trained man-power are on the horizon. The competition for water resources will increase in the future.

The demand for desalted water will be limited by its high costs to urban-metropolitan uses in areas near sea coasts. Cities near sea coasts, who have no obvious fresh water alternatives, and who also can absorb large blocks of power, would seem to be the best prospects for medium or large-scale combination nuclear -desalting plants. However, cities located near sea coasts usually dispose of their waste waters into the ocean. From their point of view, it would seem desirable that a balancing of gains and costs, in terms of water quantities and water qualities, be made between reclaiming waste waters, transporting fresh waters, and desalting saline sources.

Irrigation uses of desalted water may be possible when there exists the possibility of using desalted water for blending with poor quality supplies already on hand near a sea coast. Perhaps, there are only a limited number of such cases. In the long run, irrigation use of desalted water for high-value crops in or near urban areas may become feasible.

The market for desalting plants, especially of small and intermediate sizes, is likely to develop first. A desalting plant may well be the best answer in the short run for a metropolitan area, even though it may wish to build a large aqueduct at a later date. When there is uncertainty about growth rates, when the cost of capital is high, when an aqueduct takes fifteen years to construct -- in such situations it may pay to use desalted water in the short run until demand builds up to justify a large-size aqueduct.

These sorts of speculative statements seem reasonable. Whether they are borne out or not will depend, to great extent, upon the forces influencing the economic demand and supply of water resources. Economic analysis of water resource development is not going out of style. Clearly, economic considerations must be studied with the same intensity which we apply to the research and development of water production using nuclear energy.

## NOTES

1   The President's remarks to the Delegates of the First International Symposium on Desalination, October 7, 1965 as quoted in the Weekly Compilation of Presidential Documents, October 11, 1965.

2   Loc. cit.

3   For convincing evidence on this point see: The Value of Water in Alternative Uses with Special Application to Water Use in the San Juan and Rio Grande Basins of New Mexico, edited by National Wollman, (Albuquerque: University of New Mexico Press, 1962).

4    J. W. Milliman, "Economic Considerations for the Design of Water Institutions," Public Administration Review, Vol. XXV, No. 4, December 1965.

5    Allen V. Kneese, The Economics of Water Quality Management (Baltimore: Johns Hopkins Press, 1964).

6    For a simple exposition of this point see: Kenneth J. Arrow, "Criteria for Social Investment," Water Resources Research, Vol. I, Number 1, First Quarter, 1965.

7    Hirshleifer, DeHaven, and Milliman, Water Supply: Economics, Technology and Policy (Chicago: University of Chicago Press, Third Printing 1966). Chap. VII, "The Practical Logic of Investment Efficiency Calculations."

8    Louis Koenig, "Economic Boundaries of Saline Water Conversion," Journal American Water Works Association, Vol. 51, No. 7, July 1959 and The Future Uses of Saline and Fresh Water Resources of the United States, Department of Sanitary Engineering and Water Resources, Johns Hopkins University, June 1964.

9    Frederick E. Crever, "The Prospects for Dual Purpose Plants," Nucleonics, September, 1965, p. 49.

10   H. E. Hedger and A. M. Rawn, A Report Upon Potential Reclamation of Sewage Now Wasting Into the Ocean in Los Angeles County (Los Angeles, November 1958); A. F. Bush and S. F. Mulford, Studies of Waste Water Reclamation and Utilization (Department of Engineering, University of California, Los Angeles, Report 52-4, January 1954)

11   Hirshleifer, DeHaven and Milliman, op. cit., pp. 324-327.

12   Hedger and Rawn, op. cit., p. 90.

13   Willing Water, Vol. 10, No. 2, February 1966, p. 15.

14   Rolf Eliassen, Bruce M. Wyckoff and Charles D. Tonkin, "Ion Exchange for Reclamation of Reusable Supplies," Journal American Water Works Association, Vol. 57, No. 9, September 1965.

15   Bechtel Corporation, Engineering and Economic Feasibility Study for Combination Nuclear Power and Desalting Plant: Summary, sponsored jointly by the Metropolitan Water District of Southern California, U. S. Department of Interior, and U. S. Atomic Energy Commission, January 1966, Capter 5, p. 24.

16   Office of Science and Technology, An Assessment of Large Nuclear Powered Sea Water Distillation Plants: A Report of an Interagency Task Group (Washington, D. C.: U. S. Government Printing Office, March 1964), p. 2.

17   Crever, op. cit., p. 48.

18   Warren A. Hall, "A Method for Allocating Costs of a Water Supply Canal," Journal of Farm Economics, Vol. XLV, No. 4, November 1963.

19   Roland N. McKean, Efficiency in Government Through Systems Analysis: With Emphasis on Water Resources Development (New York: John Wiley & Sons, Inc., 1958), p. 46.

20   Hirshleifer, DeHaven and Milliman, op. cit., p. 94.

21   Water Desalination: Proposals for a Costing Procedure and Related Technical and Economic Considerations, (New York: United Nations, 1965).

22   Barnea, "A Note on a New Method of Cost Allocation for Combined Water and Desalination Plants," Water Resources Research, Vol. I, No. 1, First Quarter, 1965.

23   Bechtel Corporation, Engineering and Economic Feasibility Study, Phases I and II for a Combination Nuclear Power and Desalting Plant, December 1965, Chapter 10.

24   The Fluor Corporation, Feasibility Report on the Application of Desalination to Supplement the Florida Keys Aqueduct (Los Angeles, Fluor Corporation, March 1965), Chap. IV, p. 13.

25   Bechtel Corporation, Engineering and Economic Feasibility Study for A Combination Nuclear Power and Desalting Plant, Phases I and II, Phase III, and Summary. Copies of the three volume report (T1022300) are available from Clearinghouse, U.S. Department of Commerce, Springfield, Virginia 22151. Vol. 3, a summary, $1.25; Volumes 1 and 2, $4.00 each.

26   Phase III, op. cit., Chapter 2.

27   Department of Water and Power, City of Los Angeles, Southern California Edison Company and the San Diego Gas and Electric Company.

28   The Metropolitan Water District of Southern California, Twenty-Sixth Annual Report, (Los Angeles, California, 1964).

29   Bechtel, Summary, op. cit., Chapter 5, p. 11.

30   Office of Science and Technology, Assessment of --- Distillation Plants, op. cit., pp. 6-10.

31   Bechtel, Phase III, op. cit., Chapter 5, p. 27.

32   Ibid., Chap. 2, pp. 1-2.

33   In January 1966, The Board of Directors of the Metropolitan Water District ordered a study of a desalting plant with an initial capacity of 50 million gallons a day which might subsequently be expanded to 150 million gallons a day.   The Metropolitan Water District of Southern California, Colorado River Aqueduct News, Vol. 33, No. 1, January 1966.

34   Robert A. Skinner, "Sea Water Conversion Study in California," Journal American Water Works Association, Vol. 57, No. 6, June 1965.

35   John M. Toups, Engineer's Report on Ground Water Conditions in the Orange County Water District, February 6, 1966, Orange County, California.

36   Roy E. Dodson and Stewart F. Mulford, "Use of Distilled Sea Water at San Diego," Journal American Water Works Association, Vol. 57, No. 9, September 1965.

37   Bechtel, Phase III, op. cit., Chap. 8, p. 10.

38   Metropolitan Water District of Southern California, Colorado River Aqueduct News, Vol. 32, No. 7, July 1965.

39   Bechtel, Phases I and II, op. cit., Chap. 4, p. 3.

40   Max K. Socha, "Construction of the Second Los Angeles Aqueduct," Journal American Water Works Association, Vol. 57, No. 6, June 1965.

# 7. Strategic Economic Factors in Planning
# Nuclear Power for Desalting Sea Water

Philip Mullenbach, President, Growth Industry Shares, Inc.

We can hope to evaluate usefully the economics of nuclear power for water desalting over the next decade only after being satisfied that certain prior conditions have been defined and explicitly met.

First, that water desalting at a specific metropolitan center in the United States is found by objective economic analysis to be a reasonably promising technical and cost alternative to other methods of securing water -- such as by treating sewage discharge water, by transporting or diverting water from distant sources, or by simply expanding existing conventional sources of water. [1]

Second, that the technology of sea water desalting is being pressed on a scale and with sufficient vigor and skill as to justify the assumption that large-scale plants (150 MGD) can be usefully considered for construction in the next ten years. [2]

Third, that the major goal of present desalting development programs is to produce competitive water for municipal purposes in large quantities from sea water. For the time being, other sources (brackish water) and other markets (irrigation water for agriculture) are not ready to be considered. [3]

If these conditions or assumptions relating to alternative supplies, to technology and scale-up, and to the specific market for water are satisfied, then we will be in a position to examine the possible role of nuclear power in sea water desalting in the United States during the next decade. We emphasize the period and the place, for during the next ten years nuclear power seems certain to have become one of the major sources of energy in the United States. [4]   During much of this period water desalting will probably be in an early stage of development, whereas nuclear power development will probably have reached an advanced stage. [5] Before the end of this decade designers of desalting plants can expect to learn whether nuclear breeder reactors are the practical next step in technology (and, hence, whether prospective advanced converters represent merely an intermediate stage of reactor development).

Furthermore, our analysis will be directed at those strategic independent variables, explicit or implicit, in recent engineering studies, [6] , [7]  that seem to hold the greatest potential for influencing the future costs of energy and of desalted water. A list of these strategic factors, being economic and institutional in form, is long. Among others it includes interest rates and fixed charges (under private or municipal ownership), the economies of increasing plant size, the so-called external economies of the nuclear power industry, the cost benefits of dual-purpose power reactors, and the influence of national energy policies on both fossil fuels and nuclear power. Before examining these variables in dynamic terms, it would be well for water specialists to realize that the history of nuclear power development may carry some relevant lessons for planning water desalting today.

Looking at reactor development in terms of planning, we believe the early programs of government and industry probably ignored or gave too little attention to (a) the stimulating potentialities of competition between the largest equipment manufacturers in reducing capital costs by repetitive design and by the economies of increased plant size; (b) the great cost benefits derived from large government plants providing services or products, such as low-cost enriched uranium; (c) the powerful motivation of the private-versus-public power controversy; and (d) the rapid growth of large power loads in metropolitan areas being threatened with air pollution by burning fossil fuels. On the other hand, the early history of reactor development suggests that too great emphasis was placed on (a) justifying nuclear power by extreme assertions about the physical limitations of depleting domestic fossil fuel reserves; (b) the asserted necessity of getting the government out of reactor development as soon as possible; and (c) the abortive idea that competitive nuclear power could be readily achieved by the credits received from the sale of plutonium produced in dual-purpose power reactors. [8]   Each of these may have its complement or analogue today in the development of water desalting processes and plants.

TABLE I

Average Fuel Costs of Steam Electric Plants,
by Regions, 1964

| Region | Average fuel cost per million Btu (cents) | | | Percentage distribution of Btu of fuel consumed | | |
|---|---|---|---|---|---|---|
| | Coal | Oil | Gas | Coal | Oil | Gas |
| New England | 33.4 | 34.4 | 34.2 | 63 | 33 | 4 |
| Middle Atlantic | 26.0 | 31.7 | 33.5 | 77 | 15 | 8 |
| East North Central | 24.6 | - | 24.8 | 96 | - | 4 |
| West North Central | 26.0 | - | 24.3 | 50 | - | 50 |
| South Atlantic | 25.4 | 33.9 | 32.2 | 79 | 11 | 10 |
| East South Central | 19.3 | - | 24.6 | 92 | - | 8 |
| West South Central | - | - | 19.6 | - | - | 100 |
| Mountain | 19.2 | 25.7 | 26.6 | 45 | 4 | 51 |
| Pacific | - | 30.7 | 32.2 | - | 17 | 83 |
| Total United States | 24.6 | 32.6 | 25.3 | 65 | 7 | 28 |

Source: National Coal Association, Steam-Electric Plant Factors, 1964, 15th Edition, September 1965.

## ECONOMIC STATICS, 1966-70

This phase of analysis will consist of, first, a static description of the comparative costs of energy from nuclear and fossil fuels in private power plants of modern size (500 MWe or larger) in various areas of the United States and, second, a brief review of the cost components of desalted water and the effect of energy costs on total water cost as estimated by the available computer studies of dual-purpose reactor coupled with commensurately-sized desalting plants (up to 150 MGD). In the second part of the paper we shall assess the strategic economic factors in a dynamic manner, that is, evaluate the changes over time of the assumed independent variables.  In the third part we shall outline some of the tentative implications for public policy and planning that are suggested by the preceding economic evaluation.

### The Competitive Threshold:
### Geographic Variations In Energy Costs

As a guideline, privately-owned nuclear power plants of 500 MWe or larger are evidently capable of generating electricity at costs of roughly 4. 0 to 4. 5 mills per kwh. [9]   This range is broadly equivalent to coal, oil or natural gas priced at 20 to 25 cents per million Btu.  By way of geographic comparison, the 1964 average fuel costs of steam-electric generating plants in the United States, shown in Table I, are 24. 6 cents per million Btu for coal, 32. 6 cents for oil and 25. 3 cents for natural gas. Moreover, certain regions of the United States -- New England and the Pacific -- bear fuel costs that would give nuclear power a clear cost advantage.  Nuclear power may be competitive now in areas where one-half or more of all steam power is generated, and thus is well past the competitive threshold.

Furthermore, nuclear power costs appear to be fully competitive with fossil fuel costs in a number of coastal urban areas where water desalting is already of interest (see Table II).  Each

TABLE II

Fuel Costs of Large Steam Electric Plants
Near Selected Metropolitan Areas, 1964

| Plant Location | Installed Capacity (MWe) | Cost per million Btu (cents) | | | Percentage distribution of Btus of fuel consumed | | |
|---|---|---|---|---|---|---|---|
| | | Coal | Oil | Gas | Coal | Oil | Gas |
| California - Seal Beach (Haynes Plant) | 460 | - | 30. 8 | 32. 2 | - | 24 | 76 |
| Florida - Port Everglades | 852. 6 | - | 32. 5 | - | - | 100 | - |
| Tampa | 617 | 29. 4 | - | - | 100 | - | - |
| New York - Glenwood Landing | 400. 3 | - | 30. 2 | 34. 7 | - | 22 | 78 |

Source: National Coal Association, Steam-Electric Plant Factors, 1964, 15th Edition, September 1965.

of these fossil-fuel plant sites is in or near a large metropolitan center which requires large and growing amounts of water and electric power.  Finally, it is significant that in three of the four locations the fossil fuels are oil and natural gas, rather than coal, the most widely used boiler fuel in the United States.

## Break-even Fuel Costs

These figures are, in effect, first approximations of the current competitive position of nuclear power.  Today reactor manufacturers can judge with seeming accuracy the break-even fuel costs of fossil-fueled plants and nuclear power plants, that is, the fuel cost at which it is a matter of economic indifference whether energy for desalting is derived from a nuclear energy plant or a conventional thermal plant of corresponding size.  Approximate break-even fossil fuel costs are as follows, according to recent Westinghouse estimates (1965): [10]

| Plant size- MWe net | Single-purpose plant cents per million Btu | Dual-purpose plant-50 MGD | Difference |
|---|---|---|---|
| 300 | 25 | 22.5 | 2.5¢ |
| 400 | 23 | 21 | 2.0 |
| 500 | 22 | 20 | 2.0 |
| 600 | 20 | 19 | 1.0 |
| 700 | 19 | 18.5 | 0.5 |
| 800 | 18 | 18 | 0.5 |

These figures suggest not only the range of fossil fuel costs at which nuclear energy is directly competitive, but also that the economies of increasing plant size provide greater thrust to nuclear energy than to fossil-fueled plants.  Importantly, too, the intensity of fuel competition in dual-purpose plants is about the same as between nuclear and fossil fuel electric power plants. Dual-purpose plants for such metropolitan areas as are listed in Table II appear advantageous because they can meet the growing loads of both water and electric power.  Furthermore, the recent emphasis on the dual-purpose reactor is fully justified because the cost of low-pressure steam is lower over a wide range of conditions than from a much larger single-purpose reactor.

## Plant Size and Water Costs

The economies of increased size and the use of dual-purpose reactors would clearly help to decrease the costs of desalted water.  But at the present time the development of desalting plants has apparently not reached plant sizes that can easily be considered commensurate with the present optimum scale of nuclear power plants.  Whereas the largest desalting plant in operation or planned for early construction is only a few mgd, a water plant many times this size would be required to take any substantial fraction of the steam output of the latest second generation power reactors now being ordered (700 MWe and up). Hence, rigorous evaluation of the economics of nuclear energy for desalting should start with the lower range of dual-purpose plant capacities. The 1964 studies by Catalytic Construction Company prepared for the AEC and the Office of Saline Water show that, aside from the technology of water desalting, the cost of water is especially sensitive to four elements: plant size, interest rates and fixed charges, the prime cost of steam from the reactor, and the credit to be allowed for electric power output. The effects of these variables are illustrated by the comparative cases shown in Table III,

TABLE III

Key Factors in Water Cost Variations in Low Temperature Dual-Purpose
Plants (Assuming 6m/kwh electric power credit)

| Variables | Fossil-fueled plant | Nuclear reactor |
|---|---|---|
| A. Plant size and cost of water - cents per thousand gallons (7% fixed charges) | | |
| MWt | | |
| 200 | 45.5 | 54.8 |
| /600/ | 37.4 | 33.9 |
| 1000 | 39.1 | 30.6 |
| 1500 | 37.3 | 28.3 |

| B. Plant size and output | Water output | Net salable power | Water output | Net salable power |
|---|---|---|---|---|
| MWt | MGD | MWe | MGD | MWe |
| 200 | 18.5 | 33.8 | 26.5 | 26.6 |
| /600/ | 66.7 | 96.2 | 63.2 | 85.2 |
| 1000 | 113.4 | 158.9 | 95.5 | 144.0 |
| 1500 | 182.5 | 233.9 | 133.7 | 220.6 |

C. Fixed charges and cost of steam and power (600 MWt)

| | Steam cost ¢/MBtu | Power cost m/kwh | Steam cost ¢/MBtu | Power cost m/kwh |
|---|---|---|---|---|
| 4% | 47.1 | 5.2 | 32.1 | 5.2 |
| /7%/ | 48.6 | 5.7 | 39.6 | 5.9 |
| 14% | 52.1 | 7.2 | 60.4 | 7.6 |

D. Power credit and water cost (600 MWt and 7% fixed charges)

| m/kwh | ¢/1000g | ¢/1000g |
|---|---|---|
| 3.65 | 44.0 | 39.2 |
| 4.00 | 42.9 | 38.2 |
| 6.00 | 36.5 | 32.4 |

Source: Catalytic Construction Company and Nuclear Utilities Services, Inc. "A Study of Desalting Plants (15 to 150 MGD) and Nuclear Power Plants (200 to 1500 MWt) for Combined Water and Power Production," NYO-3316.1, Department of Interior and AEC, September 1964.

in which it is assumed that fossil fuel costs are 35 cents per million Btu, applicable to Southern California at the end of 1963. (As we have seen, this assumed fossil fuel cost appears today to be too high by a few cents, as the recent fuel costs of large thermal plants in the area have been 30-32 cents per million Btu).[11]

Brief study of Table III confirms the fact that water costs are especially sensitive to increasing plant size. A tremendous scale-up over recent desalting plant size (30 times) is implied by coupling with even relatively small power plants. Also, there is great leverage in having such capital-intensive facilities carry the low fixed charges characteristic of municipalities or public entities, rather than private power systems. Finally, even with the benefit of low fixed charges, the cost of desalted water does not approach competitively convincing levels short of water plant sizes of about 100 MGD, and reactors of far more than 200 MWe capacity are necessary to assure competitive nuclear power costs. Based on this essentially static view, the economics of water desalting with either nuclear energy or fossil fuel plants does not appear convincingly promising -- unless one permits a major relaxation of the technical and economic constraints that were necessarily imposed by the first approximations of the Catalytic Construction study in 1964.[6]

Examination of the recent Bechtel study of the Metropolitan Water District,[7] as well as the preceding Interagency Task Group Study[12] indicate that the potential economies of scale are expected to be the primary key to competive desalted water in the near future. In effect, one observes that the larger the power plant can become the greater will be the net revenues available from the sale of excess power and hence the lower the cost of water will be. Consequently, the cost of desalted water could be significantly influenced by the size and growth of the power load in the system that would be prepared to take the excess power. The reciprocal relation between the scale of production of desalted water and of excess power sold is illustrated in Table IV. The lowest estimated water cost, 27.4 cents per thousand gallons, is associated with the smallest ratio of water output to excess power for sale.

In brief, then, the static economics of dual-purpose power reactors indicate the cost advantages of large-scale reactors, with water essentially a by-product, located in large municipal water systems and enjoying low fixed charges on capital.

## ECONOMIC DYNAMICS

From this point on, the engineer and the economist may find themselves parting company. For in considering such elements of water and power economics as interest rates, external economies and national energy policies, the economist is necessarily complicating the smooth engineering analyses provided by digital computers. Data that had been put into the voluminous computations as assumptions or constants the economist must -- if he is to be productive -- reexamine and consider as dependent variables. Indeed, the economist necessarily asks the kind of controversial question that the engineer customarily finds awkward or uncomfortable to ask himself. For example, to what extent since 1954 has the price structure of coal, oil and natural gas in the United States been influenced by national policies designed to protect domestic producers from the price competition of foreign fuels? Recognizing that water and power supply are franchised monopolies and that dual-purpose plants are highly capital-intensive, what are the appropriate rates of interest to assume when mixed private and public ownership is involved? Or further, just how far into the future is it economically sensible to gauge the benefits of very large multi-purpose projects or the development expenses committed to them today? We shall start with the crucial role of interest rates.

TABLE IV

Large Dual-Purpose Reactor:
Reciprocal Relation of Water and Power Production

| Water production MGD | Excess power for sale MWe | Water cost ¢/1000 gal |
|---|---|---|
| 235 | 747 | 27.4 |
| 350 | 570 | 30.5 |
| 435 | 422 | 32.4 |
| 520 | 260 | 32.4 |

Assumptions:
3430 MWt boiling water reactor.
Fixed charges, 7% on water plant and 14% on power plant.
Excess electric power for sale at 3.86 mills/kwh.
Steam cost rising from 9.8¢ MBtu, to 15.3¢, 17.8¢ and 20.2¢.
Performance ratio (water/steam) rising from 9.1 to 15.5.

Source: F. E. Crever et al, "Potential of BWR's as Low-Cost Heat Sources for Desalting Plant Applications," Table I, p. 184, Proceedings of the American Power Conference, 1965, Vol. XXVII.

## Interest Rates and Fixed Charges

Fixed charges on capital represent between 40% and 50% of the total costs of desalted water (Table V). They are the single most important cost element, reflecting the fact that power and water plants are highly capital-intensive (that is, variable labor and material costs are relatively less important per unit of output). Therefore, the estimated costs of desalted water are especially sensitive to (a) the level of interest rate assumed and possible future changes in that rate, and to (b) the form of ownership assumed -- municipal or private, or a mixture thereof through private ownership of power facilities.

TABLE V

Composition of the Cost of Desalted Water Using
a Large Dual-purpose Reactor (3430MWt)

|  | ¢/1000g | % of total |
|---|---|---|
| Fixed charges | 10. 9¢ | 39. 8% |
| Steam cost | 8. 8 | 32. 1 |
| Chemicals | 2. 7 | 9. 9 |
| Electricity | 2. 3 | 8. 4 |
| Labor cost | 1. 9 | 6. 9 |
| Supplies and maintenance | . 8 | 2. 9 |
| Total | 27. 4¢ | 100. 0% |

Assumption:
  Fixed charges, 7% on water plant and 14% on boiling water
  reactor.  Steam pressure, 15. 4 pia; steam temperature,
  215°F. ; brine temperature, 200°F.  Performance ration,
  9. 1; water production, 235 MGD.  Excess electric power
  remaining for sale at 3. 86 mills/kwh.

Source:  F.  E.  Crever, et al, "Potential of BWR's as Low-
         Cost Heat Sources for Desalting Plant Applications, "
         Table I, p. 184, Proceedings of the American Power
         Conference, 1965, Vol. XXVII.

As shown in Table III (Part C) private utility rates of fixed
charges are more burdensome on nuclear powered than on fossil-
fueled plants.  Moreover, the municipal rates of financing put at
a cost disadvantage the large fossil-fueled plants, which are less
capital-intensive and have heavier fuel expenses.  In addition, if
the chosen interest rate should be thought of as simply a measure
of "time preference, " that is, as a rough indicator of the value of
present over future monetary benefits (or, conversely, the relative burden of future expenses as against present expenses), then
the difference between private and municipal rates of fixed
charges becomes exceedingly important in arriving at planning or
policy decisions.  For example, in the developmental stage --
when the economies of size remain to be demonstrated in desalting plants -- a smaller dual-purpose plant (e. g., 50 MGD) may be
a better economic choice at municipal rates of fixed charges than
a much larger plant (e. g. , 150 MGD)in which any substantial portion of the capital carries private rates of fixed charges. [6]

The time-preference leverage of interest rates (and fixed
charges) also shows up in the evaluation of current types of converter reactors as against prospective breeders.  Considering the
fact that a dual-purpose reactor chosen to come on the line by
1970 may well have a useful life of up to 30 years, the cost of
fixed charges obviously should be minimized if possible.  For the
probability is good that before the last twenty years of that period
breeder reactors will have proved to be a better alternative
source of nuclear energy.

Time preference seems to support the practical planning
principle that "a bird in the hand is worth two in the bush. "  This

can be crudely measured by discounting future economic benefits to their present worth; e. g. , if the compound interest rate chosen were as low as 2. 35%, then the discounted worth today of an economic benefit (excess over cost) occurring 30 years away would be zero.  Where major advances in technological progress are in prospect, present-worth calculations deserve consideration -- without being exaggerated -- when evaluating such large capital investments.

Finally, during the last two years the money markets of the United States have moved toward significantly higher interest rates on bonds and other evidence of indebtedness. [13]   This raises the question whether the interest rate assumptions in the major cost studies of dual-purpose plants remain valid.  The answer seems to depend partly on how long national monetary policy will continue to require downward pressure on bank reserves and lending conditions.  Short-term rates have recently reached the highest levels in 30 years and fiscal policy appears to have moved toward restraint of aggregate demand through selective restoration of taxes.  In view of a nearly full-employment economy and a partial war-economy, the inflationary restraints seem likely to be needed for a considerable period -- or until the nation's military posture changes significantly.  Therefore, one might expect some advance in long-term rates for state and municipal bonds.  At the present moment, the assumed rate of 3. 5% interest appears low in light of the current and foreseeable tax-free bond market for prime issues.  Current rates are substantially above 3. 5%, in fact, nearly one-seventh higher. [14]   This is a variable that the U. S. engineering studies did not evaluate, but is clearly pertinent in 1966 financing.

## Economies of Size

Next to variations in fixed charges, the economies of size most noticeably influence the cost of dual-purpose plants, assuming a given state of reactor technology.  As we have seen, the economies of increased size have been more convincingly established for nuclear power reactors than for desalting facilities. [6] Moreover, the power loads in metropolitan areas are large and they are growing in sufficient blocks as to justify increments in nuclear power capacity today that are twice as great as the fossil-fueled increments considered economic only five years ago in Los Angeles, Chicago and New York.  It is pertinent, at this stage, that the growth in urban power load has a doubling time of ten years (7% annually) whereas for municipal water demand the growth rate is only half that.  Neither of these growth rates is now a limiting factor in selecting an appropriate size for dual-purpose plants that might be planned for 1970.  On the other hand, we must recognize that the present schedules of diminishing unit plant cost (price per kwe ) as a function of size have, first, already anticipated the future benefits of external economies (to be described later) and, second, have shown a perceptible flattening of unit cost in the range of reactor size most relevant today for both water and power, namely, 500-1,000 MWe.[15]

In other words, manufacturer's bids on power reactors can hardly be expected to decline much more, if at all, as a result of increasing the capacity of water resources that might be expected to go on the line by 1970 or soon thereafter. Until the plant costs and fuel-cycle economics of breeder reactors are more clearly revealed, the economies of size have been and are today substantially reflected in the computer studies of desalted water costs. There seems to be little significant room for further improvement in unit plant cost, short of the huge multi-purpose complexes imagined by ORNL for a period some decades away and outside the scope of this paper.[16]   In terms of both economies of reactor size and the growth in urban power loads, then, the application of nuclear power to water desalting is being optimized with current reactor sizes and designs. The open question, for the water engineers and economists to answer, is the nature of economies of size for dealting plants. For the moment, the optimum size of reactor appears to be far greater than that suggested by the present stage of water desalting technology. But this optimum reactor size is not obviously greater than the size of water facility that is commensurate with the water requirements of metropolitan areas.[17]

## External Economies and Diseconomies

Most of the computer studies are oblivious to what economists refer to as "external economies." These customarily refer to the economic benefits accruing to a plant or an industry from resources or services which are outside the control of the plant or industry. For example, the so-called infant industry is unlikely to thrive without substantial "free" assistance from the surrounding industrial community or from the infrastructure of the economy. A new plant in an industrialized area starts out with the advantages of the public facilities such as highways, railroads, water supply, etc. Now, in the case of nuclear power plants such external economies are very great. Consider the fact that uranium supply, enrichment facilities, chemical processing, etc. are already in being, partly as a result of the AEC's military and reactor development programs and partly because both private and public services are being expanded or converted to meet civilian requirements. Dual-purpose nuclear power plants will receive the boost of external economies in the immediate future, whereas for fossil fuel plants no essential gain in external economies appears in prospect.[18]

To a degree the external economies of nuclear energy are measurable, but even when they are not their importance is usually evident -- particularly as the size of the industry increases and benefits of economies of scale become more pronounced. The measurable illustrations of external economies are these:

Uranium supply -- exploration, development and financing of uranium mining and milling for AEC programs have brought down uranium prices to $5 per pound of $U_3O_8$ (at least for a time).

Fuel element fabrication -- the combination of the military propulsion reactor program for vessels with the civilian power reactor program has resulted in a scale of fabricating capacity that is conducive to still lower nuclear fuel costs in the future.

Chemical processing -- heretofore the output of spent fuel elements from nuclear power plants has appeared too small to justify an industry of economical size, but the prospective level of reactor construction and operation suggests that that phase will soon be ended.

Enriched uranium -- the gaseous diffusion facilities owned by the AEC are of such a size, even though now operating below capacity, that the cost of enriched reactor fuel is far below that considered in the early '50s and conceivably may decline further. [19]

Reactor manufacturing -- as a result of repetitive use and modification of basic reactor engineering and design, it has become possible now for reactor manufacturers to quote reactors on a fixed-price basis that spreads the design costs over a large number of units.

To a degree these external economies may be reduced, or partially offset, by external diseconomies (or social costs) that are contingent upon the growth of a substantial power reactor industry. The principal case in prospect is the possibility of converter reactor capacity expanding so rapidly that the low-cost sources of natural uranium may be substantially used up before the technology of advanced converters or breeders can be developed sufficiently for commercial application. While there may be technical grounds for some concern, the world-wide uranium supply, the vast stored quantities of depleted uranium, the probably excessive military stockpiles of highly-enriched uranium and weapon-grade plutonium, and the large reserves of only slightly higher-cost natural uranium here and abroad, all seem to provide a cushion to cover the ten-year period until breeder reactors can promise relief. [20] In any case the possible increase in the cost of domestic natural uranium is not so great as to represent a significant obstacle to commercial nuclear power during the next decade and probably much longer. [21]

Important social costs of a large-scale nuclear power industry are commonly said to be the hazards of nuclear power plants located in or near urban centers and the disposal of radioactive wastes in volume. In evaluating the direct expenses of controlling such social costs of nuclear power it is well to note that fossil-fueled power plants entail their social costs as well. For example, it appears that with few exceptions the growth of urban (metropolitan) loads and interconnections with intersystem grids is now such that economically acceptable locations of power reactors need not be in or adjacent to population centers. [22]   Moreover, conventional oil or coal-burning power plants in urban centers are becoming such large sources of air pollution by sulphur and products of incomplete combustion that the electric utility industry is calling on equipment suppliers and others to mount a costly pollution abatement program that will help coal and oil-burning plants to maintain competitive parity with nuclear power plants. [23]

### Technological Discontinuities in Progress

A primary economic weakness of the cost evaluations of dual-purpose plants is inherent -- how to take account of discontinuities in technical progress in reactor design and in nuclear fuel. Current engineering studies have been largely confined to the present generation of water reactors, yet it is clear that major developmental expenditures and effort are being directed now to the advanced converters and, more particularly, to the breeders. Also, we sense that, based upon the experience of the last ten years, nuclear fuel economies may not follow a smooth curve of progress but instead move by stages as determined by advances in fuel element design and composition, in fuel fabrication, in chemical processing, in waste disposal and in institutional arrangements. The computer approach to dual-purpose reactors and to fuel-cycle costs is obviously convenient, simple and revealing. But an economist has reason to be wary of such studies when he sees in economic history the repeated interjection of "outside" influences and policies that produced discontinuities. For example, within twelve months during 1961-62 the price of enriched uranium was reduced drastically, and more recently legislation permitting (and later requiring) private ownership of fissionable material has altered the terms on which inventories will be carried by electric utility systems. [24]

### National Energy Policies

A further weakness of the cost studies completed thus far is the general assumption that national energy policies are going to remain substantially unchanged in the foreseeable future. Yet, within the last decade U. S. policy for fossil fuels has shifted drastically, from a condition of generally free competition internationally to one of protection of domestic producers of energy from the full impact of foreign competition. The Bechtel study of the Metropolitan Water District assumes that the price of residual fuel oil will rise during the next 30 years from 32. 5 cents to 35. 4 cents per million Btu and the price of natural gas from 36. 3 cents to 46. 3 cents. Because fossil fuel costs would have to drop to 23 cents per million Btu to be competitive with nuclear fuel at 14 cents per million, the Bechtel report comfortably states that the fossil fuel assumption may be "considered conservative. " It seems more likely to prove unrealistic than conservative.

Changes in the relative price of domestic fossil fuels in recent years have come about as a result of three factors: First, reduced transportation costs, chiefly railroad rates on coal; second, the progressive widening of federal and state protection of domestic producers; and, third, the appearance of nuclear energy as a huge new primary source of energy potentially available at disturbingly low cost. With respect to the first, reduced transportation rates have accounted for much of the decline of nearly three per cent in the delivered cost of coal to steam-electric plants during the last decade.[11]   (During the same period the cost of oil decreased by almost two per cent, whereas natural gas increased by more than 40 per cent. ) The energy industry states that it is aware that these cost trends could be affected by changes in legislation concerning the control of natural gas prices in the field and of imports of Canadian natural gas, by changes in import quotas on petroleum and residual fuel oil, and by other policies (state proration and extraordinary depletion allowances) that subsidize or protect the domestic fossil fuel industries.[11]

These policies are exceedingly important for nuclear energy, because they make it more certain that nuclear power will be able to compete with fossil fuels. Ultimately, of course, nuclear energy may affect widely the present elevated price structure of all domestic fuels used for power generation. Nuclear energy seems to hold some chance of penetrating the present "closed system" of mutually reinforcing elements of national oil policies -- state proration, extraordinary depletion allowances and import quotas, all of which serve to protect the prices of coal and natural gas, as well as oil.[25]   Under these circumstances it is economically conceivable, though perhaps politically uncertain that nuclear energy will within the next decade contribute to a reexamination, and perhaps modification, of present protectionist policies which could lead to appreciably lower domestic prices for all fossil fuels. In this respect the major potential addition to fossil fuel reserves -- the oil in shale and tar sands -- may have to face more difficult economic criteria than are presently foreseen.[26]

## IMPLICATIONS FOR NATIONAL POLICY AND FOR DEVELOPMENT PLANNING

This evaluation of the economics of nuclear power for water desalting is intended to be not only descriptive but also to provide a rough kind of guide -- possibly a quiet warning -- to help private and public decision makers. A few policy and planning implications logically flow from this analysis and the cost studies that are now at hand.

First, as to the pace and timing of desalting plants and their coupling with dual-purpose nuclear power plants, neither a leisurely nor a crash program seems to be justified by the obvious economic promise of dual-purpose plants. At this stage the technology and scaling-up of desalting plants appear to be a long step behind nuclear power development. Moreover, the economics of breeder reactors could significantly change the assumptions now being used in dual-purpose studies which are customarily based on converter types of water reactors. Furthermore, the present period of high interest rates should not last indefinitely, considering the maturity of our capital-intensive economy and the need for interest rates that encourage rather than retard investment.

Second, with respect to the economies of large dual-purpose power plants, it seems probable -- based on plant size and product ratios -- that desalted water will be for some years a by-product rather than a joint product of large power reactors built primarily for generating electricity. The economies of reactor size clearly represent strong leverage to improve the costs of desalted water. But one may be rightly concerned that the benefits of very low-cost power and of large power credits may weaken the incentive or distort the technology for achieving optimum desalting processes and equipment. (For a time, nuclear power technology was distorted by the "crutch" offered by the weapon value of by-product plutonium and by the low service charges on AEC-furnished materials. ) A form of economic Calvinism is not being proposed here -- that water desalting plants must prove their competitive worth without regard to low-cost nuclear power. However, just as nuclear power had to drop the plutonium crutch, so too may water desalting technology make better long-term progress if it does not become too dependent upon low-cost nuclear power.[27]

Third, considering the subtle and usually tense relations between private power and municipal power systems, it is obvious that the prospect of large dual-purpose plants could create a new set of institutional relationships -- one in which doctrinaire approaches seem singularly inappropriate. On the one hand, the economies of scale should entice the private electric utility system to go into or join with public water systems in the production of power and water. On the other hand, the public water systems may wish to see municipal or other public power systems undertake the dual-purpose plants, presumably at less cost to the consumer in lower water and power rates. State public utility commissions will need to examine carefully the joint arrangements (partly private, partly municipal) that may be developed.

Finally, with respect to national energy policies, we have seen that the first competitive impact of nuclear power was in areas of high fuel costs where coal was customarily the predominant fuel. With the prospect of large dual-purpose reactors for water desalting the competition with fuel oil and natural gas may become more intense. Thus far, nuclear power has provided a desirable restraint on delivered coal prices in the eastern United States. Conceivably, natural gas and fuel oil prices may be affected similarly. Yet it seems more likely that present protectionist policies and subsidies for domestic producers of energy will continue for a time to provide a price umbrella over nuclear power. (Interestingly, import quotas on residual oil -- but not crude petroleum -- were lifted last week. ) Continuation of such policies and subsidies will permit nuclear power to make greater inroads into the boiler-fuel markets of the three fossil fuels than would otherwise be possible. Critical reexamination of these national energy policies might be expected at some point as nuclear energy takes over a larger part of the boiler-fuel markets of oil and natural gas.

These national policies seem certain to require change and the protection of fossil fuel prices may be reduced, possibly leading to lower relative prices compared with nuclear energy. It is exceedingly important that the economics of low-cost nuclear power from breeder reactors be established soon -- both as a continuing restraint on fossil fuel prices as well as to reveal the potential role of dual-purpose reactors coupled with large desalting plants.

## NOTES

1.  Milliman, J. W. , "The Economics of Water Production Using Nuclear Energy, " Symposium on Water Production Using Nuclear Energy, sponsored by the University of Arizona, et al, March 30, 1966.

2.  U. S. Department of Interior, Office of Saline Water, Saline Water Conversion Report for 1964, Government Printing Office, 1965.

3.  Hammond, R. P. , "Nuclear Desalting for Agricultural Water, " Nucleonics, September 1965, p. 51 et seq.

4.  Tape, G. F. , et al, "Future Energy Needs and the Role of Nuclear Power, " Third United Nations International Conference on the Peaceful Uses of Atomic Energy, 1964, Paper No. 192.

5.  See, for example, Wright, J. H. and Gray, J. C. , "Advanced Reactor Systems and Their Future Applications, "Proceedings of the American Power Conference, 27th Annual Meeting, Vol. XXVII, 1965, pp. 221-232.

6.   Catalytic Construction Company and Nuclear Utilities Serv-
     ices, Inc. "A Study of Desalting Plants (15 to 150 mgd) and
     Nuclear Power Plants (200 to 1500 mwt) for Combined Water
     and Power Production, NYO-3316-1, U. S. Department of
     Interior and U. S. Atomic Energy Commission, Washington,
     D. C. (Sept. 1964).

7.   Bechtel Corporation, "Economic Feasibility Study, Phases I,
     II and III for a Combination Nuclear Power and Desalting
     Plant, " December 1965, Sponsored jointly by the Metropoli-
     tan Water District of Southern California, U. S. Department
     of Interior (OSW) and the U. S. Atomic Energy Commission,
     Volume I, II and III.

8.   Cisler, Walker L. , "Economic Feasibility: The Dual Purpose
     Reactor, " Annals of the American Academy of Political and
     Social Science, November 1953, pp. 45-49.

9.   Sporn, P. , "A Post Oyster Creek Evaluation of the Current
     Status of Nuclear Electric Generation, " Nuclear Power Eco-
     nomics - Analysis and Comments - 1964 Joint Committee on
     Atomic Energy, Government Printing Office, 1964.

10.  B. R. Scarbrough et al, "The Economics of Combined Elec-
     tric Power and Water Desalination Plants, " Proceedings of
     the American Power Conference, Vol. XXVII, 1965, pp. 167-
     172.

11.  Steam-Electric Plant Factors, 1964, National Coal Associa-
     tion, 15th Edition, 1965.

12.  Office of Science and Technology, Executive Office of the
     President, An Assessment of Large Nuclear Powered Sea
     Water Distillation Plants, a Report of an Interagency Task
     Group, March 1964.

13.  Economic Indicators, February 1966, prepared for the Joint
     Economic Committee by the Council of Economic Advisers.

14.  Standard and Poors, The Outlook, March 14, 1966.

15.  Nucleonics, November 1964, "G. E. Issues Nuclear Power
     Plant Price List, " pp. 20-21.

16.  Hammond, R. P. , "Large Reactors May Distill Sea Water
     Economically, " Nucleonics, Vol. 21, December 1962, pp.
     45-49.

17.  Water and Power, Sixty-fourth Annual Report, 1964-65,
     Board of Water and Power Commissions, City of Los Angeles.

18.  Barron, S. , "Economics of Reactors for Power and Desalin-
     ation, " Nucleonics, April 1964, pp. 67-71.

19. Lane, J. A., "The Economics of a Reactor Diffusion Complex," (ORNL internal memo, July 1964) cited by A. M. Weinberg and G. Young in "The Nuclear Energy Revolution and Chemical Processing," ORNL, February 1966.

20. Stoller, S. M. "Plutonium Recycling: Consequences for Uranium," Nuclear Engineering, January 1966, Vol. II, No. 116, p. 32.

21. Golan, S., "Optimum Nuclear Fuel Resource Utilization," Proceedings of the American Power Conference, Vol. XXVII, 1965, p. 196-209.

22. Ritchings, F. A., "Site Planning for Large Thermal Generating Stations, Proceedings of the American Power Conference, 1962, pp. 338 et seq.

23. Gerber, A., "The Impact of Air Pollution Control on the Economics of Energy Supply," Proceedings of the American Power Conference, Vol. XXVII, 1965, pp. 102-106.

24. Private Ownership of Special Nuclear Materials, 1964, Hearings, Subcommittee on Legislation, Joint Committee on Atomic Energy, 88th Cong., 2nd Sess., June 1964.

25. Mullenbach, Philip, Civilian Nuclear Power: Economic Issues and Policy Formation, Twentieth Century Fund, 1963, pp. 91-97.

26. Cf. Landsberg, H. H., "Factors in the Long-Range Competitive Setting of Shale Oil," Resources for the Future, Reprint No. 54, August 1965.

27. Barron S. and M. Zizza, "Why Not Single-Purpose Reactors for Desalting?" Nucleonics, September 1965, pp. 44-47.

# 8. Future Programming in Office of Saline Water

Raymond Durante, Office of Saline Water, U.S. Department of the Interior

In Arizona people have a day-to-day appreciation of the value of water, a term not synonymous with cost or price -- a fact that far too few seem to realize.

In 1952, the Congress of the United States authorized the Secretary of the Interior to conduct a program "to provide for the development of practicable low-cost means of producing from sea water, or from other saline waters, water of a quality suitable for agricultural, industrial, municipal, and other beneficial consumptive uses on a scale sufficient to determine the feasibility of the development of such production and distribution on a large scale basis, for the purpose of conserving and increasing the water resources of the Nation. "

This was a big order, but it apparently didn't seem so at the time. This is, of course, not peculiar to our desalting program, but is a common experience to most research and development programs. It seems that scientists can be very enthusiastic and optimistic about a new program, but as the program evolves, the engineers who must provide the operating hardware, of necessity, must be realistic, and, in turn, more pessimistic.

The optimism in the early days of the program was based, perhaps, on the fact that desalting of sea water was a known phenomenon, even Aristotle, centuries ago, had taught his students that "Vapor produced from sea water, when condensed, was no longer salt, " and as early as 1791, Thomas Jefferson issued to U. S. merchant seamen, instructions on how to build and operate a sea water distillation device.

This Nation's success in marching into the Atomic Age and approaching the threshold of the Space Age, surely indicated that the U. S. scientific and engineering community would have little difficulty in resolving the problem of cheap water from the seas in short order. Thus, the desalting program was confidently launched, without fully recognizing the economic parameters of producing "low-cost" desalted water, if by low-cost it was intended that the water be available at a price or cost comparable to existing natural sources of supply.

To enable the Secretary of the Interior to accomplish this ambitious objective, the Congress has supported this program with a series of legislative amendments to expand, extend and accelerate saline water conversion activities, and, through fiscal

93

year 1966, has appropriated a total of $81, 458, 000.  The budget
estimate of the Office of Saline Water for fiscal year 1967 is
$30, 946, 000.

As it is presently constituted, the operation of the Office of
Saline Water is divided into three categories to reach short, intermediate, and long-range goals.  To establish these goals, it
was necessary for us to study and evaluate the growing requirements for incremental sources of fresh water supplies; attempt to
ascertain desalting plant sizes that would be needed to meet these
incremental requirements; consider the time-frame in which
these requirements would develop; and, most important, endeav-
or to establish economic zones for desalted water.

Within these considerations our short-range program has
been devised to produce desalted water at the lowest possible cost
at the earliest possible date.  We believe this is necessary because even now there are places both domestic and foreign where
plants using current process and energy costs are applicable.  In
many places in the world even our most expensive desalted water
is cheaper and more reliable than natural sources of supply.  We
believe it is incumbent on us to make plant designs available for
these locations by refining and re-refining existing technology in
order to provide the most efficient processes and plants we can
devise to meet these current needs.

I should like to highlight some of the engineering work we are
conducting to continue the development and improvement of a
number of promising processes.  At the present time, distillation
processes offer the most efficient method of producing fresh water from sea water on a commercial basis.  We are supporting
development work on the multistage flash distillation process, the
multistage-multieffect flash distillation process, the long-tube
vertical (LTV) multiple effect distillation process, and the forced
forced-circulation vapor-compression process.

For two years (1962-1964) we operated a 1-million GPD multistage flash plant at San Diego, California.  The design of that
plant has served as the basis of most commercial plants that have
been built since that time.  We are opening bids for a 1.2 MGD
multistage multieffect plant which we hope will advance distillation
technology to the next plateau of economic efficiency.

We plan to substantially modify the 1-million gpd LTV plant
at Freeport, Texas, and operate it as a test bed to further advance the technology of the process and explore its economic potential.

While we are still plagued by process and operating problems
in the 1-mgd vapor-compression plant at Roswell, New Mexico,
we have developed considerable data on pretreatment of saline

waters and we have also learned that we cannot effectively extrapolate data developed in sea water desalting plants and utilize that data for brackish water plants. For this reason, we are planning to increase the level of effort to develop better pretreatment methods, and we expect soon to establish a brackish water test station to better study the unique problems presented by the diverse waters that are found at various inland locations.

The problem of scale formation, which affects all distillation cycles, is being actively studied, as is the operation and performance of components, such as heat-exchangers, pumps, deaerators, etc. We are encouraging industry to develop improved components and to work-out new techniques for manufacturing tubes and fabricating tube-bundles.

Recent developments in crystalization processes have been encouraging. A 60,000 gpd freezing process pilot plant at our research and development test station at Wrightsville Beach, North Carolina, has produced as much as 109,000 gallons of fresh water in a single day. We think freezing processes have considerable potential, particularly for desalting complex brackish waters containing iron, manganese, silica, etc.

Electrodialysis, which is currently the best process for desalting mildly brackish waters, still has a long way to go before its fullest contribution can be realized. Here again, the development of pretreatment systems is extremely important for the efficient operation of the process.

Reverse osmosis is one of the newest and one of the most promising of all desalting processes. Although we are just making some of our first tenuous steps to advance the process through the engineering phases of its development, we are very excited about its possibilities. First of all, it is a liquid to liquid process, and as such it eliminates the costly phase change of liquid to vapor and back to liquid required by distillation processes, or from liquid to solid and back to liquid as required by crystallization cycles. Since it only requires simple pressure for its operation, the key to the process is the efficiency of the reverse osmosis membrane itself.

We are supporting a broad and active program to improve the membranes to provide greater flux, longer life, and cheaper casting methods. Progress in any one of these areas will substantially improve the promise of the process.

We recently awarded two contracts, one for a 10,000 and one for a 50,000 GPD reverse osmosis pilot plant. We have used a 1,400 GPD unit to obtain preliminary data on the performance of reverse osmosis on several types of waters. We intend to extensively test these new units on polluted waters, brackish waters, acid mine-waters, and eventually--sea water.

From what we see now, based on the present status of the reverse osmosis process, it will reach its first economic application for desalting brackish waters and eventually, as the processes and engineering data continue  to develop, sea water.

For a number of years we have sponsored an extensive program to develop desalting processes using solar energy, including some fine work conducted by the Solar Energy Laboratory of the University of Arizona, which has included the operation of a pilot scale solar desalting plant at Puerto Penasco, Sonora, Mexico.  We have concluded, however, that solar distillation will find little application in the United States, and since proposals we have received for continued work do not offer sufficient economic advantage to warrant the cost of additional developmental programs, we have pretty much phased-out our work in this area.

We have designs  available for solar distillation units which offer good potential for use in areas of high solar intensity and low-volume water requirements.  Several solar stills have recently been erected by the Greek Government on small islands in the Aegean Sea with satisfactory results.  Similar applications are being considered by other governments.  If the opportunity presents itself to test our solar still designs without excessive costs being involved, we would, of course, do so.

Other desalting processes being studied by the Office of Saline Water include:  transport depletion, electrogravitational depletion, electrosorption, electrode demineralizers, environmentally modulated adsorption beds, hydrate processes, and solvent extraction.

In the overall concept of our short-range program, we have programmed the engineering development of a family of plants designed to meet current incremental water requirements.  The original San Diego desalting plant provided solutions to many problems, including (a) those encountered in higher temperature operation (up to $250^\circ$ F. ) with acid treatment to prevent scale formation, and (b) those involving control of brine level and ways to maintain equal distribution of vapor flashing in a large number (36) of evaporator stages.  In logical progression of experience the advanced technology plant is a follow-on plant to push multistage flash technology considerably beyond that obtained in the original San Diego plant.

Based on experience gained from the advanced technology plant and from 15 conceptual design studies, performed by some of this Nation's outstanding manufacturing and architect engineering firms, we will design and build a 17-million gpd test module. This module, consisting of an integrated arrangement of full-size components, such as pumps and flash stages, will be built and operated to insure satisfactory performance before committing

ourselves to an expensive large prototype plant.  The upper plant
size limit in our short-range program for the development of
large distillation plants is 50-million gallons per day.

Much of the experience and technology obtained from the construction and design programs I have just described, will be advantageously extrapolated downward and used in concurrent design
and construction of smaller plants in the range of 3 to 25 million
gallons per day, single or dual purpose plants, using fossil fuel
heat sources initially and hopefully nuclear reactors for some of
the follow-on plants; thus providing a balance to the program
which will develop desalting processes to meet a variety of size
requirements.

We have no intention of proposing the construction of a large
prototype plant simply to prove-out quantity production.  Our sole
interest will be to demonstrate the achievement of the lowest
price water possible through the best use of available technology.
It is our present conclusion that the status of engineering development needed to support the construction of an economical 50-mil-
lion gallons per day plant or larger has not yet attained the appropriate level of reliability unless one is willing to take a high technological and economic risk.

The data we obtain from operating the large test module is an
important step in the engineering development program through
which we will study scale-up problems and minimize the technological risks.

We are participating with the AEC and others, in a series of
studies, both foreign and domestic, to ascertain the engineering
and economic feasibility of large plants.  These include the study
with the Metropolitan Water District of Southern California and
the study with the Government of Israel.  Since these two studies
will be discussed by others at this meeting in considerable detail,
I should only like to comment that we are interested in participating in the construction and operation of the proposed 150-mgd
Metropolitan Water District plant, through the purchase of technology, because it will give us an opportunity to obtain data from
a plant of this size at a much earlier date than would otherwise be
possible.  Certainly, we are interested in a dual purpose plant
that indicates a desalted water cost of 22¢-25¢ per 1,000 gallons.
In addition, there are certain features of the Israeli technical feasibility study which indicate we may be interested in buying some
technology from this installation as well.

The preliminary feasibility study just getting underway in
Mexico offers, for the first time, an opportunity to really look at
the potential of viable large plants designed to produce water in
sufficient quantity to meet the gross requirements of cities, industries, and agriculture.

In terms of the short-range need, large plants -- those of 50-mgd or larger -- are the exception rather than the rule.  The present world-wide demand for desalting units for both sea and brackish waters in plants of 1 to 10-million gpd, with most of the emphasis on the lower range of the bracket.  We expect plants in the size range of 10 to 25 million gallons per day will soon be receiving greater attention.

In order to meet this need, the Office of Saline Water must continue to emphasize the development of small plant technology. Even though large single and dual purpose plants are more attractive economically, they are not feasible if their size overmatches the need for both power and water.

We are required to produce a survey of possible need for desalting equipment and we have a program to do just that.  It is, however, rather difficult to determine the basis for such a survey and much more difficult is the task to provide a comparison between cost of desalting water and alternative water cost.  Neither of these costs is easy to determine because much depends on understanding and evaluating a great variety of ground rules in use today by the various water agencies.  It also depends on the phasing of the planned program and, to a great extent, on the optimism of the water resource planners.  Even the legal and political climate is of great influence.

We all know the time factor involved in water resource planning.  Water systems must be planned 20-30 years in advance. To criticize the desalting program, as some have done, simply because there is no identifiable market is unfair to the program for a very simple reason.  Even if it is true that there is no market -- an allegation which I do not agree with -- now is the time to develop desalting equipment and prove-out its economics, while we have 5-10 years to do so in a careful properly paced way.  If we wait until the need for desalting technology becomes imperative, we would then be forced into a crash program in which we would spend substantially greater sums of money to achieve the same end.

The program as now planned, will also give industry, who eventually will be required to build these plants, an opportunity to develop better materials, fabrication methods, and systems analysis, all of which will lead to lower capital investment per unit of plant capacity.

Our intermediate range program has been developed to provide the second and third generation of improved desalting processes for the time frame of 1970-75.  It involves the operation of experimental pilot plants, studies of the application of new materials and new design concepts.  Within the time frame of the intermediate effort, no wholly new process is contemplated.

Our long-range program, a vital part of our overall effort, is centered in basic research. The basic research program was established only after an exhaustive study was made on desalting and the water problem. Scientific disciplines requiring research support were detailed and gaps in our knowledge were delineated by those studies. All of our research efforts are under constant examination both by in-house reviews and by use of consultant committees, as a result programs are dropped, continued at their current level, or accelerated, depending upon past results, future promise, and available funding.

Research is carried out by 5 divisions within OSW. They are: Applied Science, Materials, Bioscience, Chemistry, and Chemical Physics. The program is divided into the following 4 broad categories: (1) Properties of Water; (2) Separation processes; (3) Interactions at boundaries of water systems; and, (4) Properties of brackish waters, salts, brines, and by-products.

The lead time between the glassware of the laboratory and the hardware of a commercial desalting plant is long and arduous. It is unrealistic to assume that cheap desalting plants or processes to meet the great variety of requirements in terms of plant sizes, types of water and different processes will burst upon the scene like the first bright rays of the rising sun. The facts of life are that plants and process will be produced as a function of time and effort, in a broad spectrum, and they will be initially economically viable only for selective application. As experience and knowledge grow, the application of desalting technology will be in direct ratio to the lowering of product water costs and the increased cost of providing fresh water from conventional sources of supply. Then and only then will desalting come into its own in ever increasing measure.

The greatest single need to solve this Nation's water problems is to (1) provide better institutional water management techniques and (2) provide the basic technical and economic data on the wide range of alternatives from which to choose the best alternative or combination of alternatives. We, in OSW, will and must contribute our share to both needs.

Desalting is in the same general category as waste water recovery. The basic water data, applications of certain processes, etc., are common to both. Talents necessary to find answers to either the technical, social, or political problems are generally interrelated. Desalting cannot be applied in a vacuum. It must be considered in the same manner and at the same time as other alternatives such as conveyance of potable water over great distances, conservation of existing supplies by either regulatory controls or economic factors such as metering or price escalation, and waste water recovery. Decisions should be based on total system analysis. Some alternatives have only short range

benefits while others have effect only in the longer range sense.
All solutions that reallocate existing water supplies, or consist of
water reuse, will eventually have to face-up to desalting for potable incremental water. Reclaiming and recycling waste water has
its potential, but in every cycle which involves human use, the
water will pick-up 200-300 ppm of salt which present waste water
treatment processes will not economically remove.

It is obvious that saline water conversion is not a panacea for
all our water ills; it is equally obvious that atomic energy is not
an answer to all desalting problems. Our joint studies with AEC
to date clearly indicate that dual purpose nuclear reactors will, in
many areas, provide the lowest cost source of energy for the
very large plants, but for smaller plants -- those in the size
range of 1 to about 25 mgd, fossil fuel will get the economic nod.

A desalting plant doesn't know -- or care -- where its energy
comes from; it is only interested in the availability and cost per
million BTU of that energy. Desalting water can be made available at a time and place of man's own choosing, but water, unlike
electricity, is expensive to transport over great distances. It is
an economic necessity, therefore, to locate a desalting plant as
close to the point of use as possible. The problem of siting reactors because of population concentrations and objections, no
matter how unjustified or unreasonable these negative attitudes
may be, as well as unstable geological or seismological conditions, can severely limit their availability for large dual purpose
plants.

While the cost of energy cannot be minimized, there are
other considerations in desalting that must be clearly recognized.
We can be selective, and choose the most economic source of energy for a specific set of conditions and also choose the best possible desalting process in terms of the size of the facility and the
type of water to be desalted, but there are other factors that influence the cost of water to a customer. These cost considerations can be conveniently divided into two main areas: First,
factors that occur "within the skin" or the hard economies of the
technology of the desalting plant itself, such as the engineering
optimization of heat transfer rates, steam temperatures, chemistry of feed water, scaling, corrosion, fuel cost, construction
costs and many other factors. The second area to consider includes factors that bear directly on the cost of water, but are outside of the characteristics of the desalting plant and over which
we exercise little or no control, and which I choose to refer to as
"soft economics." These are the cost of money, the amount of
water needed for a specific area (i. e. , size of the plant), the
availability of a properly sized storage and distribution system,
the geographical need for blocks of power in the case of a dual-
purpose plant, etc. Much too often only the first area is considered and the second is ignored.

Within this diversified complex, we believe there are many unexplored avenues of approach. For example, we have recently discussed with the AEC the need to restudy both single and dual purpose power reactors, but within the context that surplus off-peak power be transmitted for the operation of brackish water de-salting plants two hundred, three hundred, or more miles distant. These desalting plants could be designed with either existing wa-ter storage facilities or with new storage facilities constructed for this purpose. Then, just as dump power from Hoover Dam has been utilized to pump water, surplus or off-peak power from atomic generating plants could desalt brackish water inland. I am thinking specifically of electrodialysis which requires elec-tricity or reverse osmosis which requires simple pressure, to operate the process.

As these various alternatives are considered, one must con-template the methods of financing that will be utilized in the inte-grated development and control of water supplies. It would seem that there is a need to develop a National policy in this regard as the best answer to a complex problem. Some foreign countries have established an interest-free revolving fund from which cities and communities can borrow to construct water supply facilities, with income from the sale of water made available through such facilities used to repay the loan. In a reclamation project here in the West, the sale of power pays for a substantial share of the overall project. Should the sale of power from a dual-purpose plant be used in the same manner? Should new financing plans be developed?

The whole point is, with desalting we are entering into a new dimension in the development of incremental sources of fresh wa-ter, and at this stage of the game, we should take full advantage of its flexibility and its timeliness and consider its potential ap-plication outside of the shackles of limitation that heretofore have necessarily been applied to the development of natural sources of water supply.

As we look for imaginative ways to utilize desalted water, it must, of course, be considered in the overall framework of a regional water supply system. As we plan for incremental water supplies we must study the availability, the quality, and the cost of ground or surface water; reprocessing waste water, including sewage and polluted water; and desalting.

The value of desalted water may often prove to be far greater than its cost, even though it might prove to be a bit more expen-sive than other incremental sources because of the speed and flex-ibility with which one source might provide sorely needed water as compared to another. Since it is not dependent on the vagaries of nature it can provide a back-up supply, a water insurance poli-cy. If brackish or polluted water has an economic penalty to be

associated with its use, high quality desalted water should then
have a premium associated with its economics; for example, as a
blending agent to improve the overall quality of an existing source
of supply.

As we deal with the national effects of our developing technology, we will need tough-minded technical advice at each stage of
its development on the feasibility of specific large water projects;
on the alternatives which should be considered; on the contribution
the Office of Saline Water can make to them; on their impact on
our manpower and economic resources; and finally, on the projects timing and need.

With this kind of judgment available, however, such programs of development and technology can multiply the helpful
choices available to us in determining which alternative source of
water is best for given problems. In addition, the alternative
choice available afford this country at the same time with new
means and opportunity to contribute to the welfare of the total human community.

Any new technology or a new and novel method of social
treatment of new technology must face the test of acceptability and
competition with conventional systems.   The innovative process
is not to be confused with R&D.   Both are aspects of the innovation process but innovation involves more than the development of
an idea and the organized technical work that is necessary for its
perfection.

Innovation also includes the introduction of the process into
the economy.   This in short means the development of a market
by demonstrating its reliability, maturity and its economics.   It
is for this reason that our desalting program includes the building
of prototype plants to clearly demonstrate a process and its economics.   From that moment on it will become industry's role to
promote wider application and further process cost reductions.

The Office of Saline Water is not in the water-supply business
and we have no plans to do so.

In August 1965,  President Johnson signed a new law to expand, extend and accelerate the saline water conversion program.
In closing, I would like to quote from the President's remarks at
that signing ceremony, because it dramatically summarizes the
challenge and the promise of desalting:

> A millenium ago -- in what is now Arizona -- there were
> Indians who built extensive water works, as we ourselves
> build them now.   They irrigated the lands that are now desert.
> But then drought came and their works were of no value.   The
> Indians disappeared, remembered in history as "The People
> Nobody Knows. "

In our Nation, water has long been treated by many as the concern only of the farmer and the rancher.  But we know better now.  In our complex, concentrated, urban economy and society, water has never had more meaning.  The drought being experienced now in our most populous region reminds us anew that we must not and cannot rely alone upon building bigger reservoirs, longer pipelines, or grander schemes of water works to supply this essential of life.  We can -- and because we can, we must -- develop the capacity to produce water when and where we need it at a price we can afford.

I have faith that we will succeed -- and I have a vision that such success will be one of history's most vital contributions to the cause of peace among nations.

# NATIONAL SALINE WATER PROGRAM AND CURRENT DESALTING TECHNOLOGY

Norman Hilberry, President
American Nuclear Society

# 9. The National Saline Water Program

Kenneth Holum, Assistant Secretary of the Interior —
Water and Power Development

History has many ways of dramatizing the importance we assign to solving various problems we face as a nation.

The measurement is provided in Presidential statements, messages and programs; appropriation levels and numerous Congressional actions; the record of program achievements and expansion to name just a few.

Take the Saline Water Conversion Program as a good example. It is only one facet of a much larger effort to meet mounting fresh water supply needs in years to come. And it is a new one. But it is gaining recognition and acceptance throughout the world as one of the potential, exciting new tools to be used in future water supply planning.

When the Saline Water Act was first enacted 14 years ago, the program began with an annual appropriation of $175,000. That was enough to commence building a staff and begin organizing for the future. The program carried a five year authorization. When that period of time elapsed Congress had increased the annual funding level fourfold.

The original Act was amended in 1958 -- then again in 1961 and 1965. Each time the program was reshaped. New thrusts were added reflecting previous experience and new found knowledge. Now in this current fiscal year Congress, at the request of President Johnson, has provided $20 million to support the broadened research and development effort. A new program is taking shape. And for the coming fiscal year, beginning on July 1, 1966, we are asking Congress to appropriate $29 million.

When the original Act was passed in 1952, the impetus almost exclusively came from westerners. Naturally it stemmed from their concern with the interminable water shortage problems both present and future, in the arid and semi-arid portions of our country.

The authorization specifically took note of this problem. But the Congress also included a phrase defining the broad object of the program -- "to determine the feasibility of the development of such production and distribution on a large-scale basis, for the purpose of conserving and increasing the water resources of the nation."

Water problems as we know are not peculiar to the west alone. Even now, Secretary of the Interior Stewart L. Udall has advised local and state officials of 12 northeastern states to prepare for a possible fifth year of drought.

In his capacity as Chairman of the Water Resources Council, Secretary Udall on March 16, urged that prudent planning measures be undertaken immediately to conserve present water supplies.

"This is the time of year, " he cautioned, "when water shortages are not readily evident; however, the conditions which contribute to future shortages are still present. There is no room for complacency although only a few areas are now suffering from actual shortages. "

You will recall the crises that gripped the East Coast last summer as it suffered through its longest and most severe drought on record for that area. Vermont farmers were hauling water to keep their thirsty cattle alive. New York City restaurants served water only if requested. Reservoirs feeding all the major coastal cities were at critical lows.

You will recall too, that on August 11, 1965, President Johnson directed Secretary Udall in cooperation with the Office of Science and Technology, the Council of Economic Advisors, and the Atomic Energy Commission to initiate an immediate study. Specifically, the President said the potentialities of desalting as a means of "drought proofing" these highly populated areas of the Northeast should be examined and a report made to him in six months.

We have just recently completed this study. It indicates that desalting is not the immediate answer to the overall metropolitan area water-supply problem. However, it also shows that incremental water costs there are rising rather rapidly and that desalting may soon be ecomically competitive either as a result of continued rising water cost or of improved desalting technology.

One interesting point developed by the study is that water-supply is essentially similar to power-supply. By this I mean it has the same requirements for reserve or peaking capacity that exists in the electric industry. Moreover, desalting can be expected to make a very valuable contribution in meeting these requirements - particularly as we learn more about the advantages inherent in dual purpose desalting and power plants. The advantages of combining a desalting plant with an electric generating plant are such that it would be unwise for any organization, public or private, now planning the construction of a power plant not to consider a feasibility study of coupling it with desalting facilities.

One problem that must be recognized is that we will need

more and more water to meet the demands of our rising population and our expanded industrial capabilities.  The difficulty is
that population and industrial growth geographically are often in
head-on conflict with water resources development plans.  As
populous eastern states seek to develop additional supplies of
available surface water, they are likely to find the potential dam
and reservoir sites on a stream or river already occupied by
towns or cities, homes, factories, schools, highways, railroads,
power lines, and other capital investments that would not only
make the cost of water prohibitive, but development of the site itself something bordering on the impossible.  Thus, as we continue to grow, the problem compounds itself.

Sharp contrasts are easily discernible as we study the water
problem across the nation.

While the rain which has fallen in the Northeast the past four
years is considered as of critical drought proportions, the same
amount in the Southwest would unquestionably be referred to as
"four wet years. "  Scant rainfall is a permanent fact of life in
your area.  So much of your effort from the earliest pioneer days
has been aimed at developing what you have and conserving it for
future use.  The Southwest has done a tremendous job of developing its available surface water resources.  With your tremendous
climate -- which certainly is an invaluable resource in itself --
your industrial, economic and population growth has outstripped
any comparable area of our country in recent years.  It is a tribute to the foresight and determination of the citizens and their
elected officials, who have supported water resource planners and
engineers and thus have enabled them to create some of the finest
water projects of all recorded history.

But each of us here today knows that all is not rosy.  The
precious ground water reserves which have accumulated over the
centuries have been heavily mined -- perhaps to a serious degree
-- and so you are compelled to use new tools to seek new means
of meeting your water needs.

One of our greatest problems in grappling with our water
supply problems is to fit the programs to the times.  The subtle
and yet inexorable shifts in water use that result from a more
sophisticated society and way of life -- the impact of new technology and population shifts -- all these and many other facts must
be faced.

We can no longer plan water resource development programs
on a piece-meal local basis and expect to adequately meet rising
demands.  Regional planning is necessary in order to assure full
and proper development of our available supplies of fresh water.

The first session of the 89th Congress launched a major effort to save America's existing water resources.  It authorized

the establishment of quality standards for all interstate waters.
It provided, in the Water Pollution Control Act of 1965, new resources for treating the wastes from our cities.  It created the
Water Resources Council to coordinate all aspects of river basin
planning.

A month ago, President Johnson transmitted to the Congress
a reorganization plan to transfer most of the functions of the Federal Water Pollution Control Act to the Department of the Interior.

In his message transmitting the reorganization plan to the
Congress, the President said:

> Today we face a harsh reality.  Our waters are burdened
> with blight.  We know that every river system in America
> suffers from some degree of pollution.  This menace is grow-
> ing more serious with every passing day.  We have just begun
> to take the steps to clean and restore our waters.  The task
> is immense.  The journey will be long.

The Congress has not yet acted upon this reorganization plan.
But I know that Secretary Udall would look upon these new responsibilities with the utmost seriousness.  And I know that he would
bring to the management of this tremendously important program,
the same vigor and outstanding leadership which has so characterized his administration of the Department of the Interior for
the past five years.

Some 20 months ago, a study was launched which has considerable significance for the Southwest in particular.  A three-way
feasibility study was undertaken of a large nuclear-powered dual
purpose desalting and electric powerplant.  Parties to the agreement were the Office of Saline Water, the Atomic Energy Commission and the Metropolitan Water District of Southern California.

The study was specifically aimed at evaluating a dual-purpose
plant to meet MWD's further needs.  It has now been completed.
Conducted by the Bechtel Corporation of San Francisco, the study
included two reactors, each rated at 2865 MWt, the combination
of 1800 megawatts of nuclear capacity and a 150-million gallons
per day desalting plant.  Based on a 90 per cent plant factor, it
would provide just over 1.5 million acre feet of high quality water
per year.

The four principal conclusions of the dual-purpose plant
study are:

--Construction of a large power-desalting plant is technically
practicable.

--The proposed plant could be constructed and be in operation
by the early 1970's.

--Water costs from such a plant would be 22 cents - 25 cents per thousand gallons ($70 per acre foot) and could be delivered to MWD's distribution point near Yerba Linda for an additional five cents per thousand gallons.

--A 43-acre man-made island 3, 500 feet off-shore from Orange County would provide the most economic location for the facility.

Fourteen years ago or less, the cost of producing 1, 000 gallons of fresh water from sea water ranged upward from $4. The 1-million gpd demonstration plant, which we operated for two years (1962-1964) on Point Loma, near San Diego, California, produced fresh water for slightly over $1 per thousand gallons. Now we are talking about a cost of from 22 cents to 25 cents. Moreover, the desalting cost breakthrough estimated by the Bechtel study is not based on pie-in-the-sky technology. Rather, it represents hard-headed engineering utilization of available technology plus scale-up in size, optimized for power and water production.

The 150-MGD plant will be composed of three 50-MGD modules. In order to proceed with plans for large plant construction, additional usable data will be refined to a point from which we can move forward with assurance that the desalting plant will represent the most advanced extension of the art, within the bounds of sound engineering extrapolation.

While the MWD study has been underway, we have also been participating in a feasibility study for a large dual-purpose plant in Israel. This study, conducted by Kaiser Engineers in association with Catalytic Construction Company, provides for a 100-MGD desalting plant coupled with a 200-MW nuclear powerplant. Water would be produced at an estimated 28. 6 cents per thousand gallons at a 5 per cent fixed charge rate, or 43. 4 cents per thousand gallons at 7 per cent fixed charges. Incidentally, either the MWD or the Israeli project would more than double the current installed desalting capacity of the world.

Of perhaps even greater interest to this group is another feasibility study just now getting underway.

As a culmination of the International Symposium of Water Desalination last October, an agreement was signed between the International Atomic Energy Commission, and the Governments of the United States and Mexico. It provides for a preliminary assessment of the technical and economic practicality of a desalting plant, operated in conjunction with a nuclear electric plant to provide fresh water and electricity for portions of the States of California and Arizona in the United States, and the States of Baja California and Sonora in Mexico.

This study is of special interest to us, and I think to you as

well, because it will, for the first time, provide information
which will determine for the next ten years or so the largest economically feasible and viable plant for water and power production.  The MWD and Israeli studies have optimized power and water production.  The Mexico-United States study, however, will
maximize power and water production.  It is our belief that the
economics of scale-up associated with this study will produce water at lower cost than the MWD plant.  It will permit us to take
advantage of maximum water and power production and relate that
production to markets.

Power does not appear to be a particular problem, since power grid interties could distribute the electrical energy.  But water
is not that flexible.  While the MWD study envisions desalted water only for municipal and industrial purposes, the joint Mexico-
United States study will also consider the use of desalted water
for blending purposes to improve existing supplies and agricultural water for high value crops.  This broader concept will permit
the study team to determine the largest water plant that may have
economic application to a single area.

While we have no question about our ability to desalt water at
a specific cost, we must know from an engineering standpoint
what all of these factors mean, and we must look at the overall
project in terms of the value of the water produced.

From this study we may conclude that desalted water for agriculture is out of the question for decades.  Or we may find that
maximum production of power and water brings desalted water into the realm of practicality as agricultural water in limited special situations.  Frankly, I have no intention of trying to second
guess the study outcome or of making any predictions.  The study
will stand on its merits.

And it will be performed in four stages covering data compilation on power and water needs through 1995; selection of the
best of several alternative power and water combinations to serve
these needs; determination of the economics of these alternatives;
and submission of recommendations to the two governments and
the IAEA for further action.

When the U. S. -Mexico-IAEA Agreement was signed, President Johnson said in part:

> The United States of America and our good neighbor to the
> south, Mexico, share much in common, including the great
> areas which are very short of water.  Together, with the help
> of the International Atomic Energy Agency, we are now going
> to explore a promising answer to a very difficult but a very
> mutual problem.

> This agreement will help us discover whether nuclear

power can be applied in a practical and economical way to convert sea water to generate electricity for the great arid region which joins our two countries.

This is our task and our commission.

The application of today's desalting technology is moving ahead at a quickening pace. A number of new desalting plants have been built. Others are being planned. Progress to lower the cost of desalting can be measured to a certain extent, by its acceptance in the market place as an incremental source of supply. In this regard we should bear in mind that the significant comparison is between cost of desalted water and other sources of new water -- not the cost of presently available supplies.

Two new MGD plants have been placed in operation this year in the Virgin Islands. Other MGD plants have recently gone onstream in Israel, Malta and Italy. The Key West Aqueduct Commission earlier this month awarded a $3,179,500 contract for a 2.6 MGD plant at Key West, Florida. A 250,000 GPD electrodialysis plant is now desalting brackish water at Port Mansfield, Texas. The Spanish Government is evaluating bids received for a 2.5 MGD plant for the Canary Islands, and the Government of Kuwait opened bids on March 1, for plants with a total capacity of 6 MGD to add to their present installed capacity of 13 MGD. These are but a few of the plants recently constructed or planned for the near future.

New technology continues to drive down the cost of producing desalted water. As the philosophy and the technology of desalting receive increasing acceptance there will be greater involvement of States and municipalities in planning and construction. For local interests to obtain maximum benefit from this Federal research and development program, we must develop a methodology for allocating costs of desalting projects or project systems, and a better rationale for financing capital investments and repayment formulas. Research is also needed to establish the effects of pricing on water demand and to learn more about the effects of present pricing policies on the efficiency of water use.

Achieving the goals which we must reach if we are to provide the water to meet the rapidly increasing demands of our growing population and our expanding industrial complex will require the continuing and untiring support of all our people. We cannot expect that support unless they have an opportunity to understand the magnitude of the problems.

But each of us here has an opportunity to participate in the total water resource development program. There are many new tools at our command. Desalting is one. Those of us that have responsibilities for meeting future water supply needs of our communities have an enormously important task.  Timely planning, adequate research, and intelligent action will help us meet those problems.

# 10. Operating Experiences at the LTV Demonstration Plant, Freeport, Texas

R. W. Akerlow, Manager, Special Products Division,
Stearns-Roger Corporation

Stearns-Roger Corporation has been the Operations Contractor for the Office of Saline Water Long Tube Vertical Desalination Plant at Freeport, Texas (see Figure 1) since its dedication by the then Vice-President, Lyndon B. Johnson in 1961. This Plant has been the most productive of all Demonstration Plants and at the present time has produced more than one and one-quarter billion gallons of desalted sea water; and after almost five years of operation, desalted sea water has been produced at less cost than by any other distillation process on record.

## EARLY DEMONSTRATION PLANT PHILOSOPHY

The initial goal in the program at Freeport was to demonstrate process cost and production reliability. Demonstration Plants were to account strictly for all costs and thus demonstrate the most economical process for desalting sea water. Since a major portion of water costs of plants of this size is amortization; water production was emphasized, and technical evaluation costs were minimized. Production runs of long duration were made, and process variables were observed and changed, however, major emphasis was placed on continuity of operation. Some valuable aspects of this process were demonstrated by this program.

## EARLY ACCOMPLISHMENTS

Selection of the LTV process for desalination is a wise choice. To make this a nonscaling competitive process, almost all conditions encountered during operations necessitated study and many changes were required in the plant process equipment. Some of the important items demonstrated were:

1. Extended operating runs, with a heating steam temperature of $240^{\circ}F$ and a final concentration factor of 3.0, proved the reliability and efficiency of the LTV process. During the latter phase of these runs, it was determined that increasing flow rates, over Effect 12 heat transfer surface, greatly reduced the rate of mineral scale deposition in that Effect. This was the basis for brine recirculation studies initiated at Freeport.

Figure 1.  Sea Water Desalting Demonstration Plant No. 1,
Freeport, Texas

2.    Freeport was the first major Demonstration Plant to use the pH method of scale control. (Magnesium hydroxide seeding has proven impractical during initial runs. )

3.    Plant production and heat transfer rates were increased by replacement of carbon steel tubes and plugs with aluminum brass units.

4.    Effectiveness of cross-exchangers 202 through 207 in the condensate circuit was investigated. It was determined that by converting to a flash system, the cross-exchangers could be eliminated with negligible loss in production economy, resulting in significant saving in installed Plant cost.

5.    Many instrumentation improvements were incorporated. Automatic level controllers were installed on each evaporator. A pH recorder was installed at the sea water deaerator outlet permitting closer control of acid and caustic feed systems. Numerous pressure taps and thermowells were installed to obtain better heat transfer information around evaporators and heat exchangers.

6.    Operation at a brine concentration of 4.0 (as predicted by the Wrightsville Beach data) was found to be impractical due to the heavy build-up of gypsum scale ($CaSO_4 . 2H_2O$). As a temporary expedient, until the scaling problem could be solved, the Plant was operated at a brine concentration of 3.0 in Effect 12.

## UNSUCCESSFUL LOW COST DESIGN FEATURES

In an attempt to establish the applicability of low cost carbon steel for salt water plant construction, this material was specified in as many areas within the Plant as possible. The state of the art then was such that performance could not be predicted. The theory advanced was, that if scale could be prevented by the use of a magnesium hydroxide slurry technique, carbon steel tubing and other major process equipment could be used without suffering corrosion.

The magnesium hydroxide slurry technique was never successfully operated, so the pH method, using a combination deaerator-decarbonator, was substituted. The outlet pH of the decarbonated sea water was nominally adjusted to neutral, but control of this process was minimal because of inadequate instrumentation and process knowledge. The combined effects of occasional low pH, erosive silt, and pitting from the chloride solution, led to early and continued failure of carbon steel tubing. The first failure was in the preheater tubes, next the evaporator tubes, and then the carbon steel water boxes and piping. Onstream time and maintenance costs were adversely affected due to this situation.

## REVALUATION OF DEMONSTRATION PLANT OBJECTIVES

The need for process improvements, tabulating and recording data, keeping records, and reduction of production costs brought about a development program to achieve these aims. Operating on a test cycle of approximately one month, specific, relatively independent variables were investigated. Primary objectives were to:

(a) Eliminate all scaling,

(b) Better utilize heat transfer surface,

(c) Improve distribution flow conditions in the tubes.

The long-range objectives were to further simplify the Plant and provide a sound basis for design of new facilities through acquisition of reliable engineering data.

The success of the program has instilled enough confidence in the process that the Office of Saline Water authorized increasing the length of the evaporator train at Freeport from twelve to seventeen Effects and replacing the inadequate heat rejection condenser and non-condensable gas removal equipment. This will provide Plant capability to reject heating at $100^{\circ}F$, instead of $120^{\circ}F$, demonstrating the most efficient desalination Plant installed at this time.

## DISTRIBUTION IMPROVEMENT

It is fundamental that if scaling is eliminated, heat transfer coefficients will improve and Plant downtime to remove scale will be nonexistent. Definite brine flow patterns were observed above the distributor plate, and this was correlated to the tubes which were scaling. These tubes appeared to be starved and the introduction of additional sea water to the starved tubes brought about use of the brine recycle. Recycle successfully reduced scaling in the tubes, and thereby confirmed the need for better distribution to each tube. A notched weir was designed and inserted in the tube to provide an even distribution level to all tubes during varying brine flow rates. Prior to this time, all evaporator tubes in Effects 10, 11, and 12 were scaling. Further research on the notched weir is being conducted.

## HIGH TEMPERATURE OPERATIONS

One fundamental of a single-purpose Desalination Plant is to make maximum use of heating steam over the greatest possible brine flashing range. It has been determined that, without forming anhydrite scale, the upper limit of sea water flashing range is 275°F on the steam side. Operating at this temperature, maximum benefit is derived from the improved heat transfer coefficients which occur at elevated temperatures. At present, this is an established operating procedure at Freeport. Pretreatment of sea water to increase the 275°F upper limit is now under study.

## IMPROVEMENTS IN HEAT TRANSFER

Heat transfer coefficients can be improved by controlling flow rates, distribution, and tube size. When the vapor-to-vapor temperature differential is decreased across each Effect, the heat transfer coefficients improve. During 1962, while Effect 1 sea water feed temperature was 238°F, evaporator heat transfer surface was 66,882 ft² and production averaged 1,027,000 gallons/day. By comparison, during 1964, while Effect 1 sea water feed temperature was 269°F, evaporator heat transfer surface was reduced to 48,411 ft² and production averaged 1,065,300 gallons/day. To operate at 270°F temperature without over-concentrating in Effect 12, it was necessary to raise the sea water feed to the maximum rate of 530,000 lb/hr. This rate is established by blowdown pump capacity. At this rate, the condensing temperature was 146°F, with a concentration factor of 3.26. Production for this 32-day run averaged 1,163,435 gallons/day with a sea water temperature differential of 119°F. It is obvious that both preheater and evaporator surfaces were experiencing high heat transfer coefficients. This can be attributed to flow rates of 4.1 ft/sec in the preheater circuit versus original design flow rates of 3.0 ft/sec.

## SCALE-FREE OPERATIONS AND ONSTREAM SCALE REMOVAL

When the maldistribution of brine was corrected, good deaeration was achieved, and the operating temperature limit (without producing anhydrite scale) was defined; the elimination of calcium sulfate dihydrate (gypsum) scale formation was the one problem that needed to be solved before scale-free operations could be achieved at a reasonable final concentration factor. The addition of 4 to 6 ppm of a blend of various polyphosphates (Nalco 918), effectively eliminates gypsum deposits at final concentration factors of 3.2.

Onstream gypsum scale removal was subsequently demonstrated as an effective technique which rapidly dissolves gypsum scale. Operating conditions for this technique require that the blowdown concentration factor be decreased to between 2.6 and 2.8, at which time polyphosphate (Nalco 918) is injected at 6 ppm by weight into the brine concentrate at the point where the temperature level is no greater than 165°F. Using this technique, tons of scale were removed during a controlled experimental

production run. This is an important development for water production plants where onstream time can materially affect the cost
of water.

## EQUIPMENT DEVELOPMENT

Much of the process equipment within the Plant has been
modified to increase Plant performance and decrease unscheduled
shutdowns. Major equipment improvements are as follows:

1. Deaerated Sea Water Feed Pump

   This vertical canned pump was fabricated of 316 stainless steel with Ni-resist suction bells, graphitar bearings, ceramic coated bearing surfaces, and a teflon shaft
   bearing. Very satisfactory service has been provided
   since this pump was installed.

2. Evaporator Vessels

   A recent modification to Effect 12 water box has eliminated the requirements for a distribution plate. Brine
   enters the annular water chamber, builds up a head on
   the tube sheet, and is evenly distributed into the tube
   bundle through the notched weirs inserted in each tube.

   Use of a monel mesh entrainment separator is an important development which will permit a decrease in the size
   of evaporator vessels. Not only has it been demonstrated that an 80 per cent decrease in vapor space is
   acceptable, but the entrainment of brine droplets caused
   by high vapor velocities in the low-pressure Effects can
   be eliminated.

   Intereffect brine transfer also has been demonstrated;
   this allows the brine to flash in the vapor body, thus reducing the vapor flow through the evaporator tubes.

3. Blowdown Pump

   A new brine blowdown pump was required to meet the demands of brine recirculation and demonstrate variable
   through-put operation.

4. Deaerator

   The deaerator has been improved by modifying both the
   level control system and the ejection nozzle. A slight
   increase in performance has been achieved using the recently installed Dow "Mac-Pac" packing rather than the
   original Raschig rings.

5.   Clarifier Tank

Freeport's sea water feed carries fine suspended silt
through the Plant process equipment.  The abrasiveness
of the silt has eroded many pump suction bells, pipe el-
bows, and other equipment subjected to high velocities.
In an attempt to settle out the silt and correct this problem, the initially installed clarifier-thickener has been
converted to a silt settling tank.  Some decrease has been
noted in turbidity, but the existing clarifier tank is too
small to do a complete settling job without use of an expensive coagulant.

6.   Pump Seals

The initial operation used raw sea water in the pump seal
lines.  After this was converted to product water, the
air intake into the system was greatly reduced.

## DEAERATOR-DECARBONATOR

The deaeration-decarbonation unit is extremely important in
preventing alkaline scale and corrosion.  The success of this relatively simple unit at Freeport is a definite advancement in the
desalting process.  It has been demonstrated that, with proper
control, the quantity of stripping steam can be materially reduced.
The deaerator has been operated under all conceivable operating
conditions such as operating without packing and stripping steam.

The amount of dissolved oxygen can be reduced to less than
100 parts per billion as shown by tests using the Modified Winkler
Determination method and $CO_2$ can be reduced to less than six
parts per million as shown by tests using the ASTM D 513-57
method.  These results have been obtained in a simple deaerator
where both deaeration and decarbonation is accomplished in one
vessel with a minimum heat requirement.

The most economical means of obtaining decarbonation is by
adding a calculated stoichiometric quantity of acid (plus a small
excess) to the feed water stream.  To produce a noncorrosive
feed, sodium hydroxide is added to adjust feed water pH to 6.75
after acid injection.

## CORROSION STUDIES

A continuous evaluation of construction materials has been in
force at the Freeport Plant.  A generalized summary of the results on metals and nonmetals is listed in Table I.

An impressed current protection system for carbon steel has

TABLE I

Corrosion Evaluation of Construction Materials

METALS

| MATERIAL | APPLICATION | RESULTS |
|---|---|---|
| Carbon Steel | Hot Sea Water Service    290°F,  1.0 to 1.2 brine concentration | Good |
| Carbon Steel | Brine Service  150°F,    3.5 Brine concentration, velocity  5.0 fps | Good |
| Carbon Steel | Heat transfer service | Very Poor |
| Carbon Steel | Deaerated Sea Water    200°F | Good |
| Carbon Steel | Evaporator Distribution Plates | Poor |
| Carbon Steel | Water Boxes (Heat Exchangers and Evaporator) | Poor |
| Carbon Steel | Impingement Baffles | Very Poor |
| Cast Iron | Pump Casings and Valve Bodies | Fair |
| Cast Iron | Pump Suction Bells | Poor |
| 316 ELC S.S. | Water Box Liner | Good |
| 316 ELC S.S. | Sea Water Pump Shaft, Sleeve and Liner | Good |
| 304 S.S. | Evaporator Tubes | Poor |
| Ni-Resist Type B | Pump Impellers Deaerated Sea Water | Good |
| Ni-Resist | Deaerated Sea Water Vertical Pump Bowls | Good |
| 70-30 Cu-Ni Clad | Non Deaerated Heat Exchanger | Good |
| 90-10 Cu-Ni | Heat Transfer Surface | Good |
| 90-10 Cu-Ni | Water Box Liners | Good |
| Al-Br. | Heat Transfer Surface | Good |
| Monel | Brine Pump Shaft | Good |
| Monel | Deaerated Heat Exchanger Water Boxes | Good |
| Monel | Expansion Joints (Evaporators and Heat Exchanger) | Good |
| Monel Mesh | Entrainment Separator | Good |
| Admiralty Brass | Heat Exchanger Surface | Poor |

NONMETALLICS

| MATERIAL | APPLICATION | RESULTS |
|---|---|---|
| Epoxy Lined Asbestos Cement | Non Deaerated Sea Water   150°F | Good |
| Unlined Asbestos Cement | Non Deaerated Sea Water   150°F | Good |
| Type 1 PVC | Non Deaerated Sea Water   150°F | Good |
| Type II ABS | Non Deaerated Sea Water   150°F | Good |
| Fiberglass Reinforced Epoxy | Non Deaerated Sea Water   150°F | Good |
| Baked-on Phenolic Coating | Sea Water Piping   290°F | Good |
| Coal for Epoxy | Sea Water   150°F | Good |

been installed on three heat exchangers.   Initial tests indicated that good protection was provided at 150°F or less.   Later tests indicated that adequate protection at 275°F is possible by increasing current densities.   An economic study is being conducted to determine whether this type of protection can be justified for carbon steel.

Magnesium anodes have been unsuccessful in the protection of heat exchangers because magnesium hydroxide plating on the heat exchanger surface reduces the heat transfer coefficient.

A product water treatment program has been conducted at the Freeport Plant to develop a stable product water which will not

attack municipal water systems.   Weighed specimens are exposed
to a controlled flow of product water to which has been added an
appropriate concentration of selected chemicals.   After a period
of exposure, the specimens are reweighed and the corrosion rate
established.   The materials evaluated and their usage are listed
in Table II.   Results of the corrosion studies are listed in Table
III.

## INSTRUMENTATION

The most significant improvement is the recently installed
high-accuracy evaporator instrumentation.   This instrumentation

### TABLE II

Materials Evaluated During Product Water Corrosion Control Tests

| MATERIAL | SPECIFICATION | USE IN MUNICIPAL WATER SYSTEM |
|---|---|---|
| Carbon Steel | ASTM A7 | Structural material, comparable to ASTM A53B pipe material. |
| Galvanized Carbon Steel | ASTM A7 hot-dip galvanized | Corrosion-resistant structural material and piping. |
| Cast Iron | ASTM A126B | Pump impellers and pump and valve bodies. |
| Copper | ASTM B11ETP | Structural material, comparable to ASTM B68 annealed tubing. |
| Polyvinylchloride | Unplasticized | Non-metallic piping. |
| Asbestos-Portland Cement | "Transite" Class 150 | Non-metallic piping. |
| Ni-Resist | Ni-Resist Type II Copper-Free | Pump impellers, bowls, and suction pieces. |
| Steam Bronze | ASTM B62 | Valve Bodies and Trim. |
| Silicon Bronze | ASTM B198 Alloy 13B | Valve Trim. |

### TABLE III

Calculated Corrosion Rate (MPY)

| TEST LOOP TREATMENT | A Oyster Shell | B Untreated Freeport Product | C Sodium Silicate | D Polyphosphate |
|---|---|---|---|---|
| COUPON MAT'L. | | | | |
| Carbon Steel | 12.0 | 10.8 | 0.9 | 12.6 |
| Galvanized Carbon Steel | 7.9 | 16.6 | None | 2.8 |
| Cast Iron | 13.5 | 17.5 | 1.5 | 14.4 |
| Copper | None | 0.7 | 0.1 | 0.4 |
| Polyvinylchloride | None | None | None | None |
| Asbestos-Portland Cement | 29.6 | 39.0 | 18.0 | 22.0 |
| Ni-Resist | 22.3 | 4.6 | 0.3 | 3.5 |
| Steam Bronze | 0.5 | 0.2 | 0.2 | 0.3 |
| Silicon Bronze | 0.5 | None | None | None |
| Corrosometer* | 20.5 | 9.3 | 0.1 | 8.8 |

*The corrosometer probe element is mild carbon steel, and corrosometer-
determined corrosion rates are directly comparable only to the carbon steel
coupon.

has provided detailed data which, for the first time, provides a means to analyze, by improved analytical procedures, the pressure drop over the evaporator tubes, across the distribution plate, and across the mist eliminator. Early evaluation of the data indicates that a pressure drop of three inches of water is being experienced over the evaporator tubes in the later Effects. This corresponds to a temperature rise up the tubes of $1^{\circ}$ to $1.5^{\circ}F$ which must be accounted for in calculating heat transfer coefficients. Another significant observation is the extremely low pressure drop across the mist eliminator. This not only provides a means of effectively eliminating entrainment carry-over; but, since only 20 per cent of the original vapor flow area is utilized, a significant reduction in evaporator vessel size can be incorporated in future designs.

Vapor sampling equipment and techniques were developed to obtain vapor samples at less than atmospheric pressures. With this equipment, it has been possible to determine the flow of non-condensables throughout the system. Vent studies have been useful in optimizing stripping steam rates for deaeration and venting rates.

## LARGE DIAMETER EVAPORATOR TUBES

At normal production rates and at the decreased surface previously mentioned, pressure drop readings obtained by the high accuracy instrumentation have been found to vary from about three inches of water in Effect 1 (operating at $265^{\circ}F$) to an apparent maximum of eight inches of water in Effect 12 (operating at $120^{\circ}F$). This is relatively unimportant to heat transfer at $265^{\circ}F$, but is very important to heat transfer at $120^{\circ}F$. The economic necessity to operate at $100^{\circ}F$ or less in Effect 12 makes it essential that the temperature differential penalty, associated with the pressure drop, be minimized.

The Plant was originally equipped with evaporator tube bundles which were fitted with two-inch tubes 24 feet long. Effect 12 evaporator tube bundle is presently being replaced with a bundle containing three-inch by 20-foot tubes. This modification is expected to lower the pressure drop to not more than four inches of water, when operating at $100^{\circ}F$. New vacuum equipment is also being installed to allow condensation at $100^{\circ}F$. It is expected that this modification will improve the heat transfer capability of the surface in the low pressure Effects by more than 20 per cent. Benefits other than the decreased pressure drop are expected on the basis of work by Dukler and Elliott. [1]

## DISTRIBUTION STUDIES

Equitable distribution of an optimum flow is beneficial to both scale elimination and the heat transfer. The perforated distributor plate was an elementary device provided to improve the obvious deficiencies of spilling from one inlet to the open tubes.  Excessive pressure drop, plugging, and localized bypassing between the plate and water box wall, still limit the effectiveness of the perforated distributor plate, even though the notched weirs have largely overcome the starving problem.

Stearns-Roger is making three new approaches to improve brine distribution.  The first is to provide a chamber into which the initial feed is discharged and may flash in an unrestricted manner at a point below the upper tube sheet.  The second is to allow the flashed liquid to flood the tube sheet and spill into the tubes through notched weirs, thereby eliminating the distributor plate and the high-velocity stream problem.  The third approach is the design of a distributing device which will impart a swirl and thus place a turbulent film on the tube wall in such a manner that the surface tension forces are aided by centrifugal force. Other approaches can and should be evaluated, including spray nozzles and other devices suggested by the University of California Sea Water Conversion Laboratory.[2]

The first two of these approaches have been incorporated into the overall design of the new final Effect tube bundle now being installed.  The third is a new development which will be tried in the near future.  To evaluate these major design changes, a distribution flow-measuring device has been designed and installed. It will measure the flow from nine tubes simultaneously from three adjustable positions.  Thus, the effectiveness of distribution can be determined during actual operations, from side-to-side of the entire tube bundle in two directions.


## PLANT COMPARISONS AND APPLICATIONS

The potential of the LTV process, utilizing the falling film, forward feed is superior in many respects to the presently accepted and often specified MSF process.  In a recent study made for the Edison Electric Institute[3] it was stated that MSF is a superior process for these reasons:

1.  Problems with scale formation are minimized since there is no area of contact between the evaporating brine and metallic heat transfer surfaces.

2.  The heated brine can be recycled, thereby reducing thermal energy losses and feed water treatment costs.

3.  Multistage flash permits the widest range of operating temperatures.

4.  High heat transfer rates, using surfaces of minimum cost.

5.   Adaptability to large size plants constructed of relatively inexpensive materials.

Results obtained from three reports[4, 5, 6] which document the operation of the Point Loma Demonstration Plant for Fiscal Year 1964, and the Freeport Demonstration Plant for Fiscal Years 1964 and 1965, provide comparisons that refute the claims presented in the Edison Electric Institute study. The following discussion of each assertion given above is based on the facts contained in these, OSW reports and other recent developments in the desalting art:

1.   Problems with scale formation are nonexistent in an LTV plant operating on normal sea water and observing the same maximum brine temperature as the 250°F commonly specified for MSF. Scale-free operation at 265°F maximum brine temperature has been demonstrated over a 55-day continuous operation of the Freeport LTV plant. The actual advantage lies in the once-through LTV plant which heats only normal sea water to the maximum temperature, instead of a concentrated brine recycle stream normally required in an MSF plant.

2.   The MSF process, in which recirculation is used, is a detrimental requirement rather than an advantage when compared to the once-through LTV process. Thermal energy losses and chemical treating costs are actually less for the LTV process, because LTV concentrates the sea water to three times normal as opposed to MSF concentration of less than two times normal. Thus, there is considerably less sea water to treat chemically, and a great deal less hot brine to blow down to waste. An additional advantage of the high-concentrating once-through LTV process is the greatly reduced mechanical energy requirement for pumping. In general, the pumping energy for the LTV plant is only 50 per cent of that required for the long-tube MSF plant.

3.   The Freeport LTV plant has established the highest satisfactory operating temperature in desalination use. The comparison often made between the Freeport and Point Loma plants have seldom noted that the flashing range was not the same for each (120°F versus 155°F). This variance was partially due to the difference in temperatures of the sea water available for cooling (85°F at Freeport versus 60°F at Point Loma). The latter factor was sharply illustrated when it was necessary to derate the Point Loma Plant radically before it was moved to Guantanamo.

The same process problems arise for both types of plants in condensing at low pressures; namely, entrainment and the pressure drop associated with handling of large volumes of water vapor.

4. The evaporating heat transfer coefficients achieved in the LTV system are approximately 10 to 20 per cent higher than for the condenser tubes in the MSF plant. The coefficients available in the preheat circuit are the same (in a properly designed plant) since the service is identical for all practical purposes. Additionally, the temperature potential applicable to the surfaces is much better in an LTV plant, because (a) the total range is divided into many fewer steps for a given gain ratio and (b) the evaporating surface has a relatively constant and automatically maximized temperature difference applied over its entire length, because of the continuous removal of the latent vaporization heat. These factors combine to produce a surface effectiveness in the LTV which cannot be matched by the MSF plant for identical flashing range, heat source, and heat sink temperatures.

5. The necessity to provide very large volume fixed-flow devices, and to provide flow channels and appurtenances which diminish the hydrostatic effect (and yet operate satisfactorily over low pressure differences) poses some difficult problems in a large size plant. The requirement for very large brine recirculation pumps and/or the operating difficulties associated with paralleling large pumps raises problems in an MSF system that are evidently not as critical in the LTV system.

The modular design proposed by Stearns-Roger (and presently under construction at the Freeport Plant) provides the necessary adaptability to construct large size plants. Additionally, this design can incorporate use of reinforced concrete construction without the problems associated with hydrostatic head and several other irreversibilities associated with the uncontrolled flows of the MSF system. Other attractive proposals have recently been made whereby the high efficiency and low cost of the LTV system can readily be applied in large size plants.

From these observations, the advantages proven in five years of operation and development at the Freeport Plant appear to factor in favor of the eventual acceptance of the LTV process for sea water evaporation over those presently under consideration.

In addition to the five specific reasons discussed previously, the following three other important factors enhance the position of the LTV process:

1. The thermal efficiency of the LTV process is practically unaffected by variations in production rate. Since all

circulation is controlled, the Plant can be operated at
any rate up to that obtainable with the maximum brine
temperature without need for operator adjustments or
loss of efficiency. All that is needed to arrange the LTV
system to use all available energy automatically from an
extraction turbine, is a proportional steam-to-sea water
feed ratio controller. The water plant and the turbine
can even use a common surface condenser for heat rejection, thus allowing the complete base loading of the
steam generator and producing water at a maximum rate
whenever electrical demand is down. This variable operational capability, without undue operator stress and
with maintained efficiency, has been demonstrated from
50 to 125 per cent of design rate at Freeport on several
occasions, where the Plant is operated with one man per
shift.

2.   The comparison of capital cost of plants in the range of
one to ten million gallons per day has been estimated as
follows:

(a)   For a given set of conditions and gain ratio, the cost
of an LTV plant should be from 10 to 25 per cent
less than that for an MSF plant (due primarily to
savings in tube materials).

(b)   For a given capital investment, a more efficient
plant can be obtained in the LTV process than for the
MSF process.

These two statements are the direct result of the facts
that heat transfer surface is used more effectively in the
LTV plant, and that less expensive pumps and drivers
are required. The cost of water produced in the LTV
plant tends to be further reduced by the more favorable
ratio of thermal to mechanical energy required, and the
reduced chemical treating costs. It is reasonable to assume that these benefits will accrue in a large size plant
as well as in an intermediate size facility.

3.   The land area required for the LTV plant is generally
about two-thirds of that required for a comparable MSF
plant. This factor will have increasing importance in the
years to come, particularly in island installations where
hillside areas are waste space and ideal for an LTV facility insofar as space requirements are concerned.

## APPLICATIONS TO WASTE HEAT RECOVERY

Waste heat, in one practical sense, is an energy-containing
stream which has some remaining value, but which has been de-
graded to the extent that it can no longer serve the purpose for

which it was initially required. In another sense, it can be by-product energy resulting from a process requiring relatively high temperatures. However, this heat or energy is "wasted" only if it is rejected to the heat sink without accomplishing further work. The stream turbine used to drive an electric generator (or other-wise produce useful work) can successfully recover the energy in the steam down to the same heat rejection level as a sea water evaporator, since both must reject heat to the same heat sink in the same manner. Therefore, the use of a well-designed steam turbine does not normally result in the creation of a "waste heat" source which is useful to a sea water evaporator. Several chem-ical processes and some other operations could be correctly de-scribed as resulting in "waste heat" which can be considered re-coverable for sea water distillation.

Waste heat sources at temperature levels as low as $140^{\circ}F$ can be considered practical for recovery in an LTV system. A generalization can be made that maximum sea water temperatures of $265^{\circ}F$ make all sea water evaporators users of low-grade en-ergy. The LTV system is easily adapted to heat recovery from such a temperature level. The number of Effects can be deter-mined to obtain the desired production of water at the minimum capital cost. Further, as previously pointed out, the LTV unit will automatically utilize the quantity of energy available, even though it varies from day-to-day or hour-to-hour.

## DUAL-PURPOSE PLANTS

The most frequently conceived form of dual-purpose opera-tion for a desalination plant is combined electric power and water production, using a single or common heat source. This is, in a large measure, the subject of this Symposium. The total energy utilization concept is paramount in the efficient application of a large (and, therefore, less costly on a unit-of-heat basis) heat source. This is particularly true of nuclear steam generators. However, for maximum benefit, the heat source should be fully loaded at all times. A secondary benefit derives from the use of a less costly back-pressure turbine; however, use of a back-pressure turbine requires either that the water plant be in opera-tion whenever the turbine operates, or that a dump condenser be provided. A third benefit derives from the sharing of common facilities and operating labor.

Inherent in the utilization of dual purpose facilities is the ability to market the product, in a ratio (of power to water) and quantity which falls within the design capability of the processes, and results in a true benefit to the users (as opposed to single-purpose plants for each product).

The principal benefits to be derived from use of a back-pres-sure turbine are dependent upon continuous concurrent operation of both the turbine and water plant at a base load. This is due to the inability to store electrical energy, and the probability that energy charges to power generation will not be at an acceptable level if a dump condenser must be used. This problem is attenuated by providing multiple turbines and evaporation trains so that one or more combinations can be shut down or started up with variances in electrical demand. This is necessary in water plants such as the MSF plant where efficiency is a function of production and is maximized at the design rate. The MSF system is, therefore, suited to the back-pressure turbine requirement for concurrent operation, but must be designed so that its onstream factor is comparable to that of the steam turbine-generator. Such a dual-purpose plant is not well adapted to base loading of the heat source, under varying electrical demands.

The LTV system, which is efficient over a very wide range of production rates, appears to be admirably suited to base loading, and thus maximum utilization of the heat source, even with a variable electrical demand. This could be advantageously accomplished in a large plant by supplying one or more back-pressure turbine-evaporator combinations and one or more extraction turbine-evaporator combinations, arranged such that the base load would be carried by the back-pressure turbines, and the variable load by the extraction turbines. The swing capability of the LTV plant, with maintainable efficient use of energy, makes it feasible to produce more water during off-peak electrical demand periods and thus utilize the full capacity of the heat source. This is particularly advantageous in the solution of problems associated with the large size nuclear heat sources. The heat rejection condenser for an LTV system can be sized and designed to handle the low-pressure steam from both the extraction turbine and the water plant, thus providing efficient power generation at all levels of water production (including zero) from the extraction turbine LTV evaporator combination.

The use of gas turbine-generators and waste heat boilers in combination with an LTV evaporator has been investigated in depth. Under normal conditions, one million gallons per day of water can be economically produced from sea water in an LTV system for each 7500 kw of generating capacity, utilizing only the "waste" heat from the turbine. Again, the ability of the LTV system to utilize energy available at variable rates efficiently, will maximize the benefits resulting from a dual-purpose operation.

## THE MODULAR DESIGN

Developments at Freeport, and the extensive background of chemical processing using multiple effect evaporation, has resulted in a compact design. A five-effect module of this design (see Figure 2) has been approved for installation at Freeport by OSW. The design eliminates intereffect vapor piping, cross-

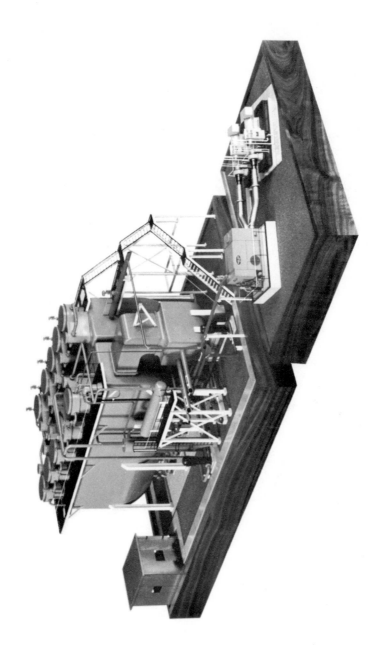

Figure 2. Five-Effect Modular Design

exchangers, flash tanks, and condensate pumps.  It maintains the highly efficient falling film heat transfer surface and utilizes it in standard tubing form.  The bundles and channels are standard design, easily removable from the vessels, and economically protectable from corrosion by use of appropriate alloys.

Figures 2 and 3 illustrate the pattern of arrangement.  This design utilizes the vessel as the structural support for the vertical bundles.  The use of reinforced concrete is admirably suited to the large flat surfaces subjected to low internal pressures and/ or the atmospheric external pressure encountered in sea water evaporators.  The modular concept reduces heat losses to the environment and provides for continuous compact design.  If additional efficiency is needed, additional modules in a folded arrangement can be added.  Use of entrainment separators has been fully confirmed at Freeport, and has made it possible to design on this greatly reduced volume principle.

This design has been proposed and priced for plants up to 7-1/2 million gallons per day and is applicable in the form shown for plants up to 10 million gallons per day in a single train. Larger sizes would most likely utilize a horizontal cylinder partially below grade, with submerged blowdown pumps.  Such a design has been given preliminary consideration and appears to be feasible for the large plants envisioned for regional type desalting plants utilizing nuclear heat sources.

## SUMMARY

The Development Program at the Freeport Plant has demonstrated the soundness of the LTV process through a continuing series of reliability performance tests, each aimed at achieving a definite goal in advancing the desalination state of the art.

The Development Program is a continuing effort which is constantly providing invaluable data establishing the reliability of the LTV process.  Some of the more significant accomplishments resulting from the Program that emphasize the advantages of the LTV process are:

1.   High Thermal Economy

2.   Low Mechanical Energy Requirements

3.   Scale-Free Operation

4.   Highest Operating Temperature

5.   Highest Productivity Per Unit Surface

6.   Efficiency Maintained Over Production Range

7.   Low Normalized Cost

Figure 3.  Cutaway of Modular Design

After installation of the five- effect modular design is completed, further extensive studies will be conducted to demonstrate the adaptability and overall efficiency of the LTV process. Verifying the feasibility of utilizing this design and process in future large-scale plants having a wide range of operating capability will be our objective.

## NOTES

1.   Elliott, L. C. and Dukler, A. E., "Aspects of Two-Phase Flow and Heat Transfer In Distillation Type Conversion Processes," Paper No. SWD/21, First International Symposium on Water Desalination, Washington, D. C., 1965.

2.   E. I. Ewoldsen, et al., "Sea Water Entrainment in Low Temperature Flash Evaporators," Sea Water Conversion Laboratory Report No. 64-3, University of California Sea Water Conversion Laboratory, Berkeley, California, December, 1964.

3.   "Survey of Current Economics of Natural and Desalted Water in the United States," the Fluor Corporation, Ltd., for Research Project RP-67, Edison Electric Institute, 750 Third Ave., New York, New York 10017, November 1965.

4.   "First Annual Report, Saline Water Conversion Demonstration Plant No. 2, San Diego, California," by Burns and Roe, Inc. for the Office of Saline Water, February 1964, PB 181684, U. S. Dept. of Commerce, Office of Technical Services, Washington, D. C., 20230.

5.   "Third Annual Report, Sea Water Desalting Demonstration Plant No. 1," by Stearns-Roger Corporation for the Office of Saline Water, September 1964.

6.   "Fourth Annual Report, Sea Water Desalting Demonstration Plant No. 1," by Stearns-Roger Corporation for the Office of Saline Water, November 1965.

7.   "1964 Saline Water Conversion Report," U. S. Dept. of the Interior, Office of Saline Water, U. S. Government Printing Office, Washington, D. C., 20402.

8.   "Summary of Performance, Sea Water Desalting Demonstration Plant No. 1," by the Stearns-Roger Corporation for the Office of Saline Water, February 1965.

9.   R. H. Jebens, et al. , "The First Municipal Sea Water Con-
     version Plant in the U. S. ," Paper No. 61-PID-4 Process
     Industries Conference of the ASME, Houston, Texas, Oct.
     4 and 5, 1961.

10.  Kays, David D. , "Desalting Sea Water in the Multiple Effect-
     Long Tube Vertical Evaporator, " Paper No. SWD/39 First
     International Symposium on Water Desalination, Washington,
     D. C. , October 1965.

# 11. Operating Experience at the Multi-Stage
# Flash Demonstration Plant, Point Loma, California

Roy E. Gaunt, Manager, Water Province Department,
Westinghouse Electric Corporation

The multi-stage flash evaporation plant was built for demonstration purposes at Point Loma near San Diego, California. Designed and constructed by Westinghouse, the 36-stage flash evaporator plant was built for the Department of the Interior, Office of Saline Water, as one of the five OSW demonstration plants authorized by the United States Congress to test the reliability, economics, and technical feasibility of various basic water-conversion methods. The purpose of the Point Loma plant was to demonstrate the feasibility of multi-stage flash evaporation. The turn-key contract was awarded in November, 1960, and the plant was completed and producing water 365 days later. See Figure 1.

When the local supply of water to the Guantanamo Naval Base in Cuba was cut off, the Point Loma plant was hurriedly dismantled, and reerected in somewhat modified form at Guantanamo. Thus, the plant was in operation only about 27 months at Point Loma. However, during this short time, we obtained a great deal of information on which to base future design modifications, and, more importantly, on how to make future predictions of the cost of producing pure water by the multi-stage flash evaporation process.

Let us consider briefly how the flash-evaporation principle is used to produce pure water. The term "flash" derives from the fact that part of a volume of hot water will change into vapor almost instantaneously when it is admitted from one chamber into another in which there is a lower pressure and temperature.

## SINGLE-STAGE EVAPORATOR

A simple single-stage evaporator, such as shown in Figure 2, consists of a heat-input section, a heat-recovery section, and a heat-rejection section. Normally, the heat-recovery and heat-rejection sections are combined in a single package. The heat-input section, called the brine heater, is a shell-and-tube heat exchanger. When the heated brine leaves the brine heater, it is forced through an orifice into the flash chamber, where the "flashing" of a portion of the brine occurs. The vapor passes through wire-mesh moisture separators to remove any droplets that might be carried along, and then passes over tubes which condense it to pure distillate. Condensation of the vapor on the tube at a lower temperature maintains the necessary pressure

135

Figure 1. Point Loma Plant

drop in the flash chamber and the recovery section.

Unflashed brine is recirculated through the tubes of the heat-recovery section to the brine heater.   The proper brine concentration is maintained by adding make-up seawater from the heat-rejection cooling water and "blowing down" a portion of the recirculating brine.

The heat-rejection section receives practically all the energy which is supplied to the heat-input section, and ejects it to a heat sink such as an ocean, river, or cooling tower.   The temperature of the coolant in the heat sink, therefore, establishes the minimum flashing temperature.

In the usual single-stage flash evaporator, approximately one pound of heating steam is required to produce a pound of distillate. This is poor energy economy, but the problem has been overcome by using a multi-stage heat-recovery section.

The multi-stage type of heat-recovery section (Figure 3) permits use of the latent heat in the vapor to reheat the circulating brine rather than eject it immediately to the heat sink.   Each stage of the heat-recovery section has a lower temperature and pressure than the preceding section.   As the brine flows from stage to stage, it gives up additional vapor with each drop in pressure.   The vapor condensed in each stage returns heat to the recirculating brine which is flowing back to the brine heater in the heat-recovery tubes.   Latent vapor heat formed in the heat-rejection section is ejected to the heat sink.

Figure 3 is a simplified schematic drawing of the Point Loma demonstration plant.   Designed as a single-purpose plant with no electric power generation at the site, the plant was rated at one million gallons of water a day.   Heat for providing steam to the brine heater was obtained from a conventional boiler burning No. 6 residual fuel oil.   Fuel cost figures used for design optimization were 50 cents a million Btu.   Electric power for the plant was supplied at 11 KV through a substation which reduced the power to 440 volts for distribution within the plant; power cost was approximately 14 mills/kwh.

The distillation part of the plant was built with 10 flash evaporator vessels and a separate brine heater.   The long tube design was employed with the brine flowing parallel to the axis of the tubes through 36 stages.   All of the seawater supplied to the plant flowed through the thirty-fifth and thirty-sixth stages; thus these two stages served as the heat sink.   Approximately 60 per cent of this warmed seawater was then introduced into the brine stream as makeup.   Normally, the concentration of the recirculating brine was about double the concentration of the seawater.

Lighted observation windows were provided at each stage,

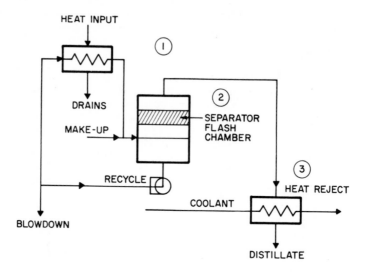

Figure 2.   Basic Flash Evaporator Cycle

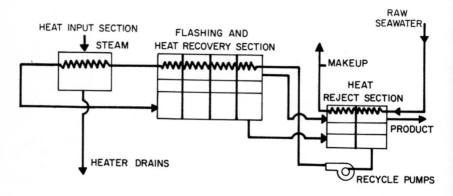

Figure 3.   Schematic of Point Loma Plant

positioned to allow visual inspection of both the surface of the shell-side brine and the wire-mesh moisture separators.

## DEMONSTRATION FEATURES

In accordance with its demonstration role, the Point Loma plant was designed to permit variation in the types of materials used, and variations in operating procedures. As a special feature, the plant was operated with two separate and completely isolated brine streams flowing in parallel in the condenser tubes and flash chambers. This arrangement permitted testing two methods of chemical treatment simultaneously. Aluminum-brass tubing was used throughout the heat-recovery condensers in one of the streams. The other stream had stages of 90-10 cupronickel and carbon steel in addition to the aluminum brass.

The plant was designed to allow variations in the velocity of the seawater, as well as variations in the number of stages operated as heat reject stages. It was also designed to accommodate inlet temperatures ranging from 200 degrees to 250 degrees. The increase in inlet temperatures from 200 degrees at the startup of the plant to 250 degrees at the time it was dismantled, is the most significant of all the achievements at Point Loma.

The warranted characteristics of the plant were as follows:

1. Product water output of one million gallons per day with purity of 50 parts per million.

2. Heat consumption of 39.8 million Btu per hour.

3. Electric power requirement 132.6 kw.

4. Chemical consumption 66.7 lbs. per day.

5. Thirty-day product water output of 30 million gallons.

The plant met or exceeded all of its warranty characteristics, as shown in Table I.

TABLE I

Performance of Point Loma

|  | Guarantee | Actual |
|---|---|---|
| Daily Output (MGD) 200°F | 1.0 | 1.0 |
| 240°F | - | 1.4 |
| Purity (ppm) | 50 | 4.0 |
| Heat Consumption (MBtu/h) | 39.8 | 39.8 |
| Electric Power (kw) | 132.6 | 107 |
| Chemical Consumption (lbs/day) | 66.7 | 61.4 |
| 30-Day Output - Continuous Run (gal) | 30.0 M | 31.6 M |

## PLANT HISTORY

The first commercial delivery of water to the city of San Diego was made on March 8, 1962. Product quality of the water was exceptionally high from the start, averaging 4 ppm to 5 ppm of dissolved solids, far better than the 50 ppm stated in the warranty. On March 10, 1962, the plant was formally dedicated by Secretary of the Interior, Stewart Udall. A 30-day continuous run with performance data being taken during the last four days of the test showed that all warranted performance characteristics were being met.

An analysis of plant performance may be misleading unless a number of factors are understood. First of all, since the plant was a demonstration plant, it was shut down on occasion for inspections and other procedures which were a part of the OSW program. One important problem, and one which would be common to other desalting plants at the same location, was caused by marine vegetation entering the system through the seawater intake. Appropriate steps were being taken to redesign the seawater intake at the time the plant was moved to Guantanamo. Mechanical difficulties, confined mostly to pumps and peripheral equipment, caused some interruptions during the first year of operation. Maintenance of the evaporators and condensers was negligible throughout the operating period of the plant.

A report issued by the operating contractors, covering the period from January 1, 1962, through June 30, 1963, disclosed that during this time some 347, 000, 000 gallons of fresh water were delivered to the city of San Diego. Although monthly production ranged from 3. 8 to 35. 6 million gallons due to the experimental mission of the plant, the average percentage of rated capacity was 71. 9 produced in 71 per cent of the time available.

During the last three months of the reported period, the daily average was 1. 15 million gallons. To some extent, the capacity of the plant was restricted by the ability of the city pumps and mains to accept the water. For short periods, approximately 10 per cent of the output was rejected.

## SCALE CONTROL

If untreated seawater is heated and concentrated as required for the distillation process, it forms precipitates which are deposited as scale on the heat transfer surfaces. If allowed to form, these deposits act as thermal insulators and reduce the efficiency of the evaporating process. The three principal types of scale deposit are calcium carbonate ($CaCO_3$), magnesium hydroxide ($MgOH_2$), and calcium sulfate. Most of the scale-forming compounds have inverted solubility curves as shown in Figure 4. Consequently, the scale problem becomes greater when the solubility of the compounds is lessened through an increase in brine temperature.

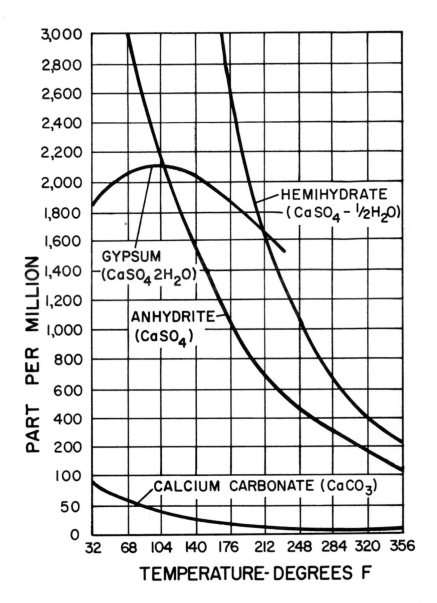

Figure 4. Solubility Curves for Scale-Forming Compounds

It has been found that scale can be controlled effectively by lowering the pH in order to increase the solubility of the carbonates and hydroxides. The warranted production of 1,000,000 gallons a day was achieved at Point Loma with top temperature of 200°F. At temperatures up to 200°F, the scale control was maintained by feeding 5 ppm of a polyphosphate-based compound into both seawater make-up lines preceding the deaerators.

In September, 1962, an acid-pH control system was installed which permitted raising the brine temperatures to 250°F. This system consisted of a 5,000-gallon acid-storage tank and a diaphragm-type positive displacement metering pump. Sulfuric acid at 66° Baume was fed into make-up lines to reduce the pH and to convert the carbonate alkalinity into carbon dioxide. This latter and other noncondensable gases were removed by air ejectors. An acid injection rate of approximately 130 ppm was used to hold the pH in the recycle stream at 7.5. The air ejectors originally installed were constructed of conventional materials for power-plant installation and showed rapid deterioration after pH scale-control was employed. Air ejectors for present-day desalting plants require the use of materials capable of withstanding the $CO_2$ attack.

## INCREASED PRODUCTION

Water production was increased substantially following the introduction of acid-pH control. On March 25, 1963, a 24-hour production of 1,243,164 gallons of water was attained. During the following month, the plant was operated 100 per cent of available time and 35.6 million gallons were produced. A new daily record of 1,389,024 gallons was set on April 14, 1963. On May 2 and 3, a plant peak of 1,400,529 gallons for a 24-hour period was established. A brine heater outlet temperature of 240° F was used.

During June, 1963, a 400-hour test run was made at 250°F. No evidence of scaling was found on the heat-exchange surfaces. Following the initiation of acid-pH control, the plant was operated regularly at temperatures ranging to 250°F, with a daily production rate of 1.4 million gallons of pure water. The excellent condition of the flash evaporator at the time it was removed for shipment to Guantanamo shows that operation of the plant at 250°F brine temperatures was completely feasible.

## ECONOMICS OF HIGHER BRINE TEMPERATURES

Some economic figures clearly demonstrate the exceptional benefits which are derived from increasing the brine temperature. The cost of the water at Point Loma was approximately $1.25 per 1,000 gallons when produced at a rate of one MGD with the 200°F brine temperature limitation. When the temperature was raised to 250°F and the production rate increased to 1.4 million gallons, the cost was reduced to $1.00 per 1,000 gallons using the same basis.

As mentioned before, carbon steel tubes were installed in several stages and their life was much longer than expected. Six hundred of these tubes withstood the rigors of their environment for 17,000 hours before failures appeared.

## LOW DISSOLVED-OXYGEN CONTENT

The freedom from serious corrosion problems in the evaporator and condensers undoubtedly resulted from the achievement of a very low dissolved-oxygen content in the recirculating brine. Noncondensable gases in the seawater, and the carbon dioxide which resulted from the lowering of the pH were vented from the deaerator to the thirty-sixth stage where they were removed. At the thirty-sixth stage an absolute pressure of 28 in. Hg was maintained by twin sets of two-stage air ejectors.

The removal of noncondensable gases from each of the stages was handled through vents which permitted passing the gases from a higher pressure stage to the next lower pressure stage. Crossover piping was provided so that venting of the gases could also be accomplished between various combinations of the stages, or to the air ejectors.

Continuing testing showed the dissolved-oxygen content of the recycle streams after they emerged from the brine heater to be 0.005 cc/liter or less.

## SELF-REGULATION

Operating experience with the plant while it was at Point Loma showed that the process tended to be self-regulating. If one phase of the process became erratic, other phases would compensate for it. The plant became exceptionally stable under transient operating conditions and did not require intensive manual supervision. The experience with this plant demonstrated that the skill level of the operating force can be the same or less than the skill level of personnel used at conventional power plants.

## THE FUTURE OF MULTISTAGE FLASH EVAPORATION

Experience at Point Loma and other installations allows some confident predictions to be made about the future costs of producing potable water by the multi-stage flash evaporation process. As shown here, the costs of producing water by the flash evaporation process have been reduced dramatically. Ten years ago, the costs ranged from $3 to $4 per 1,000 gallons; they now run from $1 to $2 per 1,000 gallons in today's relatively small plants.

Studies show that with present-day technology large amounts of water can be produced for about 25 to 35 cents per 1,000 gallons in large dual-purpose plants.

The cost of producing potable water is largely the cost of generating heat. This is determined mainly by the cost of fuel, and little can be done in a given area to reduce fuel costs. However, large multi-stage flash evaporator water desalting plants can be designed to take advantage of the economies which result from combining water production with power generation.

The flash evaporation process is suitable for dual operation with electric power plants. Heat for the flash evaporation process can be extracted from the steam turbine, or it can be supplied from a noncondensing turbine exhausting to the brine heater. Each water desalting plant must be designed to fit a specific set of conditions.

Nuclear power can be combined with the flash evaporation process to produce large economic and technical advantages. An important benefit of the combination is that the nuclear heat source becomes more economical as the plant size increases. The nuclear plant can be a dual-purpose installation designed for producing both electricity and pure water.

## TECHNICAL FEASIBILITY

In 1948, Westinghouse commenced the research, development, and construction of the first large plant for distilling seawater. Since then, the company has completed, is building, or has contracts for building desalting plants with a total capacity of nearly 25 MGD. Essentially, all of these plants use the multistage flash evaporation process.

Westinghouse is continuing research in other methods of water conversion. These are reverse osmosis, freezing, vapor compression, and electrodialysis. However, for large seawater desalting plants, we do not feel that any of these processes now approach the technical feasibility, practicality, and overall economy of multi-stage flash evaporation. This situation is expected to prevail in the foreseeable future. Multi-stage flash evaporation is the only process sufficiently developed for large water desalting plant construction today. Firm price, performance, and the completion date will be guaranteed by Westinghouse. There is no doubt that combination power and water desalting plants rated at 150 MGD and larger are possible. They can be built with complete assurance now. The confidence in the technical feasibility of large combination nuclear power water plants using multi-stage flash evaporators cannot be expressed in stronger words.

## 12. Operating Experience at the Electrodialysis Plant, Buckeye, Arizona

T. A. Kirkham, Vice-President, Ionics, Incorporated

Buckeye, Arizona is a town of approximately 2500 people, located 34 miles west of Phoenix on U. S. Highway 80. Until 1935 relatively good quality water had been obtained from a thin lens about 150 feet underground. Between 1935 and 1960, approximately 25 to 30 new wells were drilled, each with the same results: initially the total dissolved salts content was in the acceptable range of 400-500 parts per million. After pumping for 9 to 12 months, the salt content increased to about 2000-2500 parts per million. In 1960, the progressive town Council enlisted the aid of the equally progressive local Chamber of Commerce to formulate and execute an imaginative water improvement program. Manufacturers of saline water conversion plants were contacted and a survey was made to determine how much the untreated brackish water was costing the people of the town in "hidden charges." After approximately a year of study, it was concluded that a central desalting facility to provide good quality water to all people of the town for all purposes could be installed and operated at an apparent annual savings to the town, when "hidden charges" are considered, of approximately $23,000 per year. Thus the decision was made to install an electrodialysis desalting plant which was put into beneficial operation with a peak capacity of 650,000 gallons per day on September 9, 1962. The entire demands of the town have been supplied without interruption since the plant was commissioned. There have been several papers presented and published dealing with all of the factors leading up to the installation of the plant; the design, installation and startup of the plant; the guarantees provided by the manufacturer; and the operating and cost experience for the initial periods of operation.[1-8] It is the purpose of this paper to summarize the important plant performance and cost experience for the first three calendar years of operation, 1963-65.

### LOAD FACTOR, PEAK LOAD

Perhaps the most significant single consideration from a water cost standpoint is load factor. Load factor, of course, is defined as the percentage ratio of annual water production to steady, full load capability of the facility. The lower the plant load factor, the larger the total water costs due to the absorption of the fixed charges for the facility by a smaller quantity of water produced.

Thus, the study of the factors that effect peak load requirement
and average annual load requirements become very important.   In
most circumstances, data with regard to these two factors is
available for the existing water facility in prior years.   Line A on
Figure 1 shows the average daily production from the well system
on a monthly basis for the year immediately prior to the installation of the electrodialysis plant.   The average daily production for
the peak month (July) was 575,000 gallons per day and for the
minimum month (February) was 205,000 GPD.   This gives an average daily production ratio from summer to winter of approximately 2.8.   Based on an average day of the extreme weeks, the
ratio was approximately 3.3.   This condition is extreme based upon national averages, but is quite representative of towns in the
Southwest part of the United States.   The average day production
for the peak week in July was estimated to be 650,000 GPD.   Although it was recognized that there were factors accompanying the
installation of the electrodialysis facility that might tend to reduce
the peak demand such as increased water revenue rates and use of
recirculation pumps on evaporative coolers, it was decided to install an electrodialysis facility capable of 650,000 GPD because
(1) it was only conjecture that any reduced demand may occur and
(2) the excess capacity, if it did exist, would allow for further
growth of the town that was expected to result from the improved

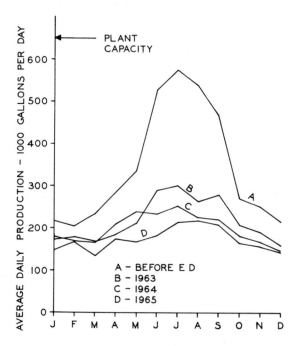

Figure 1.   Annual Variation of Plant Production

water quality over years to come.   Based upon a full load capability of 650, 000 GPD (233, 000, 000 gallons per year), the annual demand represented by Curve A (112, 000, 000 gallons per year) gives a load factor of 48 per cent.   All projections of plant operation, water costs and water revenue rates were made on this basis.

Line B,  C and D on Figure 1 show the actual measured average daily production for the years 1963,  1964 and 1965 respectively.   The major observation is the dramatic reduction in the average day for the peak month from the expected 575, 000 GPD to 300, 000 GPD for 1963,  250, 000 GPD for 1964 and 220, 000 GPD for 1965.   This resulted in a significant but, of course,  less dramatic reduction in load factor.   The load factors were 34,  31 and 27 per cent respectively for 1963,  1964 and 1965 compared to the design point of 48 per cent.   The economic impact of this reduction in load factor in terms of specific water costs is discussed later.

It is important to note the major reason behind the sharp reduction in peak demand during the summer months.   Evaporative coolers are used for air conditioning in the hot,  arid Arizona summers.   Due to the formation of scale deposits on the cooler pads, it had not been the custom to recirculate the brackish water in the coolers.   The radically improved water quality provided by the electrodialysis plant has made it possible to install recirculating pumps and thereby save more than half of the water previously used in the coolers. [6]   A significant increase in cooler efficiency was also realized.   Although this effect was considered to be a possibility in the planning period, it is now an established fact.   It emphasizes the necessity of determining and allowing for the effect of improved water quality on water production and consumption.

Figure 2 shows the average daily metered consumption in gallons per day on the same basis as Figure 1.   Of course, the values shown on Figure 2 are less than the corresponding values of Figure 1; the difference is the water "loss."   This loss is partly a true loss due to leakage and partly due to unmetered or inaccurately metered usages.   The calculated percentage loss in 1963 was 22 per cent.   This was reduced to 21 per cent in 1964 and 16 per cent in 1965, mostly due to a concentrated water meter calibration and maintenance program undertaken in 1964. [6]   A comparison of Lines C and D between Figures 1 and 2 point up the significant reduction in water loss achieved in 1965.   However, in spite of the meter inspection program, the metered consumption still decreased from 57. 4 million gallons in 1964 to 53. 4 million gallons in 1965.   This was predominately due to reduced consumption in 1965 during the months of May, June and July.

It is also interesting to note that the metered water consumption during the winter months has held relatively constant after

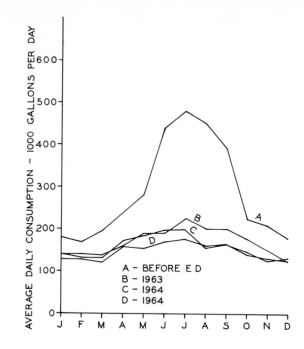

Figure 2.   Annual Variation of Consumption

the initial reduction following the installation of the electrodialysis plant.   This reduction of about 25-28 per cent can possibly be taken as an indication of the magnitude of reduction to be expected due to increased water revenue rates if no special factors are involved.   It is felt that a final stabilization of the metered consumption has now been achieved and that in subsequent years a gradual tendency toward higher consumptions will be experienced.

## PLANT PERFORMANCE AND OPERATING PROBLEMS

Table 1 is a summary of the important factors concerning performance of the electrodialysis plant.   The data are shown for calendar years 1963, 1964, 1965 for the total of the three years and for the average of the three years.   The original design basis is also shown; however, it is difficult to meaningfully compare the actual performance to the original design basis because of the radical differences in production and load factor.   Thus, an "extended design basis" is the projection that would have originally been made for the three year average production actually observed under the ground rules used to formulate the original design basis.

TABLE I

Summary of Plant Performance

| | 1963 | 1964 | 1965 | 3-yr. Total | 3-yr. Avg. | Design Basis | Ext. of Design Basis |
|---|---|---|---|---|---|---|---|
| Peak Day, kGD | 360 | 300 | 260 | ---- | 300 | 650 | 300 |
| Minimum Day, kGD | 160 | 150 | 130 | ---- | 145 | 200 | 145 |
| Average Day, kGD | 227 | 202 | 176 | ---- | 200 | 307 | 200 |
| Production, M Gal | 80.18 | 72.87 | 63.33 | 216.4 | 72.1 | 112 | 72.1 |
| Sales, M Gal | 62.03 | 57.37 | 53.37 | 172.8 | 57.6 | 93 | 57.6 |
| Production Loss, % | 22 | 21 | 16 | 20 | 20 | 20 | 20 |
| Load Factor, % | 34 | 31 | 27 | 31 | 31 | 48 | 31 |
| Blow Down, M Gal | 25.15 | 23.49 | 21 | 69.7 | 23.2 | 37 | 24 |
| Blow Down, % | 23.8 | 24.4 | 25 | 24.4 | 24.4 | 25 | 25 |
| Energy, k MWh | 602 | 606 | 476 | 1684 | 561 | 1120 | 590 |
| kwh per k Gal | 7.36 | 8.31 | 7.52 | 7.8 | 7.8 | 10.0 | 8.2 |
| Acid Consumption, k lbs. | 41 | 43 | 47.5 | 131.5 | 43.8 | 67.2 | 43 |
| Lbs. Acid per k Gal | 0.51 | 0.59 | 0.75 | 0.61 | 0.61 | 0.60 | 0.6 |
| Filter Cartridge Use | 2560 | 3200 | 4500 | 10,260 | 3420 | 2700 | 2380 |
| k Gallons of Feed Water per Cartridge | 41.3 | 29.8 | 19.5 | 28 | 28 | 55 | 55 |
| No. of Stack Disassemblies | 50 | 95 | 34 | 179 | 60 | 34 | 30 |

k   1,000
M   1,000,000

The dramatic reduction in plant production, metered consumption and plant load factor are again evident from Table 1. On the original design basis, it was expected that the plant would produce 112,000,000 gallons per year at a plant load factor of 48 per cent and that 93,000,000 gallons per year would be sold. The three year average shows a plant production of 72,100,000 gallons at a load factor of 31 per cent and metered sales of 57,600,000 gallons. In 1965, the load factor was only 27 per cent. The impact of this on specific water costs will be discussed later.

Comparing the other items of plant performance, we see that the areas where significant differences exist are the areas of energy consumption, filter cartridge consumption and number of stack disassemblies. These and other related parameters of plant performance have been primarily affected at the Buckeye plant by one operating problem. This problem has been described in the past as having to do with feed water filtration. The use of the word "pretreatment" in place of "filtration" would be more accurate. It is important to note at the start that this problem at Buckeye must still be classified primarily as one of technical interest; the costs incurred for handling the problem in the manner used to date have not increased the overall water costs to any significant extent.

The feed water for the plant contains approximately 2000 ppm total dissolved solids, up to 0.5 ppm of iron, 5-10 ppm of silica and small amounts of fine clay or sand particles. It is passed through a bank of filters containing disposable cartridges rated by the manufacturer at 10 microns. Our general electrodialysis experience and experience gained from a pilot unit run at Buckeye during 1961-62 indicated that a safe yield of 55,000 gallons of feed water per cartridge should be obtained. From Table 1 it can be seen that the three year average yield was only 28,000 gallons per cartridge and in 1965 was only 19,500 gallons per cartridge. The unusually low cartridge yield in 1965 was primarily due to a change in May 1965 from Well No. 8, which had been used exclusively up until that time, to a blend of water from Well No. 8 and Well No. 9 which was predominately from Well No. 9. Well No. 9 had been avoided in the past due to the higher level of fine silt and sand in the water from this source. The use of Well No. 8, which will be the main source in the future, can be expected to reliably yield the cartridge output experienced in 1964 or 29,800 gallons per cartridge.

Our general electrodialysis experience has indicated that, with a few exceptions, water passed through 10 micron filters such as used at Buckeye becomes an acceptable feed for the membrane stacks. The pilot plant test run in 1961-62 also confirmed this point. The full scale plant when put into operation unfortunately turned out to be an exception to a limited degree. The observation is that over a period of several weeks a coating or slime forms on the surface of the membranes and flow chambers or spacers. This slime is brown in color and analysis shows it is to be predominately silica. The slime coating is considerably more pronounced in the stacks of Stage No. 1 than Stage No. 2, is predominately in the diluting chambers rather than the concentrating chambers and favors the surface of the anion membranes over the cation membranes. It should be noted that practically all electrodialysis stacks show this tendency to form a slime coating. The problem is merely one of degree. The condition at Buckeye is more severe than one would normally expect to occur; however, it is not sufficiently severe at the present to be judged an important cost factor or to warrant the expenditure of significant sums of money for additional pretreatment equipment.

Obviously, it is the results of the slime build-up that cause the real problem. What is observed if no remedial actions are taken are (1) increase in stack electrical resistance and membrane resistance, (2) increase in energy consumption per unit of water produced, (3) increase in hydraulic resistance to flow through the membrane stacks, and (4) tendency toward polarized conditions with the accompanying undesirable scale formation and membrane damage. There has also existed at Buckeye a history of development of isolated high electrical resistance spots in the membrane stacks. The occurrence of such "high spots" has been somewhat erratic and has recently (in 1965) improved. It is felt that such high spots are also caused by slime formation but unequivocal proof is still lacking.

The remedial actions that are taken to maintain the stacks in an acceptable equilbrium condition are probably obvious. They consist of (1) disassembly, inspection and cleaning of the membrane stacks, (2) replacement of membranes and spacers as required, and (3) cleaning and chemical regeneration of the membranes if required after removal from the stack for reuse. As a direct example of the type equilibrium condition that can be maintained on a membrane stack, Figure 3 shows a plot of the ohmic resistance of stack No. 1, Stage No. 1 over the three-year period. During the early months of 1963, the stack resistance was actually less than the original design value of 10 ohms. From May 1963 through May 1965, the program of cleaning and membrane replacement maintained the stack resistance at a reasonably constant level between 10 to 12 ohms; the rate of membrane replacement was less than originally planned. The fairly sharp changes in stack resistance, particularly during the later part of 1963 and the early part of 1964, reflect the influence of isolated high spots. On May 15, 1966, the transfer to a feed water predominately from Well No. 9, which is appreciably lower in total ionized solids and therefore has a higher specific resistivity, produced the normal increase in stack resistance as shown. I think Figure 3 demonstrates that, even under the sliming conditions found at Buckeye, it is readily possible to maintain an equilibrium stack condition.

Returning to Table 1 and those items that are influenced by the sliming problem, we observe that total energy per 1000 gallons for the three-year period (7.8 $^{kwh}/kG$) is appreciably less than the guaranteed design value (10.0 $^{kwh}/kG$) as ex-

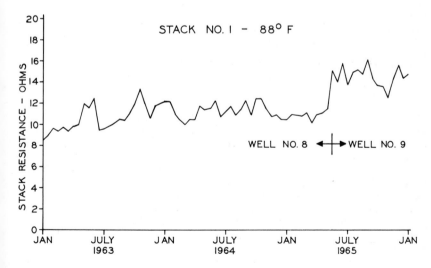

Figure 3.  Variation of Stack Resistance With Time

pected, but is also less than the extended design basis (8.2 kwh/ kG). This is partly due to operation on the lower salinity blend of Well No. 8 and Well No. 9 during 7-1/2 months of 1965. This operation also is the reason for the reduction in energy consumption from 1964 to 1965. The average number of stack disassemblies for the three-year period averaged 60 per year or approximately twice the design value. This corresponds to an average of 10 disassemblies per stack per year which, on the average, requires 6 man hours per disassembly or 60 man hours per stack per year. The unusually high number of disassemblies in 1964 was predominately due to the frequent occurrence of high spots and reflects the efforts expended to determine the cause. The sharp reduction in stack disassemblies in 1965, which was also accompanied by a sharp reduction in membrane replacement, (see Table II) appears to be associated with the switch to the blended water from Well No. 9.

TABLE II

Comparison of Annual Water Costs

|  | 1963 | 1964 | 1965 | 3-yr. Total | 3-yr. Avg. | Design Basis |
|---|---|---|---|---|---|---|
| Plant Production, Millions of Gallons | 80.2 | 72.9 | 63.3 | 216.4 | 72.1 | 112 |
| Load Factor, % | 34 | 31 | 27 | 31 | 31 | 48 |
| Electrical Power, $ [1] | 10,300 | 8,460 | 6,650 | 25,410 | 8,470 | 15,700 |
| Acid, $ [2] | 480 | 500 | 550 | 1,530 | 510 | 1,010 |
| Filters, $ | 2,560 | 2,820 | 3,960 | 9,340 | 3,110 | 2,070 |
| Membrane Replacement $ | 6,000 | 4,900 | 1,000 | 11,900 | 3,970 | 9,900 |
| Other Parts & Service, $ | 4,040 | 5,600 | 3,500 | 13,140 | 4,380 | 4,200 |
| Miscellaneous, $ | 1,140 | 2,200 | 3,000 | 6,340 | 2,110 | ----- |
| Labor, $ | 5,500 | 6,200 | 6,100 | 17,800 | 5,930 | 3,600 |
| Bond Retirement, $ | 20,500 | 20,500 | 20,500 | 61,500 | 20,500 | 20,500 |
| Total, $ | 50,520 | 51,180 | 45,260 | 146,960 | 48,980 | 56,980 |

(1) Power rate in 1963 was 1.7¢/kwh, 1964-65 was 1.4¢/kwh
(2) Acid rate was approximately 1.16¢/lb of 98% $H_2SO_4$
(3) Filter rate in 1963 was $1.00/cartridge, 1964-65 was $0.88/cartridge

## COST OF PLANT OPERATION

Under the unusual load factor conditions of the Buckeye plant, it is important to examine both the unit water costs and the annual costs. Table II shows the costs for plant operation on an annual basis. The cost of electrical energy is the largest single operating cost. The annual energy cost for the three-year average is only 54 per cent of the design basis because of the lower plant production, the lower unit cost of power and the lower energy consumption per unit of water produced. For the three-year average, the cost of filters is 50 per cent greater than the design basis in spite of the reduced plant output for the reasons previously explored. However, the incremental costs for filters extrapolated from the design basis is only $1800 per year which is not signifi-

cant.  The cost of membrane replacement for the three-year average was only 40 per cent of the design value although plant production was 65 per cent of the design value.  The unusually low
cost for membrane replacement incurred in 1965 was due to a reduced tendency toward high spot formation and general slime accumulation in the stacks and an effective program of membrane
reuse.  The average annual cost of labor over the three-year period was $5930 as compared to $3600 for the design basis.  The
original design value was based upon the part time use of a town
employee.  However, the town decided to hire an additional employee for the function and to allocate his entire salary to the
plant operation.  In spite of the higher number of stack disassemblies experienced during the three years, the plant operator has
still been able to spend a significant portion of his time on other
town functions.  Examination of the column totals in  Table II
shows that over the three-year period, the cost of plant operation
at reduced capacity has averaged $8000 per year under the design
value.  In 1965, the annual costs were $11,760 under the design
value.

Table III presents the plant operation costs in terms of cents
per thousand gallons produced.  The total water costs for the
three-year period averaged 68.0 cents per thousand gallons
compared to 50.9 cents per thousand gallons on the design basis.
The incremental cost of approximately 17 cents per 1000 gallons
is almost exclusively due to the distribution of the fixed charge
payment for bond retirement over a smaller water production and
the arbitrary allocation of higher labor charges.  The savings experienced in the cost of energy, acid and membrane replacement

TABLE III

Comparison of Unit Water Costs

|  | 1963 | 1964 | 1965 | 3-yr. Avg. | Design Basis | Ext. of Design Basis |
|---|---|---|---|---|---|---|
| Plant Production, Millions of Gallons | 80.2 | 72.9 | 63.3 | 72.1 | 112 | 72.1 |
| Load Factor, % | 34 | 31 | 27 | 31 | 48 | 31 |
| | Cents per 1000 Gallons | | | | | |
| Electrical Power [1] | 12.9 | 11.6 | 10.5 | 11.7 | 14.0 | 14.0 |
| Acid [2] | 0.6 | 0.7 | 0.9 | 0.7 | 0.9 | 0.9 |
| Filters [3] | 3.2 | 3.9 | 6.2 | 4.3 | 1.9 | 1.9 |
| Membrane Replacement | 7.5 | 6.7 | 1.6 | 5.5 | 8.8 | 13.7 |
| Other Parts & Service | 5.0 | 7.7 | 5.5 | 6.1 | 3.8 | 4.8 |
| Miscellaneous | 1.4 | 3.0 | 4.7 | 2.9 | --- | --- |
| Labor | 6.9 | 8.5 | 9.6 | 8.2 | 3.2 | 3.2 |
| Bond Retirement | 25.5 | 28.1 | 32.4 | 28.4 | 18.3 | 28.4 |
| Total | 63.0 | 70.2 | 71.4 | 68.0 | 50.9 | 66.9 |

(1)  Power rate in 1963 was 1.7¢/kwh,  1964-65 was 1.4¢/kwh
(2)  Acid rate was approximately 1.16¢/lb of 98% $H_2 SO_4$
(3)  Filter rate in 1963 was $1.00/cartridge, 1964-65 was $0.88/cartridge

approximately balance the additional unit costs for filters, other parts and service and the miscellaneous category which was not originally taken into consideration.  Although the individual cost categories vary, it is interesting to note that the total water costs for the extended design basis are essentially equal to the three-year average actually experienced.

The effect of plant load factor on unit water costs is even apparent from the limited range shown on Table III.  Table IV has been prepared to emphasize this effect.  The total unit costs in terms of cents per thousand gallons are presented for load factors of 30, 50, 75 and 100 per cent.  The base column for 30 per cent factor is oriented around the three-year average experience.  The total water costs in cents per thousand gallons decrease from a high of 68. 3 at 30 per cent load factor, to 53. 5 at 50 per cent, to 42. 8 at 75 per cent and 37. 0 at 100 per cent.  From values in Table I for peak day and average day production for 1965 and assuming the same ratios will hold or even improve as the town grows, it is apparent that a 75 per cent load factor can be achieved in the years ahead.

TABLE IV

Variation of Unit Water Costs With Annual Load Factor

| Annual Prodn. , Millions of Gal. | 70 | 117 | 175 | 233 |
| Plant Load Factor; % | 30 | 50 | 75 | 100 |
| --- | --- | --- | --- | --- |
| | Cents per 1000 Gallons | | | |
| Electrical Power | 11. 7 | 11. 7 | 13. 0 | 14. 0 |
| Acid | 0. 9 | 0. 9 | 0. 9 | 0. 9 |
| Filters | 4. 3 | 3. 2 | 3. 2 | 3. 2 |
| Membrane Replacement | 5. 5 | 8. 8 | 5. 7 | 4. 2 |
| Other Parts & Service | 5. 0 | 4. 0 | 3. 0 | 2. 0 |
| Miscellaneous | 3. 0 | 1. 8 | 1. 3 | 0. 9 |
| Labor | 8. 6 | 5. 6 | 4. 0 | 3. 0 |
| Bond Retirement | 29. 3 | 17. 5 | 11. 7 | 8. 8 |
| Total | 68. 3 | 53. 5 | 42. 8 | 37. 0 |

## WATER REVENUES

In Table V the total costs for operation of the water department of the town are compared to the total Revenues received.  Under the design basis, it was expected that 93 million gallons of water would be sold per year for $107, 000.  The expenses against this income would be $57, 000 for the electrodialysis plant and $50, 000 for basic department costs.  The net accumulation per year would be zero.  However, the basic department costs of $50, 000 were estimated and may include a small, programmed accumulation.  Also, it was expected that the $57, 000 costs for the electrodialysis plant would yield a small accumulation for a reserve against membrane replacement cost in future years.

TABLE V

Comparison of Revenues & Costs

|  | 1963 | 1964 | 1965 | Total | 3-yr. Avg. | Design Basis |
|---|---|---|---|---|---|---|
| Metered Sales, M Gal | 62.03 | 57.37 | 57.37 | 172.8 | 57.6 | 93 |
| Revenues, k $ | 79.98 | 99.37 | 108.80 | 288.2 | 96.1 | 107 |
| Basic Dept. Costs, k $ 1 | 50.00 | 50.00 | 50.00 | 150.0 | 50.0 | 50 |
| ED Costs, k $ | 50.52 | 51.18 | 45.26 | 147.0 | 49.0 | 57 |
| Net Accumulation, k $ | (20.54) | (1.81) | 13.54 | (8.8) | (2.9) | 0 |
| Average Monthly Bill, $ | 10.00 | 12.00 | 13.70 | ----- | 12.00 | 13.00 |

(1) Estimated
k    1,000
M    1,000,000

The payment of $107,000 per year was a relatively firm commitment accepted by the people of the town. Since all of the basic department costs and a major fraction of the electrodialysis costs are fixed expenses, it was also apparent that approximately $100,000 per year had to be collected by the water department, independent of the quantity of water actually sold. To obtain the additional $57,000 per year required, the revenue rates for water were increased in September of 1962 as shown in Table VI. The average monthly water bill was expected to increase from approximately $6.00 per month to $13.00 per month. However, as previously explained, the town residents had been spending an estimated $80,000 per year in "hidden charges" which were projected to be radically reduced or completely eliminated. Thus, the projected program for cash flow from the people for water and water oriented needs merely called for the diversion of $57,000 from the "hidden charges" account to the town water department account with apparent possible savings to the town residents of $23,000 per year.

In 1963, due to the reduced quantity of water sold at the rates established in September of 1962, only $80,000 was collected in revenues. Although the annual costs for electrodialysis were down slightly due to the lower water consumption, the water department suffered a net deficit of $20,500 in 1963. In the spring of 1964 it was recognized that the reduced water consumption was here to stay for the immediate few years. Since approximately $100,000 in annual revenues had to be generated, a second increase in the water revenue rates was established as shown in Table VI, effective June 1, 1964. Although the quantity of water sold in 1964 slipped another 10 per cent to 57 million gallons, the total revenues received by the water department increased to a respectable $99,000 and produced a net deficit for the year of only $2,000. The average monthly bill was $12.00 per month, which was still less than the commitment called for under the design basis. In 1965, which was the first full year at the higher water

TABLE VI

History of Water Rates

| Water Usage 1000's of Gallons | Price per 1000 Gallons $ |
|---|---|
| Before Electrodialysis | |
| First 5 | 3.00 + |
| Next 15 | 0.35 |
| Next 20 | 0.30 |
| Next 20 | 0.25 |
| Next 20 | 0.20 |
| Over 80 | 0.15 |
| Immediately after Electrodialysis | |
| First 2 | 4.40 + |
| Next 5 | 1.15 |
| Next 13 | 0.90 |
| Next 15 | 0.70 |
| Next 25 | 0.55 |
| Next 40 | 0.45 |
| Over 100 | 0.35 |
| Effective June 1964 | |
| First 2 | 6.00 + |
| Next 5 | 2.15 |
| Next 13 | 1.50 |
| Next 15 | 1.00 |
| Over 35 | 0.65 |

+ Minimum Monthly Bill

rates, the revenues collected increased to $109,000 while the department costs decreased to $95,000, primarily due to a decrease in costs for operation of the electrodialysis plant. A net accumulation of $13,500 was realized for 1965.

On a three year total basis, the sale of 173,000,000 gallons of water (62 per cent of the design basis) produced revenues of $288,000 (90 per cent of the design basis) against department costs of $297,000 (93 percent of the design basis). The net result was a deficit of $8,800 over the three-year period. The average monthly bill for the three-year period was $12.00 per month. It is apparent that the revenues and costs for 1966 will run very close to the 1965 figures and that the net accumulation generated in 1966 will wipe out the accumulated three-year deficit and put the water department into the black. It is also apparent from the 1964-65 figures that an annual break-even condition can be achieved at an average monthly bill of approximately $12.00 to $12.50.

## IMPACT ON THE COMMUNITY AND THE FUTURE

The decision to install the electrodialysis plant at Buckeye was made strictly on the basis of the economics of providing a better overall water supply to the town at reduced total water

costs when hidden charges are considered.   However, it was obviously a hope and expectation that the town would experience
commercial, industrial and residential growth as a result of the
improved quality of the water supply.   Buckeye is primarily an
agricultural community.   Unfortunately, due to climatic conditions, the crops in 1964 and 1965 were poor and this has produced
a negative effect on the economy of the town.   Thus, we are observing the results of two factors, one of which is favorable and
one unfavorable.   The observations are as follows:

1.   Residential Construction

In 1962 there were 80 permits issued on construction of
$166, 100; in 1963 there were 96 permits totaling
$336, 600.[7]   However, in 1964, the number of permits
decreased to 88 and in 1965, the number was reduced to
77.   The experience in 1964-65 was felt to be due to the
agricultural depression.

2.   Other Construction

Two new apartment buildings have been built.   The first
was an 18-unit building, completed in 1963; the second
was a 24-unit building, completed in 1964.   A new bowl-
ing alley was built in 1963 at a cost of $250, 000.

3.   Industry

Two companies have moved into the Buckeye area with
operations that are dependent upon good quality water.
Jackson and Perkins, the largest grower and shipper of
roses in the world, has set up growing and packing facilities in the Buckeye community.   Quick Cooling Company
has established facilities at Buckeye for growing, washing and packing grapes.   Both companies depend upon the
superior quality of the water at Buckeye for all phases of
their operations.

4.   Use of Home Appliances

There has been a general and substantial increase in the
use of home appliances that are related to water.   These
include dish washers, clothes washers, electric water
heaters and evaporative coolers.   The sale of dish washers and clothes washers was essentially nonexistent
prior to the advent of the improved water supply.

5.   Consumption of Electrical Energy

The increased consumption of electrical energy in Buckeye is another important indication of progress.   The

local utility franchise taxes have shown an annual increase of 10-15 per cent compared to 2-3 per cent in the
years prior to installation of the electrodialysis plant.
This increase is almost exclusively in the electrical utility area and is primarily associated with increased use
of electric power in the residential areas.

While each of the foregoing indications of growth and progress is not large when considered separately, the total does reflect substantial progress. I think, however, that it would be correct to say that the progress that has been achieved is less than
originally expected. The agricultural failure of 1964-65 is a factor and it would only be conjecture to attempt to describe the additional progress that would have resulted if the agricultural depression had not occurred.

What about the future? I feel the ingredients exist for a substantial growth in the years ahead. The leaders of the town and
the people of the town are progressive and imaginative. The fact
that they independently took the step in 1962 to improve their water supply is testimony to this. They are proud of their desalting
plant and are particularly proud of the fact that they accomplished
the feat without any financial aid from Federal, State or local
agencies. Buckeye is located in an area of the Southwest that has
experienced substantial growth and is destined to achieve even
greater rates of growth in the years ahead. Several years may
pass before the real opportunities for growth at Buckeye materi-
alize. When they do, I'm sure that Buckeye will be prepared to
accept the challenge and I'm equally certain that the improved water quality that Buckeye has to offer will play an important role in
the success story of the town.

## NOTES

1.  Katz, W. E., "Design of Medium-to-Large Electrodialysis
    Water Demineralizer - Several Hundred Thousand to Several
    Million Gallons Per Day," Symposium sponsored by Office of
    Saline Water and American Chemical Society, Washington,
    D. C., March 27, 1962.

2.  Katz, W. E., "Effect of Electrodialysis Field Experience on
    Economics and Design," First European Symposium of Euro-
    pean Federation of Chemical Engineers, Athens, Greece,
    June 1, 1962.

3.  Hamner, W. G., "Brackish Water Becomes Fresh," March
    1963, The American City Magazine.

4.   Kirkham, T. A., "Report on Design, Installation, Startup
     and Operation of Ionics 650, 000 GPD Electrodialysis Plant,
     Buckeye, Arizona, " Division of Water and Waste Chemistry,
     American Chemical Society, Los Angeles, California, April
     4, 1963.

5.   Carollo, J. A. and Hunt, H. , "Desalinization of Reclaimed
     Water and Brackish Water, " delivered before the Water Rec-
     lamation Tour, May 28, 1963, sponsored by the County Sani-
     tation Districts of Orange County, Santa Ana, California.

6.   Hamner, W. G. and Katz, W. E. , Journal American Water
     Works Association, 1964, 56, 1537, 1542.

7.   Barnhill, K. G. , "The 650, 000 GPD Buckeye, Arizona,
     Electrodialysis Water Desalting Plant, " American Water
     Works Association, 55th Annual Conference, Chicago, Illi-
     nois, March 19, 1964.

8.   Gilliland, E. R. , "The Current Economics of Electrodialysis"
     presented at the First International Symposium on Water De-
     salination, Washington, D. C. , October 3-9, 1965.

# 13. Operating Experiences at the OSW
## East Coast Test Facility, Wrightsville Beach, North Carolina

Walter L. Barnes, Jr., Manager, and Wilfred J. Hahn, R & D Test Station,
Office of Saline Water, U.S. Department of the Interior

This paper is largely concerned with the operational aspects of the
OSW Research and Development Test Station at Wrightsville Beach
with the presumption that interested persons have read the description of the test station facilities as appears in the 1963 and
1964 OSW Annual Reports. A portion of the paper will be devoted
to the Pilot Plant Operational experiences.

The primary mission of the test station is to provide the site
and services required for the centralized testing of sea water conversion processes in the pilot plant stage of development with
provisions for bench scale corrosion testing of construction materials proposed for use in sea water conversion plants.

When operation of the test facility began in February, 1963,
the maintenance and operation was conducted by contract with the
Koppers Company of Pittsburgh, Pennsylvania. The contract was
administered by the station manager who was the sole OSW employee at the station. During the course of the Koppers M & O
Contract, study was made to determine whether savings could be
achieved by utilizing OSW personnel for maintenance and operation. The study showed that savings approaching $50,000 annually
could be realized. Therefore, on December 16, 1964, the contract with Koppers was terminated and operation by OSW began.
At the present time, there are nineteen employees in the test station complement. They consist of the manager, process engineer,
chemist, lab assistant, operations supervisor, accountant, pur-
chasing agent, three secretaries, two mechanics, an electrician,
a machinist, four boiler operators, and a caretaker. The pilot
plant contractors have their own technical and operating personnel.

Station services are supplied to contractors with a high degree of reliability. Other than planned down time for improvements, repairs, or for new pilot plant tie-ins, our nonpredictable
power outages average less than four annually.

The major portion of the station operating equipment is associated with the boiler plant. Four boiler operators are employed
on a continuous rotating shift to operate and generally maintain the
steam generators, including auxiliaries such as the fuel oil and
feed water systems, the station air compressors and fire water
booster pumps. During the past fiscal year, steam was being
generated 361 of the 365 days.

Since opening in 1963, the test station equipment within the battery limits has not required major overhaul and/or replacement. Approximately 30 per cent of the structural steel has been repainted and the remainder will require painting this year. Only normal maintenance has been required in the boiler plant. The equipment and piping of the pilot plants are affected by atmospheric corrosion at a much faster rate than the station facilities probably because of the concentration of equipment into rather small areas creating wind breaks and shade conditions. This condition indicates that the exterior treatment of future production plants and the economic considerations thereof deserve further study for plants to be located in marine atmospheres. Outside the battery limits, two major maintenance projects have been undertaken involving the sea water intake system. The 24-inch duplex strainer on the sea water feed is of cast iron construction with monel baskets. The seats for the sliding gates at the strainer inlet and exit were integrally cast with the body and corroded severely after approximately one year of operation making the strainer, in effect, simplex. The strainer was removed, machined, and fitted with replaceable stainless steel seats. Stainless steel was selected due to availability and for economic considerations. The other major maintenance outside the battery limits is a continuing project involving the sea water intake pumps. Each of the three vertical turbine type pumps has been removed and overhauled. In general, only the renewal of bearings and/or wear rings is required. One of the pumps is epoxy coated cast iron with Ni-resist impellers. The other two pumps are all bronze. In the case of the cast iron pump, two of the three Ni-resist impellers have been replaced. The Ni-resist impellers showed evidence of impending stress corrosion failure at the junction of the scroll and shroud and the passages were otherwise severely eroded. Bronze impellers were used as replacements because of the long lead time for Ni-resist. New Ni-resist impellers are now being stocked for future replacements. General maintenance within the battery limits has been at a minimum.

A substantial portion of the test station management effort is in direct support of pilot plant operations. The areas of service include supplying special skills for modifications, laboratory services for other than routine analyses, centralized buying and stocking of commonly used materials, chemicals, lubricants, etc. All services to contractors are properly documented for cost and capital equipment accounting purposes.

The test station chemical laboratory is expanding continually to provide capability for varied and complete chemical analyses of sea water and analyses of scale formation products from heat exchange surfaces. Additionally, bacteriological analyses are also being performed. Qualified laboratory personnel spend considerable time developing and documenting the methodology of all unusual analyses. It is hoped that the first series of these techniques will soon be published in technical report form. As a

general service, the laboratory performs and distributes, on a
daily basis, a partial analysis of the sea water feed to the plant.
A complete sea water analysis is performed and distributed on a
monthly basis.

There is no doubt that the centralization of utilities, man-
power skills, laboratory services, and the direct government control of centralized purchase, stocking and distribution of common
use items has resulted in significant savings in the pilot plant
program.

The responsibilities of the test station staff also include technical surveillance of the pilot plant activities.  To understand our
method of surveillance one must first understand the organizational structure of the Office of Saline Water.  The organizational
chart is shown in Figure 1.  For our purposes here, I have shown
only the structure under the Assistant Director for Development
and Engineering.

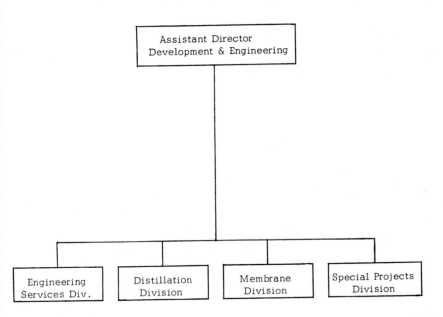

Figure 1.  Organization Chart (Partial)

The test station projects to date have consisted of those processes which would fall into the special projects or distillation categories.  The technical divisions; distillation, membranes, special projects, are responsible for preparing the contractural objectives of each pilot plant contract.  These objectives are, of
course, arrived at through inter-office discussions to assure that

needed knowledge is obtained and that effort is not being dupli-
cated.  After the objectives are agreed upon, the contract is prepared with those objectives specifically outlined therein.

After the pilot plant construction is started, the responsibility for construction and operation surveillance is transferred to
the Engineering Services Division of which the test station is a
part.  We report the day-to-day activities of construction and operation through the Chief of Engineering Services to the technical
division involved.  The test station responsibility is, in essence,
to assure that the contractural objectives are being attained.
This method of operation permits full utilization of the talents of
field personnel and removes a burden of detail work from the
technical divisions.  However, since the technical divisions are
ultimately responsible, the authority granted to Engineering Services for process changes and/or modifications is limited.

The test station accounting staff is responsible for the internal audit of all on-site expense vouchers submitted for reimburse-
ment by the contractors.

In the relatively short life of the East Coast Test Facility,
twelve different pilot units have been tested.  The results obtained
from each are summarized hereinafter.  Also, mention is made
of future operating plans where applicable.

## GENERAL ELECTRIC

The first pilot plant placed in operation at the test station was
designed and built by the General Electric Company.  The purpose
of this plant was to test two new methods of developing thin films
on both the condensate and sea water sides of a vertical tube distilling plant.  The pilot plant contained two effects of a proposed
multi-effect evaporator.  The first effect contained specially designed tubes with a fluted surface on the condensate side and a
plane surface on the sea water side.  The second effect contained
double fluted tubes, i.e.; a fluted surface on both sides of the tube.

In the first effect, a thin sea water film was generated by using a mechanical wiper to spread the feed evenly over the smooth
inner surface.  Surface tension effects of the falling condensate
maintained a thin film on the raised flutes on the outside surface.
The generation of thin films reduces the resistance to heat transfer and facilitates obtaining a high heat flux with nominal temperature driving forces.  Overall transfer coefficients of up to 4000
Btu/hr. $^{\circ}F$ $ft^2$ were obtained in the first effect with a $5^{\circ}F$ driving
force.  However, the mechanical complications of driving the wip-
er blades detracted from the overall potential of this type unit for
large sea water conversion plants.  A report has been published
by the Office of Saline Water on the work described above. [1]

The double fluted tubes installed in the second effect and subsequently used as replacements in the first effect resulted in lower overall heat transfer coefficients. Stability and reliability were, however, much improved. Parametric testing over an evaporating temperature range of from 130 to $275°F$ was completed in May 1965. The final report on this phase has not yet been published. However, it is possible to describe qualitatively the results of this program. In the second effect with a five-foot tube length, the transfer coefficient varied from a low value of approximately 1700-1800 Btu/hr.$°F$ ft$^2$ at the lower evaporating temperature to a high of around 2700 as the atmospheric boiling point was approached. The transfer coefficient again decreased slightly at elevated temperatures. The results in the first effect with a ten-foot tube length followed the same pattern but the transfer coefficients were, in general, 15 to 20 per cent lower. All of these values are based on nominal smooth tube dimensions and may be divided by a factor of 1.28 to estimate transfer rates based on the developed area of the fluted tubes.

## W. L. BADGER AND ASSOCIATES

The long tube vertical (LTV) distillation process was pioneered by W. L. Badger in a pilot plant initially erected on dock space at the International Nickel Company's sea water corrosion laboratory at Wrightsville Beach. The plant was moved to the test station early in 1963 to continue work on the seeding technique for the prevention of calcium sulfate scale at elevated evaporating temperatures. While these tests were highly encouraging, there were some unresolved complications at the end of the program.

The procedure used by W. L. Badger was essentially as follows: Incoming sea water was treated with sulfuric acid to minimize the residual alkalinity and then passed through a stripper to remove air and carbon dioxide. The deaerated sea water was then heated to approximately the evaporator temperature and calcium sulfate seeds, recovered from the reject brine, were injected at the inlet to a delay column. The sea water and seeds then passed through a single effect LTV evaporator. Tests indicated that an evaporating temperature of approximately $300°F$ could be reached without scale formation in the LTV. However, some scaling did occur in the hottest sections of the feed heater. Refinements in equipment and procedure have been proposed to overcome this problem. The test program was completed in 1963 and the plant has now been dismantled.

## BALDWIN-LIMA-HAMILTON CORPORATION

For several years, The Baldwin-Lima-Hamilton Corporation (formally The Griscom-Russell Company) had conducted scale control tests on a six-stage flash distillation plant at the International Nickel Company site. This plant was also moved to the test station in 1963 to continue the test program. Previously, Baldwin - Lima-Hamilton had undertaken programs involving seeding techniques for control of alkaline scale, the use of proprietary compounds such as poly-phosphates, and pH control of alkaline scale. At the test station, emphasis has been placed on defining the temperature and concentration limits of acid addition for control of alkaline scale and on the use of seeding for control of calcium sulfate scale. A report on pH control in flash plants was given at the First International Symposium on Water Desalination. [2]

Following closely the work on seeding by W. L. Badger Associates, Baldwin-Lima-Hamilton has confirmed some of the basic premises of the treatment. For example, seeding is effective in relieving supersaturation following a heating operation, but does not appear to be effective in prevention of deposition when present during the heating cycle. The technique is considered promising in flash distillation.

In December, 1965, Baldwin-Lima-Hamilton completed construction of a new 25,000 gallons per day, 16-stage flash plant at the test station. This plant is designed for operating temperatures up to 350°F. Initial operations have been aimed at confirming operating limits for pH control of alkaline scale, particularly as they apply to a tamdem design. The 16-stage plant operates normally over a 50°F temperature span with auxiliary heat rejection. Future plans include further investigation of calcium sulfate seeding for scale control.

## W. R. GRACE AND COMPANY

In June, 1964, W. R. Grace started operational testing of a 10,000 GPD sea water descaling pilot plant. This pretreatment process plant was designed to remove essentially all calcium and magnesium from the incoming sea water while producing a fertilizer compound as a byproduct. The sea water was treated with phosphoric acid and ammonia to precipitate calcium and magnesium ammonium phosphate. A similar compound is marketed by a W. R. Grace subsidiary under the trade name "MagAmp."

Calcium and magnesium were removed very effectively in the tests performed and the residue was found to have significant fertilizer value. The treated sea water was also tested in both a vapor compression and a forced circulation evaporator at high temperatures ($\approx 275°F$) and high concentrations. In one test, the concentration was raised to approximately 20 per cent dissolved solids and none of the normal scaling compounds were found after several hundred operating hours. However, the pH of the recirculating brine was very low and a sludge like material containing primarily iron and phosphate was encountered. Although this problem might be alleviated by refinements in the pretreating step or additional chemical treatment, work on this process was discontinued because the overall economic balance between treatment costs and byproduct sales was proving not to be as favorable as originally anticipated.

W. R. Grace then undertook pilot plant testing of an alternate pretreatment process involving only partial removal of calcium. The treated water in this case would have to be used in conjunction with a method for control of the alkaline scales such as the pH control discussed previously. This process involved the precipitation of calcium carbonate by adding lime and magnesium carbonate. Both of these materials could be generated or recovered in the plant and there would be no byproduct. The only raw material required would be limestone, which is relatively inexpensive. Because of the reduction of the calcium content in the treated sea water, distilling plants could presumably operate at either higher temperatures or high concentration ratios. This pilot plant work was only partially successful, possibly due to the necessity of using existing equipment which was specifically designed for the ammonium phosphate process. The decision was made to continue work on the lime-magnesium carbonate process at the laboratory level and to retain the pilot plant for possible modification and use in the future. A report on the above work was given at the First International Symposium on Water Desalination.[3]

## AQUA-CHEM COMPANY, INC.

In 1964, Aqua-Chem Company, Inc. started test work on a 3,000 gallon per day horizontal spray film evaporator. This was a package unit which had previously been tested on synthetic sea water. The original unit incorporated a vapor compressor as the energy source.

As the name suggests, the heat transfer tubing was oriented in the horizontal plane with the sea water sprayed over the outside surface of the tubes and steam condensed on the inside surface. High heat transfer rates could be expected because of the thin sea water and condensate films formed. In addition, film buildup was minimized by the shortness of the flowpath around the circumference of a tube as compared to the flowpath down the length of a vertically oriented tube such as in the LTV process.

Initial tests were performed with 5/8" diameter tubes in the bundle and overall transfer coefficients in excess of 1100 Btu/hr. $^{\circ}F$ ft$^2$ were consistantly obtained. Later tests using 1-1/2" diameter tubes showed approximately 20 per cent increase in transfer rates. The geometry of the tubes in the later tests undoubtedly provided for better sea water distribution and accounted for the increased efficiency. An additional increase in tube size to 2-1/2" diameter showed no further improvement.

Also during the program, the vapor compressor was replaced with raw steam from the station boilers and a parametric study of transfer rate versus evaporating temperature was conducted over

a range of from 100°F to 230°F. As might be expected, the transfer coefficient decreased in the vacuum range to a low value of
approximately 800-900 Btu/hr. °F ft². Again, proportionally
higher values were obtained with the larger diameter tubes.

A third series of tests were conducted using several schemes
for injecting a waxy drop-wise condensation promoter on the
steam side. The overall transfer coefficient using the 1-1/2"tube
was increased initially to greater than 2,000 Btu/hr. °F ft² and
was maintained above 1850 by injection of the promoter during operation at a frequency of about every 36 hours. Use of the promoter on the 5/8" tubes was not nearly as effective probably due
to the greater difficulty of accomplishing even distribution down
the length of the smaller diameter tube.

In June 1964, the test unit was shipped to Roswell, N. M. to
be operated by Aqua-Chem on scale control testing with the brackish water feed used in the 1,000,000 GPD demonstration plant located there.

## MIDWEST RESEARCH INSTITUTE

In November 1964, Midwest Research Institute started a series of tests to determine the effects of feed water pH and oxygen
content on the corrosion of mild steel tubes used in a falling film
evaporator. Two test trains with a common feed tank were used
and all tests were performed at an operating temperature of 250°F.
The only difference between the two trains was the inclusion of a
vacuum deaerator in one train only. The pH levels of interest
were 7 and 8. Actually, it was not practical to exercise complete
control over the oxygen content. The train without a deaerator
operated with oxygen at the saturation value for the inlet feed temperature and pressure conditions and the second train was operated at the lowest value obtainable which was normally 0.3 - 0.5
ppm. All dissolved oxygen measurements were made with a gal-
vanic cell instrument. A third variable studied was the effect of
heat flux on corrosion.

In general it was concluded that mild steel was not a satisfactory material from a corrosion standpoint for sea water distilling
units operating at temperatures above the atmospheric boiling
point. In aerated sea water, the gross corrosion rate was on the
order of 150-250 mg per day per sq. decimeter (mdd). Corrosion
rates generally increased as the temperature driving force, or
heat flux, was increased. Corrosion was less at an operating pH
of 8 than at 7. And finally, the corrosion rates on the deaerated
side were roughly one-half those on the aerated side. The program was completed in August, 1965. A report has been published by the Office of Saline Water on the work described above.[4]

## STRUTHERS SCIENTIFIC AND INTERNATIONAL CORPORATION

Struthers has two pilot plants at the test station. The first was completed in October 1963, and has a nominal capacity of 15,000 gallons per day. The second plant, based on the same process, was completed in July, 1964, and is rated at 200,000 gallons per day. These plants feature controlled crystallization in a butane freeze desalination process with the use of direct contact heat exchange throughout.

The 15,000 GPD plant was operated from October 1963 to September 1964 using a horizontal vibrating basket centrifuge for ice-brine separation and washing. This was a standard unit with a nominal tonnage capacity (based on coal dewatering) of approximately 10 times the ice production capacity of the plant. This was the smallest unit of its type commercially available at that time. Over capacity of the centrifuge may have been a factor, but several problems specifically related to centrifugation of ice crystals were encountered and product water salinity standards were never attained. Steady state operation of the integrated plant was also very difficult to obtain due to lack of surge capacity between the individual process components.

In September 1964, a small piston type countercurrent ice separation and washing column was placed in parallel with the centrifuge. After some initial difficulties the column was successfully operated at a capacity approaching 6,000 GPD. Along with other process modifications, continuous ice-brine separation facilitated steadier operation and a preliminary analysis of process components was obtained. The relatively high product rate obtained with the small separation column ($\approx 3000$ GPD/ft$^2$) indicated that the crystallizer could produce some of the largest ice crystals ever observed in the freeze desalination program.

Other units of the process showed less promise. The melter-condenser operated successfully only at relatively large temperature differentials (8-12°F) between the melting ice and the condensing butane vapor discharge from the primary compressor. In the design, it was hoped to operate at between 3 and 5°F $\Delta T$'s. Tests made at approximately 25 per cent of design capacity indicated that the liquid-liquid sea water precooler also required large temperature driving forces. Roughly four times the design value was obtained by extrapolating to 100 per cent capacity.

In September 1965, it was decided to continue with the crystallizer study by installing a larger separation column to handle higher production rates. Since centrifuge separation in the small plant had proved unsuccessful, this unit was removed to make room for the new wash column. The program presently in progress places emphasis on determining the effect of crystallizer operating variables on the ice crystal quality as measured by photomicrographs and the permeability of a packed bed formed from these crystals.

## SWEET WATER DEVELOPMENT COMPANY

Construction of the first pilot plant in the United States based on a hydrate conversion process was completed in March 1965. The Sweet Water Development Company process uses propane as both a refrigerant and a hydrating agent. Liquid propane is evaporated in direct contact with sea water to chill the mixture to the hydrating temperature of approximately 38°F. Hydrate crystals form in a similar manner to the ice crystals in a butane freezing process and must be separated from the brine before decomposition to potable water and liquid propane. The liquid propane is then recycled to the crystallizer to complete the cycle. The primary energy input is through the main compressor which pumps propane vapor from the crystallizer to the hydrate decomposer.

One of the unique features of this process is the use of staged liquid cyclones, or hydroclones, for the separation of hydrate crystals from the brine. Twelve stages are used in the pilot plant. The overhead of each cyclone is enriched in hydrate content and then diluted with the underflow from the next cyclone down the series. Product water is recycled for washing in the last cycle and then brine underflow from the first cyclone is rejected. To date, the separation efficiency of the cyclones has been considerably less than predicted from bench scale tests. Among the possible causes of this poor performance are emulsification of the propane-hydrate-brine feed to the cyclones, unpredictable geometry effects in scaling up from the bench scale to pilot plant cyclones, and changes in the hydrate crystal characteristics from bench scale to pilot plant. Most of the hydrocarbon processes tested to date have within the system some vessel which tends to trap particulate matter. This dirt, which may be produced by system corrosion, or introduced with the sea water feed, can adversely affect process performance. The Sweet Water Development Company test program is continuing with emphasis on overcoming the problem areas outlined above.

## COLT INDUSTRIES, INC.

The Fairbanks-Morse Division of Colt Industries, Inc. has been actively engaged in developing a vapor compression vacuum freezing desalination process for several years. This was initially a joint venture with the Israeli Government and four 60,000 GPD modules are now operating in Eilat, Israel. The initial test module, used by Colt in Beloit, Wisconsin, was modified and shipped to the Wrightsville Beach test station in October 1965.

In the vacuum freezing process, the pressure is reduced in the crystallizer to approximately 3.3 mm Hg. absolute, which corresponds to the boiling point of water at a temperature of approximately 26°F. At this triple point of water then, boiling and freezing takes place simultaneously. Ice and water vapor are formed roughly in accordance with the ratio of the latent heats or 7.5 to 1. Water vapor is continuously removed by a vapor compressor which discharges to the product ice which is used as the condensing heat sink. The ice is separated from the brine and purified by countercurrent washing in a piston type column.

The Colt process is in a fairly advanced stage of development and initial testing at Wrightsville Beach has been very promising. With minor modifications to the freezer agitation and continual effort to reduce noncondensible leaks to the system, the production has been steadily increased to a rate in excess of 100,000 GPD. At this time it appears that the vapor compressor is the limiting component in regard to the maximum production rate obtainable from this module. An advanced compressor design is scheduled for installation and testing later this summer.

Since the ability to produce a good quality potable water product with this process has been well proven, the test emphasis is on improving reliability, increasing the production rate per unit capital cost, and decreasing the energy input per unit of product. In this regard, Colt is experimenting with an aluminum plate type heat exchanger for precooling sea water feed, which has a clear cut initial cost advantage over standard tubular exchangers. In addition, the plate type exchangers installed at Wrightsville Beach are operating at an overall approach temperature of $2^O F$, or less, between the incoming sea water feed and the outgoing brine and fresh water product. This close approach has an important affect on the thermodynamic efficiency of any process. In the first 1000 hours of operation, Colt has demonstrated the ability to produce product water with a total energy consumption of less than 60 kwh/1000 gallons. It is hoped that higher efficiency in the new compressor will both increase production and decrease unit energy consumption.

## KOPPERS COMPANY, INC.

The newest pilot plant at the test station was just completed in February of this year. This plant, designed and built by Koppers Company, Inc., is based on a hydrate desalination process using Freon-12 as both a refrigerant and the hydrating agent. The design also has enough flexibility to permit operation on a propane-hydrate cycle later in the test program. Freon-12 hydrate forms in sea water at about $50^O F$ and 45 psig. As previously mentioned, propane hydrate forms at $38^O F$ and 58 psig. This demonstrates one of the potential economic features of the hydrate processes, that of reducing the heat exchange duty by choosing a hydrating agent to operate close to the average ambient temperature for the plant location.

The Koppers plant incorporates two different wash-separation devices which have proved to be technically feasible in bench scale tests. The first involves batchwise filtering to form a compact cake, followed by displacement of brine with fresh water product. Approximately 5 units are required to handle the continuous production of hydrate in the crystallizer. The second device is similar to the piston type wash column used in the freezing processes. Operation of this column differs hydraulically in that pressurized wash water flow is required to obtain reasonable production rates with the smaller hydrate crystals, and higher pressure drops throughout the column impose added mechanical design problems. There is, of course, no significant operating data from the pilot plant as yet.

During this calendar year, we expect to have at least two additional pilot units operating at the test station. In addition, the test station staff expects to prepare and submit to OSW, Washington, a task proposal for a materials test program. As presently visualized, this proposal will suggest a test bed type of installation providing a wide range of plant operating conditions, each consistently maintained. It is expected that the proposal will further suggest that, under a data-sharing agreement, private industry be allowed to make use of the test bed. Several heat exchange equipment manufacturers have shown a genuine interest in cooperating in such a program not only from the standpoint of standardized testing, but also due to the lack of natural sea water at company laboratory or research locations.

The test station staff is dedicated to the advancement of the program by assisting all divisions of OSW wherever possible and by consistently insisting upon the elimination of duplicate effort among pilot plant contractors at Wrightsville Beach, and other locations. As a part of the Engineering Services Division and in line with our responsibilities to the technical divisions of OSW, there are many areas in which the test station facilities can be utilized to furnish important data. We will continue to search out these areas with suggestions and task proposals for developing the desired information.

## NOTES

1.  Office of Saline Water Research and Development Progress Report No. 105, "Economic and Technical Evaluation of the Wiped Film Evaporator, " by Ralph E. Anderson and Charles W. Lotz, General Electric Company, Burlington, Vermont.

2.  First International Symposium Report No. SWD/24, "Methods for Scale Control in Flash Systems, " by R. A. Tidball and R. E. Woodbury, Baldwin-Lima-Hamilton Corp. , Philadelphia, Pennsylvania.

3. First International Symposium Report No. SWD/95, "Removal of Scale Formers with By-Product Recovery," Murrell L. Salutsky and Phil Messina, W. R. Grace and Company, Baltimore, Maryland.

4. Office of Saline Water Research and Development Progress Report No. 166, "Corrosion in Carbon Steel Heat Transfer Surfaces," by E. P. Shea and W. R. Hollingshad, Midwest Research Institute, Kansas City, Missouri.

## 14. Analysis of Selected Water Desalting Processes

Roy G. Post and R. L. Seale, Professors
Department of Nuclear Engineering, The University of Arizona

Previous papers have presented the status of most of the various processes of water desalting which are currently under investigation by the several groups under contract to the Office of Saline Water, as well as by certain private organizations. These studies are at varying levels of development. A wide spectrum of demonstrated and ultimate energy requirements are suggested for the various systems in these studies. An attempt to generalize on the characteristics of these systems leads to the conclusion that those utilizing relatively low quality heat energy are the ones which have the highest specific energy requirements, while those with the lower specific energy requirements need high quality electrical or mechanical energy. This is summarized in Table I, which is taken from the Interagency Task Group Report submitted through the Office of Science and Technology in March 1964. [1] (Note that the high quality energy requirements are stated in terms of thermal energy requirements with an assumed 33% conversion to electric efficiency. This implies a relatively high quality thermal energy source >600F). If we pursue this matter a bit further, we see that the really dramatic change shown in Table I occurs when we progress from systems which involve the removal of water from brine or brackish water. Specifically, we have reference to the electrodialysis technique as opposed to the distillation, freezing, and reverse osmosis techniques which involve the removal of water from the input brine. The distillation and freezing techniques suffer from the additional disadvantage of only partial recovery of the energy necessary to accomplish the phase change involved in the processes. This limitation also exists in the vapor compression system. Again, if one attempts to generalize about the properties of the various demineralization techniques, one would say that those involving the smallest transfer of energy and/or process-mass transfer would tend to be more desirable.

The energy requirements inherent to the ion exchange processes are relatively low. However, ion exchange is of limited value unless an economical means of performing reversible work on the ion exchange surface is readily available. In the technique as generally practiced today, the necessary work is accomplished by the expenditure of chemical or electrical energy. It is, therefore, relatively expensive. Ion exchange resins offer the least expensive high-surface-area media of the type needed to accomplish ion exchange. We would like to mention a scheme which could be of particular interest in those areas in which brackish water conversion is needed. The system is one proposed by

TABLE I

Basic Heat Energy Requirements for
Six Saline Water Conversion Processes

| | Energy required, Btu per gallon of product water | |
|---|---|---|
| | 1963 technology | Estimate for 1980 technology [1] |
| Processes Using Heat | | |
| Multistage flash distillation | 1,020 | 610 |
| Long tube vertical distillation | 1,020 | 610 |
| | | |
| Processes Using Electricity[2] | | |
| Vapor compression distillation | 610 | 360 |
| Freezing | 610 | 360 |
| Reverse osmosis | 510 | 310 |
| Electrodialysis | 250 | 150 |

1.  The estimated 1980 energy requirements are for high efficien-
    cy processes and are not applicable to processes using low-
    cost energy.
2.  The energy values given for the "electrical" processes are the
    thermal energies for the appropriate electrical power genera-
    tion at 33 per cent plant efficiency.
3.  The electrodialysis process is applicable to the conversion of
    brackish water only.  See p. 29.

Dr. D. E. Weiss and his associates of the Australian Scientific
and Industrial Research Organization, and called, appropriately
enough, Sirotherm. [2]   Sirotherm is a resin-bed ion-exchange
process.  The unique addition to the technology embodied in the
Sirotherm process is that the required reversible regeneration of
the ion exchange resin is performed using thermal energy, rather
than the more expensive electrical or chemical energy, as is the
case in the more conventional ion exchange processes.  In Figure
1, a flow sheet for the Sirotherm process is shown.

Input brine flows through a demineralizing bed resulting in the
production of product water.  A counter-flow arrangement with the
ion exchange resin in a continuous process of being regenerated is
envisioned.  If one can obtain a suitable resin so that the mineral
content can be absorbed on the ion exchange surface from the
brackish water at some low temperature ($\sim$75F) with subsequent
regeneration of the resin by back-flushing with saline water at a
higher temperature ($\sim$170F), a very attractive scheme is possible.
The crucial point, of course, is the dependence of ion exchange
capacity of a resin surface on temperature.  It is desirable that
the amount of water required to regenerate the resin should be
kept as low as possible.  Numbers of the order of 50 to 1 for the
ratio of product water to regenerating water volume have been
mentioned by Dr. Weiss and his associates.  This is a proposal
of merit although still in the laboratory research stage, that has

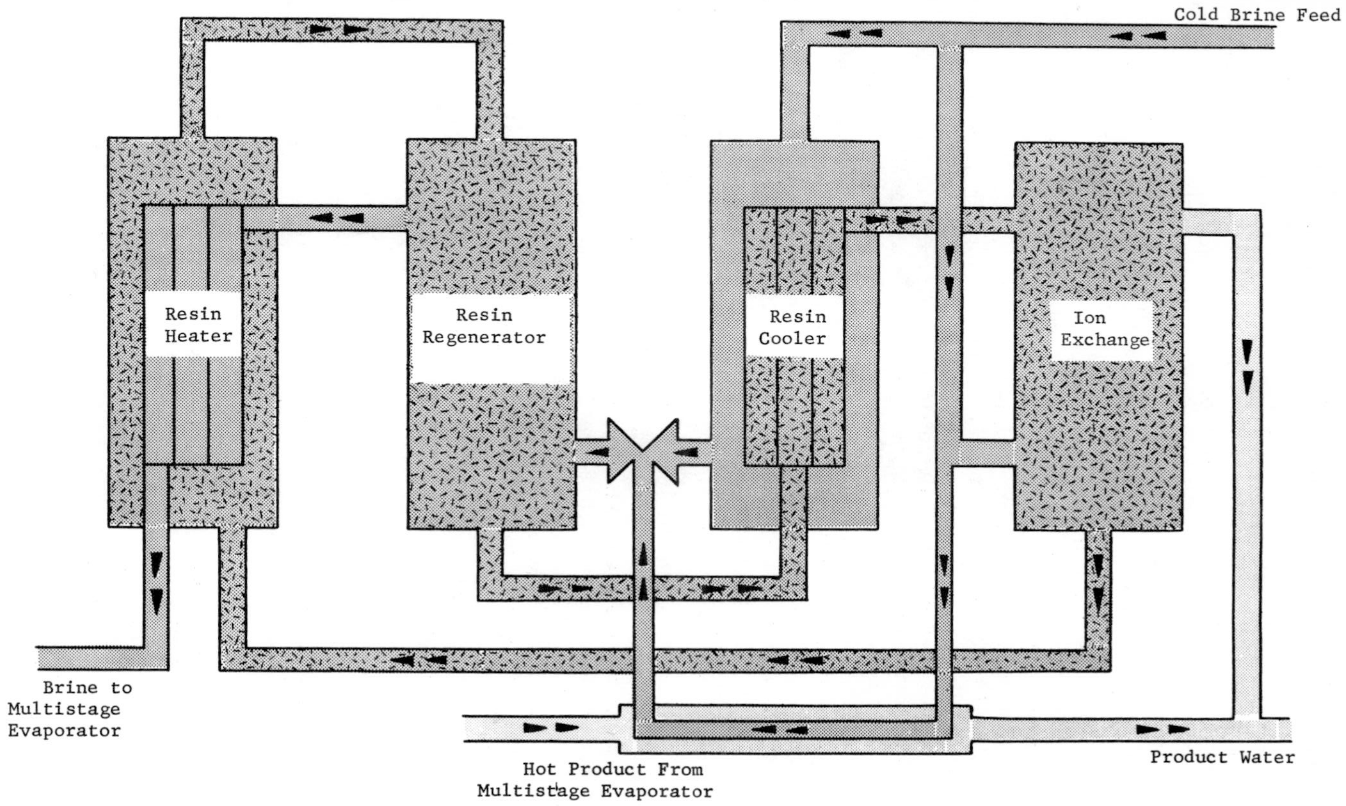

Cold Brine Feed

Product Water

Ion Exchange

Resin Cooler

Hot Product From
Multistage Evaporator

Resin Regenerator

Resin Heater

Brine to
Multistage
Evaporator

Figure 1. Sirotherm Process

particular application to brackish water areas. It seems to offer a
somewhat fresh and direct approach to the desalting problem.

We would also like to mention another aspect of the brackish
water problem being investigated in the Nuclear Engineering Department at the University of Arizona.  This investigation is sponsored by the University's Engineering Experiment Station.  Interest in this particular system grew out of the realization that, in
areas in which brackish water is available inland, there are definite and distinct advantages in carrying the water treatment to the
point of dryness.  The disposal of large volumes of enriched
brines is a serious problem and one which, if not properly handled, could contribute in a drastically adverse way to the level of
contamination in the streams and other water sources in that area.
In the desalting systems currently under development, evaporation
to dryness is not considered feasible due to the limitations imposed by the system thermodynamics as well as by corrosion and
scale formation problems.  In one solution we are evaluating, the
fluidized bed technique is used to evaporate brackish water solids
to dryness.  The many advantages of the fluidized bed in process
industries have long been recognized.  They offer a means of
evaporating to dryness economically.  An additional advantage of
the system is that, since complete evaporation is achieved  there
is no need for pumping excess water and large heat exchanger
areas are not required to recover the energy put into water which
is ultimately dumped. *  In the University of Arizona design, the
maximum utilization of the input heat is obtained through the use
of a multistage, counter-current, multiple-effect evaporator terminated by the fluidized bed.  In essence, a series of more-or-
less conventional evaporators are fed brine from successive
stages, each of which extracts a portion of product water as pro-
gressively more saline water proceeds through the system.  The
input brine is used to condense the steam that is produced in the
next evaporator with the resultant recovery of most of the energy
that is put in the system in the form of usable heat.  A flow diagram for this system is shown in Figure 2.

The evaporators used in the system are quite conventional.
(See Figure 3).

In Figure 4, the results of a series of calculations for different sized systems are shown.

In all cases, a feed brine temperature of $70^{\circ}$F is assumed and
the heat input required as well as the temperature of the product
water is shown as a function of number of stages in the system.

---

* Some work had been done in attempting to adopt this process to
saline water production.  Specifically, a study was carried out by
Battelle Memorial Institute in which a fluidized bed was used as
the terminal stage on a vapor compression unit. [3]

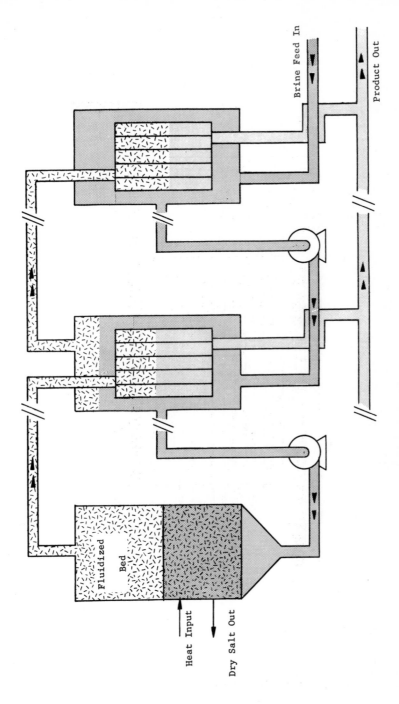

Figure 2. Fluidized Bed - Multistage Evaporator System

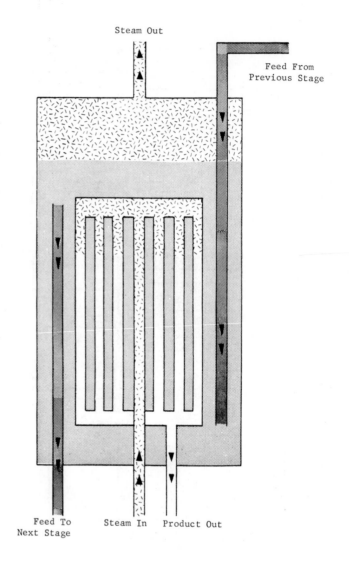

Steam Out

Feed From
Previous Stage

Feed To
Next Stage

Steam In

Product Out

Figure 3.  Evaporator - Stage Detail

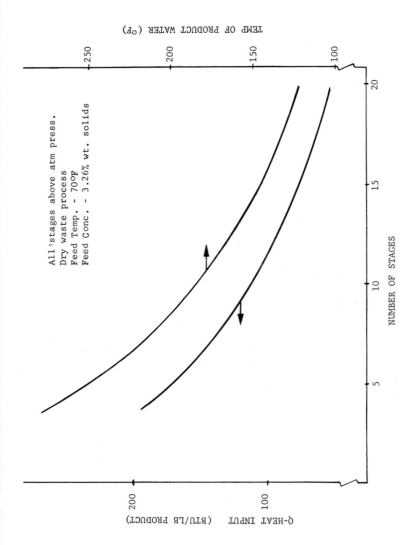

Figure 4. Fluidized Bed - Multistage Evaporator System

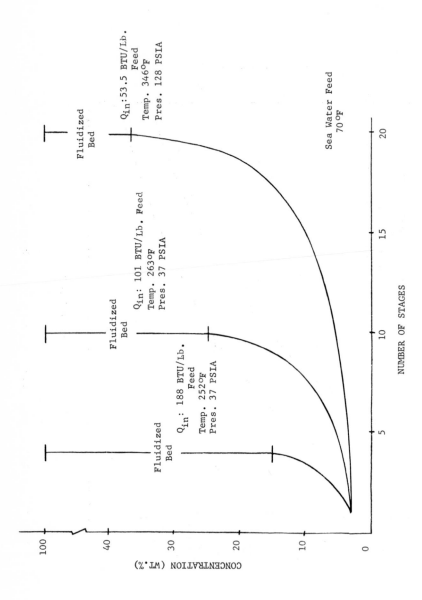

Figure 5.   Concentration Profile

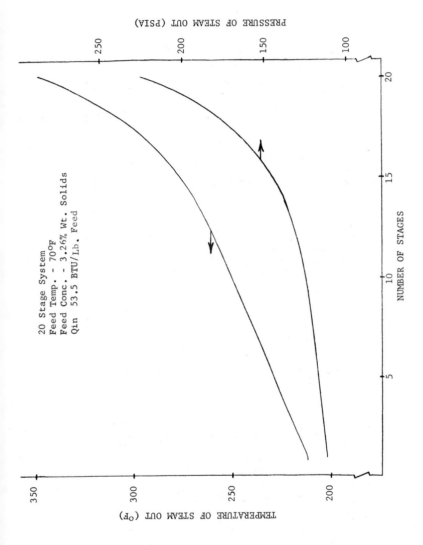

PRESSURE OF STEAM OUT (PSIA)

TEMPERATURE OF STEAM OUT (°F)

20 Stage System
Feed Temp. - 70°F
Feed Conc. - 3.26% Wt. Solids
Qin 53.5 BTU/Lb. Feed

NUMBER OF STAGES

Figure 6.   Temperature-Pressure Profile

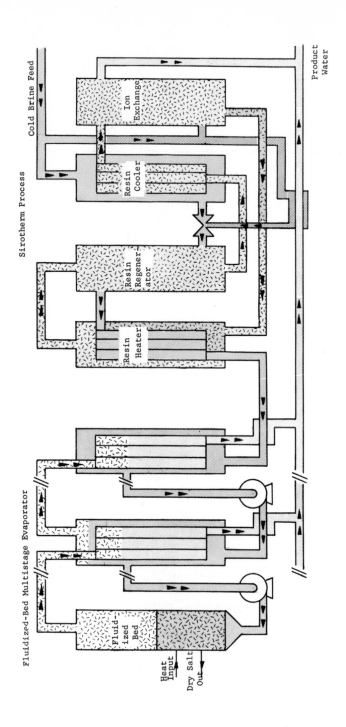

Figure 7. Combined Fluidized Bed – Sirotherm Water Desalting System

The number of stages, heat inputs of the order of 50 BTU's per pound of product at product water temperature of about 120°F are obtained. It is also evident that a relatively large number of stages is desirable for this system. In Figure 5, the concentration profile as brine progresses through several systems of this type is shown.

Profiles are shown for systems which have either 4, 10 or 20 stages of evaporator prior to the fluidized bed termination stage. Also shown are the heat input requirements, the fluidized bed operating temperature requirements and the bed operating pressure. The rather marked decrease in heat input requirement evident in the previous figure is also indicated. A decrease from 188 BTU's per pound of feed for a four-stage system to only 53.5 BTU's per pound of feed for a 20-stage system is achieved. In Figure 6, temperature and pressure profiles for the 20-stage system are shown. This traces the pressure and temperature through each state from the input to the output of the 20-stage system.

In Figure 7, a flow sheet for a system made up of a Sirotherm stage coupled to an evaporator fluidized bed system is shown. Thus the waste disposal problem of the Sirotherm system can be relieved by adding such a special distillation system to process the Sirotherm blowdown.

This paper illustrates the potential for special process and combinations to solve specific problems of water desalting. Other factors, the need for small plants for specialized applications in isolated locations will also justify special solutions and often higher costs. The need for large plants is real and pressing but the opportunity to serve the needs of large numbers of small communities is also challenging and can be an important byproduct of the technology developed for the large systems.

## NOTES

1.  "An Assessment of Large Nuclear Powered Sea Water Distillation Plants, " A Report of an Interagency Task Group, Submitted to the President's Office of Science and Technology, March 1964.

2.  "The Sirotherm Demineralization Process - An Ion Exchange Process with Thermal Regeneration, " Weiss, D. E., Bolto, B. A., NcNeill, R., Macpherson, A. S., Siudak, R., Swinton, E. A., Willis, D., The Journal of the Institution of Engineers, Australia, July-Aug., 1965.

3.  "1962 Saline Water Conversion Report, " Office of Saline Water, United States Department of Interior, January 1963.

# IMPACT OF
# NEW WATER SOURCES

Donald H. White, Professor and Head
Department of Chemical Engineering
The University of Arizona

## 15. Problems and Potentials of Concentrated Brines[*]

W. F. McIlhenny, Inorganic Research Department, Dow Chemical Company

All desalination plants will be fed a saline, nonusable solution, and will produce both a usable product water and a concentrated solution of soluble salts which must be discarded or otherwise disposed of. Many of the problems encountered in the design and operation of desalination plants are due to the omnipresent brines.

The soluble salts in the plant effluent represent a potential source of industrial chemicals, which may be economically recoverable, and under certain favorable conditions can possibly reduce the cost of the water produced.

The feed, the waste, and the intermediate salt-containing streams are all basically similar. They all contain the same dissolved salts in a water solution. The streams will vary in total dissolved solids concentration but not in the chemical characteristics of the solutions.

### BRINE OCCURRENCE AND COMPOSITION

The water distributed on and under the earth's surface is preponderantly saline. Usually its content of dissolved minerals is too great to permit it to be used for drinking or for irrigation purposes, and too low to enable the minerals to be recovered economically.

Brines have been defined, rather arbitrarily, as solutions containing more than 35,000 parts per million of dissolved solids, so solutions with concentrations exceeding that for ocean water are called brines. The upper concentration is determined only by the solubility of the dissolved compounds at the temperature of the brine, and may run as high as 350,000 parts per million.

The feed brine would be sea water, if the desalination plant were located near the ocean, and would be most probably a subterranean brine if the desalination plant were at an inland location. Very generally, most of the subsurface brines occur in

[*] This work was sponsored in part by the Office of Saline Water, United States Department of the Interor, under Contract No. 14-01-0001-392.

187

sedimentary formation between a few hundred and a few thousand feet below the surfaces.

In a majority of cases, the brine is a fossil water, usually of ultimate marine origin.  The saline content can also arise from the direct intrusion of sea water into an aquifer, by leaching of the soluble minerals from the ground, or by the resolubilization of previously precipitated solid salts.  The salinity of above ground brines is often increased by evaporation from streams or from salt lakes. [1]

When the chemical compositions of a large number of brines from all parts of the world are compared, a general characteristic of the brines becomes evident:  That the dissolved solid content of each brine is composed almost entirely of some combination of the same seven ions.  These are the four cations:  sodium, magnesium, calcium, and potassium and the three anions:  chloride, sulfate, and bicarbonate.  These seven ions are also those present in the greatest amount in sea water.

The only chemical constraints are that the cationic equivalents be equal to the anionic equivalents, and that the solubility-product constant of any possible compound not be exceeded.  Several of the four cations may be present in extremely low concentrations in a particular brine, or one or two of the three anions may be almost entirely absent.  Of the cations, sodium is usually present in the greatest concentration, and chloride is most frequently the anion of highest concentration.  Potassium is usually the least concentrated cation, and bicarbonate the least concentrated anion. [2]

Minor ions can and will occur in a brine at differing, but usually low concentration levels.  Lithium, barium, aluminum, cesium, iodide, rubidium, sulfide, bromide, strontium, borate, silicate, and fluoride, and the heavy metal ions are frequently found in concentrations greater than one part per million.

Infrequently, one of the usually minor ions will be present at a moderate concentration level, or even at a higher concentration level than one of the so-called major ions, as in the alkali lakes of western North America, where the borates occur at high concentrations in surface brines.

Sea water is the most widely distributed saline water and is arbitrarily the lower limit of concentration for a brine.  The oceans cover 361,000,000 square kilometers or 70.8 per cent of the earth's surface, with a total volume of 1,370,323,000 cubic kilometers.

It was confirmed by the Challenger Expedition in 1884 that the waters of the oceans of the world vary very little in the ratio of the dissolved ions, and only slightly in total concentration.  The oceans of the world represent an almost homogeneous solution.

Because of this homogeneity, because almost all brines are of marine origin, because deserts border the coast of the intercon- nected oceans for more than 33, 000 kilometers, and because a majority of operating desalination plants are using sea water as a feed; sea water will be used throughout this paper as a standard for the feed material to a desalination plant.

Sea water is the most complex solution ever likely to be en- countered by man.   The chemical composition of sea water is giv- en in Table I. [3, 4]   Of the 74 elements which have been found in sea water, 33 are listed in order of abundance.   All are shown as elements, although several occur in the form of more complex ions such as sulfate, bicarbonate, phosphate, and boric acid. Many metal ions partially exist in solution as complex ions or compounds.

TABLE I

Elements in Solution in Sea Water of Salinity 35% [3, 4]

| Element | Concentration |
|---------|---------------|
| Chlorine | 19, 353 mg/Kilogram |
| Sodium | 10, 760 |
| Sulfate | 2, 712 |
| Magnesium | 1, 294 |
| Calcium | 413 |
| Potassium | 387 |
| Bicarbonate | 142 |
| Bromide | 67 |
| Strontium | 8 |
| Boron | 4. 6 mg/liter |
| Silicon | 3 |
| Fluorine | 1. 3 |
| Lithium | 0. 17 |
| Rubidium | 0. 12 |
| Phosphorus | 0. 07 |
| Iodine | 0. 06 |
| Barium | 0. 03 |
| Aluminum | 0. 01 |
| Iron | 0. 01 |
| Zinc | 0. 01 |
| Molybdenum | 0. 01 |
| Selenium | 0. 004 |
| Copper | 0. 003 |
| Arsenic | 0. 003 |
| Tin | 0. 003 |
| Uranium | 0. 003 |
| Vanadium | 0. 002 |
| Manganese | 0. 002 |
| Nickel | 0. 002 |
| Titanium | 0. 001 |
| Silver | 0. 0003 |
| Thorium | 0. 000005 |
| Gold | 0. 000004 |

190 W. F. McIlhenny

## DESALINATION PLANT EFFLUENT

Most modern desalination plants control alkaline scale formation by adding acid to destroy the alkalinity and shift the bicarbonate-carbonate-carbon dioxide equilibrium. This is almost universally followed by a degassing (sometimes called deaeration) to remove the liberated carbon dioxide and the dissolved gases in the sea water.

Alternative scale control methods are; to add nucleation control agents (such as the polyphosphates) at levels of 2-5 parts per million, and to furnish a preferential precipitation surface by adding a slurry of the scaling material.

Chemicals may be added to prevent biological fouling of the low temperature system by mollusks, algae, or bacteria. Antifoams are sometimes added to control brine carryover, and materials have recently appeared on the market that are claimed to be effective in controlling calcium sulphate formation. The effluent and internal streams will contain all of these chemicals. To be effective, most of these must be added at concentration levels exceeding all but a dozen of the naturally occurring dissolved elements in sea water.

The concentration of the final effluent is partly determined by the economics of the desalination plant and partly by the type of process chosen. All processes, however, are limited by the solubility of the various forms of calcium sulphate. The brine will be discharged at a temperature as close to the inlet water temperature as is economically feasible. At this temperature, gypsum ($CaSO_4 \cdot 2H_2O$) is the calcium sulfate form which limits the design of desalination plants. The solubility limits of the various forms of calcium sulphate are shown in Figure 1. [5]

Higher brine concentrations are entirely feasible, but the cost of obtaining the higher concentrations must be balanced by the benefit obtained. At concentrations of more than five times sea water (corresponding to a dissolved solids concentration of about 18 per cent), the cost of obtaining incremental fresh water from the brine becomes more than it is worth.

Using these criteria, the quantity and chemical composition of a probable brine effluent from a sea side desalination plant can be estimated. This is shown in Table II for a plant capacity of ten-million gallons per day of water product, and alkaline scale control by acidification and decarbonation.

## CHEMICAL PRODUCTION FROM BRINES

From the four major cations and two major anions present in the effluent brine approximately 20 minerals can be recovered, if

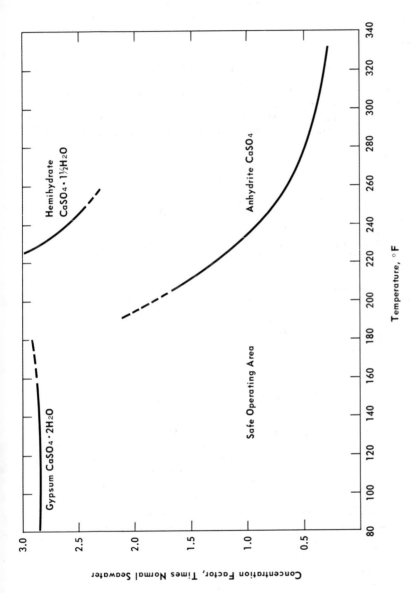

Figure 1. Solubility of CaSO₄ in Concentrated Seawaters

only the processes of evaporation and fractional crystallization are considered.[2] In general, these minerals are complex salts of eight simpler chemical compounds. The number of chemical compounds recoverable is, of course, increased if other materials are added to the brine. Thus, by adding hydroxyl ion from calcium hydroxide, magnesium hydroxide can be precipitated.

In a single processing step, several products can be obtained from the brine effluent. These first generation products are shown in Table III.[6] From these can be produced other second generation products. Many of the second generation products are basic heavy chemical products fundamental to a chemical industry. Examples are chlorine, caustic soda, hydrochloric acid, and magnesium oxide.

TABLE II

Probable Composition and Characteristics
Desalination Plant Effluent Brine

Plant Capacity:  10 MGD Distillate
Brine Concentration:  105,500 ppm dissolved solids
Brine Concentration Factor:  3 times Normal Sea Water
Brine Flow:  41.7 x $10^6$ pounds per day
           4.6 x $10^6$ gallons per day
Temperature:  12-15°F above coolant
Specific Gravity:    1.078 (depends on temperature)
Oxygen:    0 ppm
Carbon Dioxide:    0 ppm
Alkalinity:    0 ppm
pH:  6.9

TABLE III

First and Second Generation Chemicals and Uses

| First Gen. Chemical | Second Gen. Chemicals | Principal Uses |
|---|---|---|
| NaCl | $Cl_2$<br>$H_2$<br>NaOH | Plastics, organic solvents<br>Ammonia, plastics, fertilizers<br>Paper, rayon, soap |
| $MgCl_2$ | HCl<br>MgO | Metal industries, other chemicals<br>Refractories, steel production |
| $Mg(OH)_2$ | MgO | Refractories, paper |
| $Na_2SO_4$ | | Paper, synthetic detergents |
| $Br_2$ | $C_2H_4Br_2$<br>$CH_3Br$ | Gasoline additives<br>Grain fumigant, disinfectant |
| $K_2SO_4$ | | Fertilizers |
| KCl | | Fertilizers |
| $MgSO_4$ | $H_2SO_4$<br>MgO | Rayon, metal industries, chemicals |
| $CaSO_4$ | | Plaster, construction materials |
| $CaCO_3$ | CaO<br>$CO_2$ | Chemicals, construction material<br>Dry ice |

TABLE IV

Chemicals Currently Recovered Commercially
From Natural Brines (2)

Bromine, $Br_2$
Calcium carbonate, $CaCO_3$
Calcium chloride, $CaCl_2$
Calcium sulfate, $CaSO_4 \cdot 2H_2O$ (Gypsum)
Chlorine, $Cl_2$
Hydrogen, $H_2$
Iodine, $I_2$
Lithium sodium phosphate, $Li_2NaPO_4$
Magnesium chloride, $MgCl_2 \cdot 6H_2O$
Magnesium hydroxide, $Mg(OH)_2$
Magnesium sulfate, $MgSO_4 \cdot 7H_2O$ (Epson salt)
Potassium chloride, KCl
Potassium magnesium chloride, $KMgCl_3 \cdot 6H_2O$ (Carnallite)
Potassium sulfate, $K_2SO_4$ (Potash)
Sodium bicarbonate, $NaHCO_3$ (Baking Soda)
Sodium borate, $Na_2B_4O_7 \cdot 10H_2O$ (Borax)
Sodium carbonate, $Na_2CO_3$ (Soda ash)
Sodium chloride, NaCl (Common salt)
Sodium hydroxide, NaOH (Caustic soda)
Sodium sulfate, $Na_2SO_4 \cdot 10H_2O$ (Glauber's salt)

In a recently completed research contract with the Office of
Saline Water, a survey was made of the present production of
chemicals from saline solutions.[2] A partial listing of the present
production of chemicals from brines is shown in Table IV.

A substantial portion of the present production of some chemicals is based on sea water or a brine as a raw material source.
More than 30 per cent of the total world production of sodium
chloride is obtained through the solar evaporation of sea water,
and an additional considerable amount produced from landbased
brines. The entire production of bromine in the world is obtained
from brines, with about two-thirds coming from sea water. A
major fraction of sodium sulfate production and a substantial part
of potassium salt production originates from natural brines.

Magnesium compounds, including the oxide, carbonate,
chloride and sulfate, are produced in large volume from both sea
water and landbased brines. In North America, the quantity of
magnesium oxide produced from sea water and brines is three
times that obtained from solid ores. Almost all of the more than
154, 000 short tons of magnesium metal produced annually in the
world comes from sea water.

Although the greater part by far, of the world supply of potassium compounds is mined from bedded deposits, significant quantities of this element are recovered from both subterranean and
surface brines, of which the water of the Dead Sea is a classic
example. Recovery of potassium compounds from sea water itself
has not quite become a commercial reality, not because the technology is lacking, but because of the economic competition from
other sources.

Three of the minor elements found in sea water are produced commercially from brines.  Approximately one-quarter of the to- tal world consumption of boron compounds is recovered from lake brines in California.  This brine is also a significant source of lithium chemicals.  Underground brines occurring in the North American States of California and Michigan and in Japan, are the source of perhaps 40 per cent of the total world production of the element iodine.

The present large-scale recovery of basic minerals from brines is convincing evidence that brine-processing technology is wide spread and quite well advanced on commercial levels.

In the same survey for the Office of Saline Water, we inten- sively examined each of the known commerical brine-processing operations and compared the technology. [2, 7, 8, 9]  We could find very few instances of the application of newly discovered or more advanced technology.  Each of the 160 commercial or suggested recovery processes for 51 different products fits very neatly into 10 chemical engineering unit operations, or unit cells.  These are shown in Table V.

The product from the unit cell is usually either sufficiently impure, or of an improper physical form, so that further purifi- cation and product treatment is required.

The portions of the recovery processes subsequent to the ini- tial unit cell, required for converting the initially obtained mate- rial into marketable form, can also be reduced to a relatively small number of different unit cells.  For each type of unit cell, the fundamental engineering relationships (physical size, influent and effluent conditions, throughput, etc. ) will be similar.  Relia- ble engineering data, including estimated equipment costs, are available in the literature for the same, or very similar oper- tions.  By employing these relationships, it is possible to obtain fairly close approximations of the required plant equipment sizes, the necessary capital investment, and the operating costs for each unit cell, and therefore for the entire process of a complete re- covery operation.

TABLE V

Chemical Engineering Unit Processes
Employed in Commercial and Proposed
Recovery of Chemicals from Brines[2]

Absorption
Adsorption
Distillation
Electrolysis
Evaporation
Flotation
Freezing
Ion exchange
Oxidation-reduction
Precipitation

## VALUE OF THE EFFLUENT

A particularly vexing question, and one which is particularly important when the effect of chemical recovery on the water costs is considered, is the value of the chemicals dissolved in the de-salination plant effluent brines. Since the dissolved materials are present chiefly as ions, and since a cation must be removed along with an anion, the dissolved materials can associate in more than one way to produce different sets of chemical compounds. It is quite incorrect to speak of compounds in solution in a multicomponent brine.

The maximum possible value any brine can have is the minimum cost of the several alternative ways to reconstitute the brine by dissolving chemicals in water at the location of the brine. No brine can be worth more. Because the calculation of a large number of cases is tedious, a computer program has been developed to allow the calculation of a minimum cost, maximum worth.[2] The maximum worth of sea water is shown in Table VI.

The brine will certainly be worth much less than this actual value. Figure 2 shows the meager information available on this relative price of a chemical in the dissolved state and as a solid product. It may be seen that a material in a dilute dissolved state is very roughly worth one-tenth of its value as a marketable product. We can conclude that the actual value of the dissolved solids in a dilute brine is about one-tenth of the maximum possible worth.

### TABLE VI

Calculated Maximum Worth of Sea Water

The cost of synthesizing one million pounds of sea water from the lowest-cost combination of sources of dissolved materials available.

| Compound Used | Weight Need Pounds | Cost per Million Pounds of Sea Water |
|---|---|---|
| $H_3BO_3$ | 26.3 | $ 1.39 |
| $Mg(OH)_2$ | 3,110.0 | 44.20 |
| NaBr | 85.0 | 34.00 |
| $NaHCO_3$ | 195.0 | 4.97 |
| $SrSO_4$ | 28.5 | 0.92 |
| $CaSO_4 \cdot 2H_2O$ | 1,760.0 | 3.70 |
| KCl | 737.0 | 8.85 |
| NaCl | 27,200.0 | 136.00 |
| $H_2SO_4$ | 1,739.0 | 20.95 |
| HCl | 2,575.6 | 125.00 |

Total cost of compounds used     $ 379.98

The cost of synthesizing 1000 gallons of sea water is the maximum possible worth = $3.24. (Actual worth is about 0.32 $/1000 gallons.)

## ECONOMICS OF CHEMICAL PRODUCTION

Three conditions must exist before a potential product can be considered as a candidate for production. These are:

1. The product must be produced in a saleable form.

2. A market must exist.

3. The price at which the product can be sold must allow for a satisfactory return on the capital investment.

The chemical recovery process must be designed to meet the first condition. In a brine, the chemical is in a dissolved state; homogeneously dispersed through and surrounded by a continuously changing water matrix. The chemical is not ordinarily saleable in this condition.

We must, if we plan to sell the chemical, recover it by separating from the solution, purify it by removing unwanted impurities, manipulate it into a physical condition that a customer will accept, and place it in a container to protect our previous efforts.

As a potential source of minerals, the brine must compete with all naturally occurring sources of these same minerals. The potential brine products are all heavy chemicals. They are widely available at a low price and the effect of transportation cost is quite pronounced.

It is likely that at a desalination location there may be more attractive raw material sources for all of the potential products. The pertinent cost comparison to make is between the costs of mineral recovery processes using the desalination plant effluent and competing sources, rather than between the desalination plant effluent and the saline water fed to the desalination process.

It would be extremely unwise to base an industrial venture on the use of any save the most economically attractive source of raw material available.

### Chemical Production Capital

It is a general characteristic of the chemical industry, and in particular of those plants producing basic chemicals by continuous processes, that the total plant investment required is relatively high in relation to the total value of the products. [10]

The actual plant investment in a chemical plant is a statistic which is not widely available. There are, however, some general methods by which the capital investment can be estimated with some degree of accuracy, and from which some generalizations can be made.

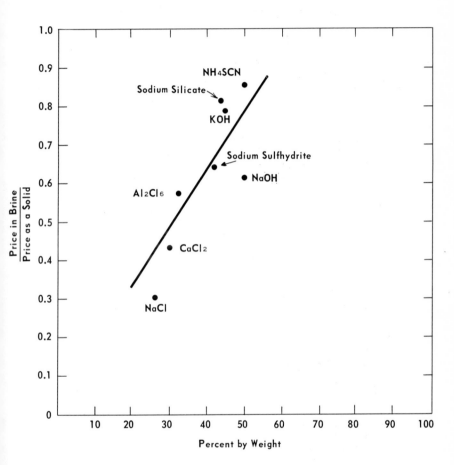

Figure 2.  Prices of Chemicals in Solution and as a Solid

The "Turnover Ratio" is widely used to compare the economics of production of one chemical with those of another, and in making preliminary estimates of the capital requirements of proposed processes. [11] The "Turnover Ratio" is defined as:

$$TR = \frac{\text{Market value of products in dollars per ton}}{\text{Plant Investment in dollars per annual ton of production}}$$

Turnover Ratios for a large number of chemical products have been calculated and are shown in Table VII for some representative inorganic chemicals. The average for all manufacturing industries is 1.92 and the United States chemical industry median is 1.47. Mining, a closely associated industry, has a median ratio of 1.03.

The Turnover Ratio is dependent on the size of the plant, because the capital cost per unit of production decreases by a power factor (0.6 to 0.8) as the plant size increases. If we limit our consideration to plants producing inorganic chemicals in the range between 10,000 and 100,000 tons per year, the average Turnover Ratio will be very nearly 1.0.

TABLE VII

Turnover Ratios

| Product | Capacity T/Yr | Turnover Ratio $/T//$/Ann T |
|---|---|---|
| Aluminum sulfate | 8,700 | 1.05 |
| Ammonia | 105,000 | 0.89 |
| Ammonia | 35,000 | 0.81 |
| Calcium phosphate | | |
| Super phosphate | 20,000 | 0.70 |
| Triple super phosphate | 50,000 | 0.54 |
| Calcium oxide (lime) | 150,000 | 1.73 |
| Caustic soda | 4,000 | 0.38 |
| Chlorine | 5,000 | 0.45 |
| Phosphoric acid | 40,000 | 1.21 |
| Portland cement | | 1.00 |
| Potassium chloride | 187,000 | 0.42 |
| Sodium carbonate | 280,000 | 0.32 |
| Sodium sulphate | 52,000 | 1.13 |
| Sulfur | 12,000 | 0.67 |
| Sulfur | 55,000 | 1.42 |
| Sulfuric acid | 84,000 | 0.76 |
| | 280,000 | 1.31 |

United States Industry Medians

| | |
|---|---|
| Chemicals | 1.47 |
| Mining | 1.03 |
| Glass, cement, gypsum | 1.29 |
| Aircraft and parts | 4.38 |
| Food and beverages | 3.22 |
| Metal products | 2.28 |
| All industry | 1.92 |

So, for the type of product we are able to produce from a desalination plant effluent brine, we can afford to invest in the
recovery plant only as many dollars as we expect to recover in.
gross sales in one year.

The price at which the product is sold includes any return on
investment, so the Turnover Ratio includes the average return on
investment for this type of chemical product.

A second and more general way to estimate the capital is to
consider the type of operation.  The investment in a plant producing a chemical from a dilute brine will be determined largely by
the amount of the dilute brine moving through the plant and therefore, if the rate of production is fixed, by the concentration in the
brine of the desirable mineral.

In a desalination plant, a unit operation is being performed.
The plants are constructed of corrosion resistant materials, and
a fluid is being handled.  The desalination plants also represent
the cheapest known method of dewatering, and are useful as a
standard for a fluid processing plant.  The capital investment in a
desalination plant as a function of the amount of liquid fed is shown
in Figure 3.  Even in a very large plant, the capital cost is at
least 0. 50 $/gallon/day of product water, or at present blowdown
ratios about 0. 30 $/gallon/day of sea water fed.  We can estimate
our capital requirements from Figure 3 at the quantity of brine
fed to the chemical recovery process.

### Chemical Production Operating Cost

The annual cost of operating a chemical recovery plant may
be estimated using the Office of Saline Water "Standardized Procedure for Estimating the Cost of Saline Water Conversion, "
dated March 1956, which is based on a 20-year amortization
schedule. [12]

When all costs are included: supplies, maintenance labor,
payroll extras, overhead, administrative expenses, amortization
of fixed and working capital, taxes, insurance, interest on capital,
and operating labor as a function of total plant investment; an
equation may be derived for the operating cost:

Operating cost $/yr. = 1. 083 (Energy cost + raw material cost)
        + 0. 1132 (Total plant investment)

It should be noted that this equation gives the actual operating cost.
No profit or return on the capital investment is included.

It must be emphasized that all chemicals actually produced
from brines require additional processing beyond the separation
from solution stage, and that any potential products will, in all
probability, also require extensive additional processing after the
recovery stage to be put in a saleable form.

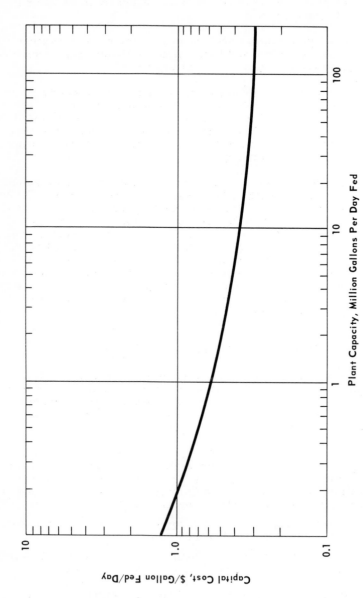

Figure 3. Desalination Plant Capital as a Function of Amount of Feed Liquid

A pressure drop of at least 50 feet of fluid head will probably be required to pass sea water or brine through any separation process equipment when all of the losses through pipes, pumps and vessels are considered. We can then estimate the minimum operating cost likely for the production of a chemical from a desalination plant, if we assume no cost for raw materials, no additional raw materials, no energy other than head loss, and that the plant investment is a function of the amount of brine fed.

The minimum cost does not include several important costs which must be included in the sale price. Distribution costs are often included in the manufacturing cost. Distribution may be by truck, rail, ship or barge, or by pipeline for liquid materials. Shipping rates are varied, many and complex depending on volume and material shipped, distance transported and carrier type.

Bulk chemicals are often sold on an FOB basis, where the customer pays all freight charges. Products are also sold on a freight-allowed basis wherein the manufacturer pays the freight cost. In the type of basic chemicals considered here, the freight-equalized rate is often used. The freight equalized rate is designed so the customer pays the same freight charge no matter where the chemical originated.

Local property taxes must also be included. The cost statement is usually prepared before Federal and State income taxes of about 52 per cent on the average are considered, and the relative attractiveness of a venture is usually determined by the profit after taxes.

The hypothetical minimum production cost is shown in Table VIII for the chemical production from the effluent from 10 million-gallon-per-day desalination plant being fed normal sea water and operating with a brine outlet concentration three times that of the feed. The cost of production is $238,872 per year.

### Potential Chemical Product Value

For each desalination plant, a given amount of each of the dissolved components appears in the effluent, almost always corresponding to the amount in the feed to the plant. These components have a potential value as a marketable product.

We can estimate this potential value by calculating the throughput of the component and multiplying this throughput by the value of the component in its usual selling form. This has been done for the brine effluent from a 10-million-gallon-per-day desalination plant and the results are shown in Table IX.

For example, through a chemical recovery plant following the

## TABLE VIII

Brine Chemical Production Cost
(Hypothetical Minimum)

Basis:
1. Effluent from 10 MGD Desalination Plant
2. $41.7 \times 10^6$ lb/day Brine
3. $4.6 \times 10^6$ GD Brine
4. 105,525 ppm dissolved solids in Brine
(Concentration Factor = 3)
5. 330 Operating days/year
6. Capital = 0.45 $/gallon fed/day
7. 8.0 mil/kwh power
8. 83% power efficiency
9. 50 feet fluid head energy loss
10. No raw material cost
11. No return on investment

A. Plant Investment

$$= \text{(gpd brine)}(\$/\text{g fed/day})$$
$$= (4.636 \times 10^6)(0.45)$$
$$= \$2,086,200$$

B. Power Required

$$\$/\text{yr} = \frac{\text{(lb/yr brine)(fluid head)}(\$/\text{kwh})(\text{kwh/ft lb})}{\text{(Efficiency)}}$$

$$\$/\text{yr} = \frac{(41.725 \times 10^6)(330)(50)(0.008)(3.766 \times 10^7)}{(0.83)}$$

$$\$/\text{yr} = \$2,506$$

C. Recovery Plant Operating Cost

$$\$/\text{yr} = (1.083)(\text{Energy cost + Raw Material Cost})$$
$$+ (0.1132)(\text{Plant Investment})$$
$$= (1.083)(2506) + (0.1132)(2,086,200)$$
$$= \$238,872/\text{yr}$$

desalination plant 7992 tons of potassium will pass each year. Potassium is usually marketed as KCl, and the market price for an agricultural grade is $24/ton. The potassium value in the KCl is worth the ratio of the weight of potassium to KCl, or $46/ton of potassium. The value of the potassium passing through the plant is then $367,362 per year.

In each case the cheapest and most widely available source of each element, is used as the selling form, and to establish the values. It is these cheapest values against which our potential products must compete for the market.

Carbon and nitrogen are not considered further, because more attractive sources of each exist, and recovery of either carbon or nitrogen from sea water in competition with coal, oil, natural gas and air is unlikely.

We can compare the value throughput of each compound with our estimated minimum cost of production to determine whether the recovery of the chemical would be a profitable business venture. In using the operating cost, we must remember that no profit or return on investment is included.

TABLE IX

Potential Chemical Values Effluent from a 10  MGD Desalination Plant

| Element in Sea Water | Concentration ppm | Recovery Plant Throughput T/Yr | Selling Form of Element | Value of Element in Selling Form | Potential Value Through Plant $/Yr |
|---|---|---|---|---|---|
| Cl | 19,353 | 399,707 | NaCl | $16/T | $6,395,312 |
| Na | 10,760 | 222,232 | NaCl | 23 | 5,111,336 |
| SO4 (S) | 2,712 | 56,012 | CaSO4 | 18 | 1,008,216 |
| Mg | 1,294 | 26,726 | Mg(OH)2 | 68 | 1,817,368 |
| Ca | 413 | 8,530 | CaSO4 | 18 | 153,540 |
| K | 387 | 7,992 | KCl | 46 | 367,632 |
| HCO3 (C) | 142 | 2,933 | - | - | - |
| Br | 67 | 1,384 | Br2 | 430 | 595,120 |
| Sr | 8 | 165 | SrSO4 | 133 | 21,945 |
| B | 4.6 | 95 | Na2B4O7. 10H2O | 384 | 36,480 |
| Si | 3 | 62 | - | - | - |
| F | 1.3 | 27 | CaF2 | 92 | 2,484 |
| Li | 0.17 | 3.5 | LiOH. H2O | 3,740 | 9,590 |
| Rb | 0.12 | 2.5 | - | - | - |
| PO4(P) | 0.07 | 1.4 | H3PO4 | 155 | 217 |
| I | 0.06 | 1.2 | HI | 630 | 756 |
| Ba | 0.03 | 0.6 | BaSO4 | 82 | 49 |
| Al | 0.01 | 0.2 | Al(OH)3 | 191 | 38 |
| Zn | 0.01 | 0.2 | ZnO | 324 | 65 |
| As | 0.003 | 0.06 | As2O3 | 117 | 7 |

By comparing our $238,900/yr. cost with the throughput value of a potential product in Table IX, we can see that from sea water, only NaCl, Mg(OH)$_2$ and bromine (those products being produced now) and sulphate as gypsum and potassium are potential products. No others are even close to being potentially profitable. Indeed, it can be shown that the production of all elements below strontium in concentration in sea water, if produced together, would not be profitable. [13]

We can also compare our $2,086,200 plant investment with the potential value to determine if the Turnover Ratio would be of the proper magnitude. We find in this case that the Turnover Ratios would have to be lower than the industry experience for bromine, sulphate, and potassium.

An additional point not often considered in recovering chemicals is the depletion allowance available to a mineral producer which would not be available to a sea water chemical producer. Many of the elements have depletion allowances of 15 to 25 per cent when mined. For example, there is no depletion allowance for magnesium produced from sea water but magnesite, dolomite and brucite, among alternative sources of magnesium are allowed a 15 per cent depletion allowance and olivine 25 per cent.

## Effect of Concentration

If the value of the potential product is equated against the cost of production, a break-even concentration of the desired element can be determined. This is the concentration of the wanted element at which the cost of recovery will just equal the product value.

Annual value = annual production cost = \$238,872

$(ppm \times 10^{-6})(T/yr. \text{ of brine})(\$/T \text{ in selling form}) = \$238,872$

$$\text{break-even ppm} = \frac{\$238,872 \times 10^6}{(T/yr. \text{ brine})(\$/T \text{ in selling form})}$$

These break-even criteria have been calculated for the seven major ions and some of the minor ions and are shown in Table X. The break-even concentrations vary from 2168 for sodium to 9 for lithium, but average 587 for the 16 elements listed. By comparison of the tabulated break-even values with the concentrations in an expected plant effluent, the potentially profitable constituents can be selected.

## Chemical Market Considerations

The need for chemical recovery from saline waters must, of necessity, be considered only as part of the total resource requirements of a region. The relative needs, the local short and long-range requirements and the effects of by-product recovery on the local economy must all be considered. [6]

As a potential economic source of the saleable forms of the minerals it contains, the brine discharged from a desalination

### TABLE X

Break-even Concentrations in Brine

| Element | Value in Selling Form | Break-even Concentration | Actual Brine Concentration |
|---------|----------------------|--------------------------|----------------------------|
| Cl      | \$16/T               | 2,168 ppm                | 58,059 ppm                 |
| Na      | 23                   | 1,509                    | 32,280                     |
| Mg      | 68                   | 510                      | 3,882                      |
| SO$_4$  | 18                   | 1,928                    | 8,136                      |
| Ca      | 18                   | 1,928                    | 1,239                      |
| K       | 46                   | 754                      | 1,161                      |
| Br      | 430                  | 81                       | 201                        |
| Sr      | 133                  | 261                      | 24                         |
| B       | 384                  | 90                       | 13.8                       |
| F       | 92                   | 377                      | 3.9                        |
| Al      | 191                  | 182                      | 0.03                       |
| Li      | 3,740                | 9                        | 0.51                       |
| PO$_4$  | 155                  | 224                      | 0.21                       |
| Ba      | 82                   | 423                      | 0.09                       |
| I       | 630                  | 55                       | 0.06                       |
| As      | 117                  | 297                      | 0.009                      |

plant must compete with all naturally occurring sources of these same minerals.   The occurrence of other natural sources of the same minerals in the area must be considered.   For example, the proposed site for a desalination plant may lie relatively close to subterranean bedded salt or to extensive magnesite deposits.   It is not an unlikely situation that a known aquifer carrying a natural brine saturated with sodium chloride and containing three or four per cent of magnesium chloride may underlie the geologic formation carrying the saline water of the same composition proposed as the feed to a desalination plant.   In these cases, saleable forms of both sodium chloride and magnesia could be produced from the more concentrated natural source at a lower cost than from the brine discharged from the desalination plant.

It is perfectly valid to say that the desalination process has increased the value of its feed brine as a source of the contained minerals, but its value may not have been up-graded sufficiently to economically justify its use in comparison with other sources.

In Table XI is shown the 1963 production and consumption of the five potentially economical products and a comparison between these and the amounts through the chemical recovery plant of Table VIII.   The potential amounts would be a substantial part of the United States' production and would have a considerable impact on the market.

## Effect of Chemical Recovery on Water Costs

The fresh water production from a desalination plant can justifiably be credited, then, only with the lowering in mineral recovery costs which would result from the use of its effluent as a raw material instead of the most economically attractive of the other sources.

Although a lower recovery cost is a necessary criterion, it alone is still not a sufficient condition to warrant applying a credit to the fresh water production.   The other necessary condition is that all the recovered products be sold at prices sufficiently

TABLE XI

Production and Consumption of Potential Products

| Product | 1963 U. S. Production | Potential Plant Production* | % of U. S. Production |
|---|---|---|---|
| NaCl | 30, 644, 000 T/Yr | 565, 251 T/Yr | 1. 8% |
| MgO | 847, 611 | 44, 445 | 5. 2 |
| $K_2O$ | 2, 865, 000 | 9, 652 | 0. 3 |
| $CaSO_4$ | 10, 388, 000 | 28, 625 | 0. 3 |
| $Br_2$ | 101, 667 | 1, 363 | 1. 3 |

*Effluent from 10 MGD Desalination plant, all effluent used for chemical production.

higher than their respective production costs for a suitable return on the plant investment. If these two conditions are both realized, then the fresh water cost can be credited with the difference between the cost of recovering the by-products from the desalination plant effluent and the estimated cost of their recovery from the next most economically attractive source.

Market considerations will dictate whether any products can be produced, and whether any credit for the effluent brine can be used to lower the cost of produced water. Under the most favorable conditions the cost reduction could be in the neighborhood of 10 cents per 1000 gallons. [2]

An integrated water-chemical production plant has some attractive features. If chemical production is desired, it should be considered at the time the water plant is designed.

## EFFLUENT DISPOSAL

Production of a concentrated brine creates an additional vexing problem. That is -- what to do with the waste effluent. Smaller plants at a seaside location may return the concentrated brine to the ocean if proper attention is paid to the design of the effluent outfall, and to the effect on the local marine ecology.

The waste brines will be concentrated, above ambient sea temperatures, oxygen free, unbuffered by the removal of alkalinity and may contain additives or suspended solids. Until this effluent is mixed with the ocean it will not support marine life.

It is quite probable that the brine, if not used in chemical production, will be mixed with the large quantity of condenser cooling water from the desalination plant, and also the cooling water from the power plant if it is located reasonably near.

The production of a single, or multiple chemical, except for major production of sodium chloride, will not change the volume or salinity of the brine to be discharged. Very little effect on the outfall and discharge costs can be expected from chemical production. At inland plants, the disposal problem is more severe, and in many cases may be design limiting. Our present modern method of disposal-dilution, would be impractical in a water-short area requiring a desalination plant.

Alternatives to discharge are: drying to a solid, solar evaporation, holding until dilution is practical, and reinjection into the same or a different underground formation. The relative merits of each will depend on the local surface and underground topography of the desalination plant areas.

## BRINE PROBLEMS

Several problems arise in handling saline solution such as brine, but none are unique to concentrated solutions.  A principal one is the uncertainty of engineering design information on the physical parameters of a concentrated solution.

Theories of multiple-component concentrated solutions are not well developed, and reliance must be placed on past experience and pragmatic equations.  Parameters such as boiling point rise, heat capacity, thermal conductivity, enthalpy, and viscosity can only be predicted with uncertain accuracy, or measured under the conditions for which the design information is required.

The internal brine streams and brine effluent will be certainly no more corrosive than the incoming fully oxygenated sea water. They are, however, solutions of electrolytes and the selection of materials of construction which are both economical and effective will continue to be a problem.

## SUMMARY

-As our knowledge of desalination increases, we can expect to develop more sophistication in the chemical management of the feed, internal, and effluent fluids.  Chemical control of biological fouling, corrosion inhibition, viscosity control, inhibition or modification of scale formation, prevention of foaming, promotion of desirable condensation modes, and wetting of surfaces, will all be practiced to allow the most economic type of plant operation.

A desalination plant is much more closely related to a chemical plant, than it is to the historical type of water collection and distribution systems with which municipalities and even industry is familiar.

Only a few basic heavy inorganic chemicals are possible as chemical products.  These products must be competitively produced, and must be marketable.  Most of the potential products are widely produced and even more widely used.   Market considerations will be the most important factor in determining what products if any will be produced, and whether any credit for the effluent brine can be used to lower the cost of produced water.

Under favorable market conditions, modest decreases in the cost of water are possible by the production of chemicals from the effluent brine.

## NOTES

1. Hem, J. D. "Study and Interpretation of the Chemical Characteristics of Natural Water, " U. S. Geological Survey Water-Supply Paper 1473, U. S. Government Printing Office, Washington, 1959.

2. Dow Chemical Company, "A Feasibility Study on the Utilization of Waste Brines from Desalination Plants, " Final Report, Contract No. 14-01-0001-392, Office of Saline Water, August 1965.

3. Goldberg, E. D. , "The Oceans as a Chemical System, " in The Sea, Vol. I, Interscience, London, 1963.

4. Sverdrup, H. U. , Johnson, M. W. , Fleming, R. H. "The Oceans, " Prentice Hall, Inc. , New York, 1942.

5. McIlhenny, W. F. "Ion Exchange Pretreatment, " First International Symposium on Water Desalination, Washington, D.C., October 6, 1965.

6. McIlhenny, W. F. , Muehlberg, P. E. "The Utilization of By-Products and Related Effects on the Cost of Desalinated Water, " Seminar on Economics of Water Desalination, United Nations, New York, October 1, 1965.

7. Tallmadge, J. A. , Butt, J. B. , Solomon, H. J. "Minerals from Sea Salt, " Industrial and Engineering Chemistry, Vol. 57, No. 7, pp. 45-65, July 1964.

8. United States Bureau of Mines, "Mineral Facts and Problems," Bulletin 585, 1960 Edition, U. S. Government Printing Office, Washington, 1957.

9. W. R. Grace and Company, "Mineral By-Products from the Sea, " Office of Saline Water Research and Development Report 91, PB 181588, March 1964.

10. Bauman, H. C. "Fundamentals of Cost Engineering in the Chemical Industry, " Reinhold Publishing Company, New York 1964.

11. Kiddoo, Gordon, "Turnover Ratios Analyzed, " Chemical Engineering, Vol. 58, pp. 145-148, October 1951.

12. Office of Saline Water, "A Standardized Procedure for Estimating Costs of Saline Water Conversion, " PB 161375, March 1965.

13. McIlhenny, W. F. , Ballard, D. A. "The Sea as a Source of Dissolved Chemicals, " 144th National American Chemical Society Meeting, Los Angeles, April 3, 1963.

# 16. Environmental Factors Relating to Large Water Plants*

Herbert M. Parker, Staff Consultant, Pacific Northwest Laboratories,
Battelle Memorial Institute

Since moving to Richland with the atomic energy project in July, 1944 until today, March 31, 1966 I have lived on the banks of the Columbia River, during which time I could have watched the passage of $7.28 \times 10^{14}$ gallons or 592 cubic miles of water toward the ocean. This meets any reasonable criterion of quantity. The criterion of relevance is less firmly assured. It does appear, however, that our considerations for 22 years of the environmental factors involved in the release of large volumes of single-pass reactor cooling water to the Columbia River will have some degree of application.

The growth of nuclear energy has been characterized by extremely careful attention to the influence of effluents of all kind from atomic energy plants. The excellent record has been established largely as the result of thoughtful anticipation of major problems, continuing extensive control and monitoring programs, and continuing research on the environmental effects. The results are believed to be superior to those achieved in most, if not all, endeavors involving release of environment-disturbing agents. It is easy to take the cynical position that these standards are easily achieved when supposedly unlimited funds are available from government sources, and will not be matched by private industry. Experience to date with the relatively infant nuclear power industry refutes this cynicism. A report of releases to the atmosphere shows these to be about one-thousandth part of the accepted permissible limits. Releases to water sources are characteristically at about 1 per cent of permissible limits.

Admittedly, these results depend in part on the regulating influences of government licensing and compliance procedures. The impact of nuclear energy in its other than peaceful applications has necessarily brought about the present degree of control, in response to public apprehension.

It seems likely that future large-scale desalination plants

---

* This review is a combined effort of a number of my associates in the Pacific Northwest Laboratories of the Battelle Memorial Institute, including: Dr. W. L. Templeton, Marine Biology; Dr. R. F. Foster, Fisheries and Environmental Science; Dr. C. C. Coutant, Aquatic Biology; Dr. D. W. Pearce, Environmental Science; R. T. Jaske, Nuclear Engineering; R. H. Moore, Desalination Engineering; whose help I wish to acknowledge.

powered by nuclear energy will carry with them the legacy of ul-traconservative control of environmental releases. It is by no means inconceivable that otherwise identical systems, one pow-ered by conventional means and one by nuclear energy could end up with more rigorous control for the latter.

When we use the term "ultraconservative" in this context, we may seem to imply that releases are unreasonably restricted. Rather, we mean that conservatism in the nuclear energy case is out of proportion with that in most other cases, and applaud the growing awareness of the overall national need for respecting and restoring the quality of the environment in all aspects.

When large-scale nuclear power and desalting plants are built, one can expect that the total releases of radioactive material to the atmosphere, ground, and water from routine operations will scale up approximately in proportion to the nuclear power level (thermal megawatts).

The general experience with civilian power reactors has de-veloped in the range of about 600 MWt, with new plants coming on line at about 1800 MWt and the next generation designed for about 3000 MWt. The dual purpose reactor at Hanford is capable of 4000 MWt. Thus, extrapolation to 8000 MWt with a water capacity approximating 500 MGD does not call for very large scaling fac-tors. It seems reasonable to conclude that releases of radioactive material from major nuclear desalting plants will present rela-tively minor affronts to the environment. * Some differences will doubtless develop for dual purpose plants, including the possibility of leakage of contaminated steam from the heater stage into the water to be evaporated. The general tendency would be to accu-mulate such contaminants in the brine waste. The exception would be tritium, which in the form of tritiated water would mix isotop-ically and appear equally in the potable water and the brine wastes. For our purposes, this eliminates tritium as a significant hazard in the brines, as it would first be limiting in the potable water.

The obvious major factors adversely affecting the environ-ment are the temperature and salinity of the large volumes of re-leased brines. Pretreatment of the process water may remove some constituents of value to marine or aquatic life, e. g. the car-bonate ion, and substitute a disagreeable one such as the sulfate ion. Corrosion products from the very large heat transfer sur-faces may add toxic materials to the brine. We shall return to these points after first making some observations derived from past experience.

Man's treatment of his water resources in grouping himself together in towns and cities, and in developing an industrial

---

*The adequacy of protection against a major malfunction is not discussed here.

posture falls far short of distinction.  All of us know the old fish-
ing spot that no longer supports fish, and the old swimming hole
that is now a cesspool.  On the grander scale, we can point to the
degradation of a nation's major water resource as in Holland,
where in the period 1900 to 1915, the Rhine salmon runs decreased
by a factor of 5, and by 1930 they were virtually eliminated.

Less well-endowed nations such as Holland and England have
found it necessary to move earlier and further in the direction of
centralized control of water and organized study of the environmental effects of its manipulation.

The Dutch have struggled long and effectively against salt
contamination, both from the sea and as carried to them in the
Rhine, which is 65 per cent of their total water supply, as upriver
industrialization increased both salt and sewage content.

Another case of some relevance is the management of cooling
water for central power stations in England.  About 40 per cent of
these stations accept the use of sea water or estuarine water despite the problems of corrosion in the condenser tubes.  The
British currently use about 25,000 MGD.  The estimated similar
demand in the U. S. is 200,000 MGD by 1980.  Stations with limited supply recirculate the water, with an average evaporative loss
of 1 per cent.  It is reported that along one 50-mile stretch of industrialized river, 20 per cent of the river flow is evaporated.

The environmental effects of the release of this heated water
have been studied somewhat sporadically.  The effects, as reported by Central Electricity Generating Board scientists, are
relatively moderate.  Most conspicuous is the stimulation of undesirable blue-green algae growth.  At least as much practical
trouble arises from fogs created by the cooling towers and by ic-
ing of roads in winter.  The British system is helped by the relatively low temperature increment and the lower temperature of
the receiving waters, vis-a-vis the United States.

In the United States, some states limit the exit temperature
to 90°F.  Recommendations of the Ohio River Valley Sanitation
Commission require the receiving water temperature not to exceed 90°F at any time, 73°F from December to April, with no increment whatsoever in streams suitable for trout propagation.  In
some observations of releases into the Delaware River at 95°F to
100°F, the characteristic blooming of blue-green algae has been
noted with accompanying increase in biochemical oxygen demand,
production of odors and fishy tastes, and clogging of filter intakes.

The structure of the system of organisms in heated rivers
changes in favor of heat tolerant species, usually to the detriment
of better quality fish.  Where there is sewage or other organic
pollution in addition, the two factors in concert can be highly detrimental to water quality through the acceleration of growth and

decay and the intolerable demands on dissolved oxygen content.

Experience with sewage disposal of principal cities provides some knowledge of the mixing of waste and receiving water in volumes comparable with those contemplated in large scale desalination.  The theory governing mixing and dispersion of a fresh water effluent in the sea is fairly well established.

At the Hanford Works, there has been a considerable body of experience on the release to the Columbia River of very large volumes of water used for single pass cooling of nuclear reactors. These waters carry the combined insults of increased temperature and radioactivity.  The engineering design for the return of this water has required virtually no modification.  This illustrates the general thesis that the main effects of a new effluent can be predicted sufficiently well to justify site selection and engineering methods.

In detail, a quite different story is told in which some of the more significant environmental factors were not foreseen, and have been brought to light by continual monitoring and research over the operating life of the reactors.

As predicted, there has been no time at which drinking the water, swimming in it, or using it for irrigation purposes outside the reserved area has caused real concern.  The expectations of effects on life forms in the river have been less successful. Salmon was the most obvious resource to be protected.  Before the reactors were operated, external radiation of salmon was studied at the University of Washington, and the uptake of radionuclides of strontium, barium, lanthanum and sodium by goldfish was observed in the University of Chicago.  No spectacular effects were noted in either laboratory.

A fish laboratory was installed at Hanford at startup to observe the effects on salmon eggs and fingerlings in the actual reactor effluent at various dilutions with river water.  Again, the effects were minimal except at concentrations far higher than those to be released.  Dramatic effects occurred when the reactor was shut down, an effect traced to the addition of soluble oil for certain process steps.  As the research continued, the presence of any demonstrable radiation effect in the laboratory fish became suspect.  It was eventually shown that the unirradiated inlet water was actually more toxic than the exit water due to chlorine added in water treatment.  Ultimately, the adverse effect at high concentrations was found to be caused neither by radiation nor by temperature increment but by the addition of chemicals to inhibit corrosion in the reactor tubes.  Safe limits for such additions were determined experimentally.

In turning from the laboratory to field studies in the river, new findings were made.  The laboratory fish, fed clean food, refused to accumulate much radioactivity from the water, although some $Na^{24}$ was measurable. In the river, $P^{32}$ was the predominant signal in whitefish and other mature resident forms (the young salmon migrate to the sea before they learn too much about this form of eating). It was soon found that small organisms in the river (e.g. plankton) accumulate $P^{32}$ by factors approaching one-million. They serve as food for intermediate forms, which in turn transmit the $P^{32}$ to the whitefish and others.

In more recent years, we have shown that $Zn^{65}$ which is only moderately concentrated in the relevant freshwater organisms is accumulated quite markedly in oysters on the coast some 20 miles from the mouth of the Columbia River, but fortunately not in hazardous quantities. In the river, the large sturgeon with a different feeding method accumulate $Na^{24}$ as their chief contaminant. In total, the affairs of some 70 radionuclides as they pass through food chains of plants, insect larvae, insects, snails, birds, and fish have been investigated.

At Hanford, the recent addition of the large dual purpose plant has increased the heat burden without adding to the radioactivity matters that have engaged much of our attention. We have not been able to demonstrate significant effects from this factor. From time to time, fish in the Western rivers suffer from infestation by a Columnaris organism. It is probable that such attacks are favored by higher temperatures, but we have not succeeded in showing it.

Sophisticated laboratory work can provide balanced ecosystems to trace many of these sequences in controlled laboratory conditions, but the total natural environment is too complex and interwoven to be reliably simulated.

Dr. Foster, the writer, and others, reported on "North American Experience in the Release of Low-Level Waste to Rivers and Lakes" at the 1964 Geneva Conference on Peaceful Uses of the Atom. It was shown there that the water releases from large-scale atomic energy installations present unique problems at each site; in each case, satisfactory control has been achieved as a result of adequate planning plus continuing monitoring and research.

The British experience at the Windscale plant shows an analogous case of disposal into an ocean. Disposal into the sea is constantly open to international criticism, so that this case has had lengthy examination covering sea-bed materials and 70 marine species. A local Welsh custom of eating red seaweed has required and received attention. Otherwise, there has been no particular problem with this effluent. The convenient radioactive signal makes it possible to trace the effluent over some 300 miles of coastline and some 30 miles out to sea, a warning that coastal releases may not be as local in their effects as is sometimes implied.

Similarly, the emptying of the slightly more saline water of the Mediterranean Sea into the Atlantic Ocean can be traced practically across that ocean.

Let us next outline the main effects of temperature and salinity on marine and aquatic organisms.  I shall here rely on notes provided by Dr. Templeton, who was one of the principal Windscale investigators, prior to joining the PNWL.  He, in turn, has drawn heavily from excellent reviews by Dr. O. Kinne in Vol. 1 and Vol. 2 of the Annual Review of "Oceanography and Marine Biology" edited by Harold Barnes and published by George Allen and Unwin Ltd. , 1963 and 1964.

Temperature and salinity are two of the most potent physical factors in the life of marine and brackish water organisms, since they largely characterize the physico-chemical properties of the medium.

There is a complex correlation between the biological effects of temperature and salinity: temperature can modify the effects of salinity, and salinity can modify the effects of temperature.

Changes in temperature and salinity alter the physical and chemical properties of water and organisms react to the total environment; therefore, detailed effects ascribed to temperature and salinity alone cannot be defined.


## TEMPERATURE

Sea and brackish water areas close to continents have a temperature range of $27^\circ F$ to $109^\circ F$, with organisms existing within the range of $32^\circ F$ to $95^\circ F$, the species range being narrower.

In general, the total range of temperature tolerated is smallest in marine forms and larger in brackish and fresh water.

The temperature range tolerated is often more restricted during the sexual phase than during the asexual phase.  In many species, it is narrow during early development, then increases somewhat and finally decreases again in the senile adult.

Rate of change is important.  Many fishes cannot survive a sudden temperature change of more than $11^\circ F$ to $14^\circ F$, though some species can tolerate a gradual change of up to $54^\circ F$.

At the upper extreme, many organisms are killed by temperatures not far above those to which they are accustomed; and species from cold water may have an upper lethal temperature which lies below the lower lethal temperature of closely related species in warm water.

Among intertidal marine organisms, lethal temperatures tend to increase as a function of height above low water level.

The main causes of heat death are insufficient supply of oxygen, failures in process integration, water loss by evaporation, enzyme interference, lipid change, change in protoplasmic viscosity. At the highest temperatures protein becomes denatured.

## Metabolism and Activity

In general, rates of metabolism and activity increase with increasing temperature over most of the temperature range tolerated. It is not just that simple since growth of fish is not entirely temperature dependent, e. g. , in some fish the growth rates decrease in the order 86°F, 77°F, 95°F, 68°F, 59°F. In the three highest levels, the growth rate is very high in the first few weeks and then levels off. Trout, for example, are most active between 50°F and 54°F with a rapid decrease at 63°F to 68°F.

## Reproduction

.Of special importance are the effects of temperature on reproduction, and in most cases the reproductive processes are confined to narrower ranges than the majority of other functions. Under normal conditions, many animals breed either at a definite temperature or at a definite temperature change.

In many cases, a slowly rising or falling temperature will induce maturation of sexual products. Spawning may then be initiated by more extensive or more sudden temperature changes in the same directions. Rates of embryonic development too are greatly affected by temperature. In the case of herring, for example, the eggs hatch after 40-50 days at 33°F and 6-8 days at 61°F.

## Distribution

The most obvious effect of temperature on distribution is exclusion of species from areas with unsuitable temperature conditions. Less obvious are effects on growth rates and length of life. Temperature may affect distribution by altering rates of metabolism and activity, time to maturity, efficiency of food conversion; rates of sexual and asexual reproduction; length of time available for sexual and asexual reproduction; relative timing of reproductive periods; rates of survival and development in offspring.

Horizontal and vertical distributions are partly temperature dependent. Temperature differences may also constitute barriers to migration from sea to rivers and vice versa.

## Adaptation to Temperature

Nongenetic adaption or acclimation, that is, involving non-genetic changes in the response mechanism, is well-known. In the lobster, thermal acclimation from 58°F to 73°F was complete in 22 days. In fish, this can be as short as 4-5 days, and in microorganisms, a few hours. The rate of acclimation tends to increase with temperature and seems to be proportional to growth. Within a given species it depends on age and metabolic rate.

In most cases, acclimation to a higher temperature tends to shift the lethal temperature up. The marine greenfish had a lower lethal temperature of 55°F after acclimation to 82°F and of 40°F after acclimation to 54°F. In invertebrates there are reports of inverse compensations.


## SALINITY

The effects of salinity on marine and brackish water invertebrates and fish are less than those of temperature. Main effects are functional; i.e. through changes in total osmoconcentrations; relative proportions of solutes; coefficients of absorption and saturation of dissolved gases; density and viscosity.

Salinity may also affect an organism indirectly by modifying the species composition of the ecosystem. All these aspects of salinity as an ecological and physiological factor make it sometimes difficult to assess the specific cause of the observed effects.


### Salinity Tolerance

The total range of salinity tolerated is usually larger in animals living in brackish water than in those living in sea or fresh water.

Salinity tolerance may be different at different ages, in different life cycle stages, and in the two sexes. In many species, it is most narrow during early ontogeny, then increases somewhat and finally decreases again in the senile adult. Thus eggs of the shore crab, Carcinus maenas, develop only in salinities between 28 and 40°/oo, while adults can tolerate down to 4°/oo for long periods. Eggs of the fish Cyprinodon macularis develop in salinities up to 70°/oo and adults up to 80-85°/oo.

Hatched young are frequently less sensitive and during early growth may even tolerate a wider salinity range and more pronounced fluctuations than old mature individuals.

Studies concerned with experimental determinations of lethal salinities are far less in number than those concerned with lethal temperatures.

## Reproduction

In general, salinity affects reproduction less obviously than temperature since diurnal and annual salinity variations are usually not as pronounced and as regular as those of temperature. Consequently, salinity is of less importance as a timer or coordinator for breeding, migration or other activities associated with reproduction.

Sterility or reduced reproductive potential is seen in the low salinity areas of the Baltic. Reduced reproductive performance has also been reported in fresh water animals penetrating into brackish water.

## Temperature-Salinity Combinations

The combined effects of temperature and salinity on tolerance and survival have been investigated.

In the lobster, Homarus americanus, the upper lethal temperature is lowered by a decrease in the salinity. The lower lethal salinity is raised by an increase in the level of thermal acclimation. These relationships are, in addition, a function of the oxygen content of the water. A number of species can tolerate subnormal salinities better at the lower part of their temperature range and can often tolerate supranormal salinities better at the upper part of their temperature range. On the other hand, other species are more successful in a low/high combination.

It is reported for anadromous fish, rapid transition from fresh water to salt water may be facilitated by relatively low temperatures.

The salinity tolerance of freshwater organisms in low salinities at moderate temperatures gave a 2 to 3-fold increase in survival time for a decrease of $18^{\circ}F$.

In applying these results to the desalination case, we should note that although temperature and salinity are not truly separable parameters, research is notably deficient because the experimenter has not varied the ambient temperature in the seasonal cycles that are vital in nature.

Work is also deficient in the area of artificially increased salinity in the sea and in the modification of composition by removal of carbonate and substitution of sulfate, as is planned in some desalination plants. Despite these deficiencies, we judge that the background of information far exceeds that which was available for nuclear energy plant releases. Moreover, the food chain considerations can be less elaborate, because one is not here cycling material toxic to higher forms, as applies to radioactive material.

The principal source of uncertainty perhaps comes in scaling up to the extremely large volumes in plants contemplated for the 1980 period.

Let us next attempt to relate the observations to large desalination plants. To establish perspective, nature is now and will remain the major desalinator. The evaporation from the Pacific Ocean alone is 139 million MGD. The total run-off water of the United States would be more than doubled by desalination equivalent to a one per cent increase in the Pacific Ocean evaporation. Thus, desalination on the sea coast, at least, must be relatively local in its consequences. California's thirst may modify the California coast, but it is not likely to affect neighboring countries or even neighboring states to any degree.

Large nuclear fired sea water distillation plants have been studied by an Office of Science and Technology Task Group, covering a range from 1500 MWt to produce 170 MGD by 1968 to 25,000 MWt producing about 1700 MGD by 1980. The Bechtel Corporation Engineering and Economic Feasibility Study for a 150 MGD plant for the Metropolitan Water District of Southern California is a model for the immediate future in which the environmental factors have been carefully scoped. We shall accept the general patterns shown in these reports. For the 150 MGD plant, a brine effluent of equal volume at twice the normal salt content and at 80°F will be produced. This can be combined at will with about 1500 MGD of cooling water, at temperatures between 80°F and 90°F. According to the specific analysis given, the combined effluent would just float on normal sea water. Its effective salinity would be on the order of 38°/oo. The general patterns of the effluent plume in the sea can be calculated and isothermal envelopes showing temperature increments of say 5°F and 10°F above ambient sea temperature derived. The linear dimensions of these figures are a few miles for the 5°F increment and about one mile for the 10°F increment. The probability of serious disturbance outside the 5°F increment isotherm and with the modest salinity increment seems to be quite limited. Within this zone, only the general nature of the changes can be inferred from existing studies of temperature-salinity effects. With a just-floating brine, the actual mixing to the sea floor is difficult to assess. At worst, one might postulate a modification of the ecosystems over an area of a few square miles.

More generally for the postulated plants, the released effluent is calculated to be slightly denser than the receiving water. * Such discharges would tend to flow out over the sea bed and tend to maintain both salinity and temperature well above normal. The dual insult would seem to be well within the range that could cause

*The Metropolitan Water District proposed plant produces more electricity per unit of water than do the usual projected plants. Hence, the high volume of cooling water without salt increment.

serious imbalance of the marine organism structure. When the operation is scaled up to the proposed 1980 type of plant, the potentially affected area may be large enough to influence a considerable stretch of coast line. If a series of such giant plants is proposed for a particular coast, the mutual interaction would need to be better definable than it is today. This definition should come in adequate time by close study of the actual effect around disposal points of the new generation of plants.

The separation of the hot primary brines from the large masses of hot cooling water offers the opportunity for controlled mixing to study the behavior of mixtures of various temperature and salinity. For experimental purposes, the addition of a third stream of raw sea water to extend the range of control over temperature and salinity, while increasing the cost of product water at that plant, could be a national asset in promoting reliable prediction of the effects of even larger plants. Such a study could also encompass the possibility of pulsing the mixing ratios of the effluent streams as a means of inducing more rapid mixing and dispersion.

The ecological situation off the California coast, as an example, is a complex one and its study quite limited until recently. In one recent study, between 300 and 400 species of macroscopic animals were noted within an area of 1650 square yards on a sloping bottom at depths of 10 to 20 yards. Rational study and follow-up of such areas can nowadays be done by a kind of scuba diver's lottery in which the diver throws rings of one-tenth, one-quarter or one square meter cross-section, and examines in detail the populations on which they fall. Similar but less engaging improvements in collection of the suspended plant and animal populations have been made.

The environmental effect of seacoast discharges for at least moderately sized plants is judged to be predictable to the first approximation in terms of temperature and salinity factors. Past experience suggests that a careful search for less obvious factors should be made, especially as these may work synergistically with the main factors. The radioactivity factor, while predicted to be minor, cannot be completely dismissed. Hanford experience would also indicate a careful study of the water modifications used to reduce deposits in the heat exchanging systems. The removal of carbonate by addition of sulfuric acid is a case in point. In addition, some proposals include the use of spent sulfuric acid from petroleum refining. This will introduce traces of organic compounds; some aquatic and marine organisms are critically sensitive to traces of organics. Both the brine wastes and the cooling waters pass over unprecedented areas of heat exchanger surface. The composition of these surfaces is expected to be aluminum alloys for the lowest temperature processes, aluminum brasses, admiralty bronze, monel, or cupro-nickel alloys in the intermediate range, and titanium, hastalloy, or Inconel at very high temperatures.  The introduction of leached contaminants in trace quantities may lead to undesirable uptake in organisms exposed over their life cycles.  The choice of heat exchanger materials and added agents to keep them clean is likely to be governed by engineering and economic factors.  The possible effects on the effluent have to be promoted to equal partnership in these considerations.

The severity of possible effects will be influenced by process temperatures directly and by enhanced corrosion rates.  Increased temperatures will be attractive for engineering efficiency.  The choice of distillation process affects the final temperature of the hot brine, being favorably lower for flash distillation.  However, about the same total energy is involved so this may be offset by increased heat in the cooling water.  If the temperature of the combined effluent is driven above $90^{\circ}F$, the risk to marine organisms can be expected to rise sharply.

With one exception, the construction of these plants in estuaries may be expected to cause less tolerable conditions.  Although the resident estuarine populations are accustomed to more change in both salinity and temperature, those that migrate from upstream to the ocean and back can only do this when conditions are just right for them.  Major estuarine effluents which could amount in the 1980 plants to a fair-sized river could be expected to kill the migrators.  The exception would be an estuarine plant with an effluent pipeline carried well out to sea in the pattern of estuarial flow.  It might be tempting to search for a location in which the increased temperature and salinity of effluents could be rapidly balanced by mixing with the cooler, fresher estuarine waters.

The placement of inland plants for treatment of brackish waters in dual purpose plants presents such a wide diversity of situations that generalized analysis is impractical.  In an arid area with copious brackish water in the underground sediments, one can visualize a plant of modest scale in which the segregated hot brine could be injected deep into the ground as is currently practiced in the East Texas oilfields at a scale of about 15 MGD.  The large volumes of cooling water would presumably require the unpopular cooling towers, which would alter the local microclimate.  Operated in an arid area, such a change could even be advantageous.  Alternatively, the brine from brackish water may be rich in certain minerals, relative to sea water and its evaporation in shallow ponds commercially attractive.  Beyond the removal of large land areas from natural use, this would present only the microclimate problem.  In both cases, cooling water could be allowed to percolate to the ground water.

A more appropriate location for an inland plant from the economics viewpoint might be on a river whose salt content has been increased by industrial waste and by run-off from irrigated land.  Such a situation might arise, for example, in the Lower Colorado

River basin. The growth especially of the blue-green algae would undoubtedly be stimulated. Its decay would increase the oxygen demand and tend to produce off-odors. Both increased temperature per se and the competitive demand for oxygen will adversely affect the better quality fish. Lower forms of life which are suitable food for higher forms may be reduced or eliminated, and forms foreign to the original biota invade the area. The effects should normally be more pronounced where the river is sluggish. The detrimental factors would increase markedly in a river already bearing sanitary wastes. An undefined length of the river could be totally spoiled. These qualitative predictions apply essentially to the heat increment, and the same consequences would result from the operation of a power station of the same large thermal output in the absence of desalination. The added insult from the increased salinity is more difficult to anticipate. Since one is dealing with brackish water, not sea water, the salt increment might not be markedly damaging in river disposal. The release of corrosion contaminants could be significant.

The extreme case would involve discharge into a lake of modest size. Here both the temperature and salinity of the lake could be permanently increased to intolerable levels.

For all inland locations, the utilization of part of the effluent for irrigation is one possibility worth consideration. Because of the large mass of cooling water, the salinity of the combined effluent is not greatly increased. Agricultural research on salt-tolerant species is showing considerable promise, and the temperature, after a preliminary cooling step, should not be objectionable. Unfortunately, irrigation is a summer solution only. It has already been shown that temperature increments in the winter are undesirable for the better fishes. Elimination of these is a price that may have to be paid for power and potable water in some regions.

In summary, anticipated environmental changes for all except mammoth water plants on the sea coast seem to be moderate enough to place no obstruction on plans to push ahead. Inland, the conditions would require very careful assessment of each proposal.

In all cases, past experience suggests that some factors not accounted for in advance will turn up to disturb the balance of nature. All observers agree that the ultimate extent of the environmental degradation can only be found by a continuing program of field studies. Such studies should begin as soon as a new site is favorably considered in order to define the unique ecosystems there. They should continue for at least several years after the start of plant operation. Generally, a monitoring program should continue through the life of the plant. In most cases, the research aspects may be gradually reduced with time. Often, once a plant is installed, its capacity will be increased at intervals. This may require a prolongation of the studies.

The order of magnitude of a comprehensive program might involve about ten professional scientists and engineers for three years prior to startup with three to five years at the same intensity afterwards. Thereafter, the effort might be reduced to a half about every five years through the life of the plant. The type of program involved is typified in the NAS-NRC publication "Oceanography 1960 to 1970," Section 5, "Artificial Radioactivity in the Marine Environment," although radiation problems would not be the principal interest. The integrated cost over the lifetime of a water plant would be of the order of 5 million dollars. Presumably a complete program will be needed for each new plant at least until the general body of knowledge has increased. Also, the probable cost is a rather flat function of the size of the plant. On this basis, and as an order of magnitude only, the cost of environmental research can be reflected as an increment to the legitimate cost of water, numerically:

| Water Produced | Incremental Cost per 1000 Gallons |
| --- | --- |
| 5 MGD | 10. 0 c |
| 50 MGD | 1. 0 c |
| 500 MGD | 0. 1 c |

The increment is severe for small plants for which the research can reasonably be viewed as an investment in the future development of desalination. At capacities above 100 MGD, the incremental cost is less than one per cent of the delivered price. It is then clearly a sound investment in maintenance of the quality of the environment.

## NOTES

1. Saline Water Conversion Report for 1964: U. S. Department of the Interior, Office of Saline Water.

2. An Assessment of Large Nuclear Powered Sea Water Distillation Plants: Report of an Interagency Task Group; Office of Science and Technology; March, 1964.

3. Appendices to the above, published separately. TID-19267 UNC

4. Engineering and Economic Feasibility Study for a Combination Nuclear Power-Desalting Plant (sponsored jointly by Metropolitan Water District of Southern California, U. S. Department of Interior, (Office of Saline Water) and U. S. Atomic Energy Commission) prepared by Bechtel Corp., Phases I & II -- TID 22330 Vol. 1, Dec. 1965; Phase III -- TID 22330 Vol. II, Dec. 1965; Summary -- TID 22330 Vol. III, Jan. 1966.

5. Desalination Research Conference, Woods Hole, 1961, Publication 942 NAS-NRC, 1963.

6. Desalination Research and the Water Problem, Publ. 941 NAS-NRC, 1962 (A summary of the above Publ. 942).

7. Advances in Conversion of Sea Water to Fresh Water; J. G. Muller, Chem. Engrg. Progress, Vol. 59, No. 12, Dec. 1963.

8. Study of 150 MGD Desalted Water-Power Dual Plant for Southern California; H. T. Holtom, L. S. Galstaun: First Int. Symposium on Water Desalination, Washington, D. C., Oct. 1965.

9. The Importance of the River Rhine for the Water-Economy of the Netherlands; J J. Hopmans, Water Pollution/Sem. 5 p. 154.

10. The Rotterdam Municipal Waterworks: J. J. B. Bijker, Water Pollution/Sem. 5 p. 223.

11. Radioactive Waste Management at the Hanford Works. H. M. Parker, Hearings before the J. C. A. E., Jan. 1959.

12. North American Experience in the Release of Low-Level Waste to Rivers and Lakes, H. M. Parker, R. F. Foster, I. L. Ophel, F. L. Parker, W. C. Reinig, Third Int. Conf. on the Peaceful Uses of Atomic Energy, Geneva, 1964.

13. Wasted Water, R. J. Baldauf, Science Vol. 149.

14. Disposal of Radioactive Wastes, Vol 2., Monaco Conference Proc. I. A. E. A. 1960.

15. Radioactive Waste Disposal into the Sea: Safety Series No. 5 I. A. E. A. 1961.

16. Disposal of Radioactive Wastes into Fresh Water: Safety Series No. 10 I. A. E. A 1963.

17. Methods of Surveying and Monitoring Marine Radioactivity: Safety Series No. 11 I. A. E. A. 1965.

18. Ecological Aspects of the Disposal of Radioactive Wastes to the Sea; W. L. Templeton: Ecology and the Industrial Society: Blackwell Scientific Publications, Oxford 1965.

19. Dispersion in the Irish Sea of the Radioactive Liquid Effluent from Windscale Works of the U. K. Atomic Energy Authority; J. Mauchline and W. L. Templeton, Nature Vol. 198, No. 4881 p. 623, 1963.

20. Water Quality Criteria: Publ. 3A. State Water Control Board of California, J. E. McKee and H. W. Wolf.

21. Stream Life and the Pollution Environment, A. F. Bartsch and W. M. Ingram. Public Works Publications, Ridgewood, N. J.

22. Heat as a Pollutant: R. T. Jaske, Water Quality Control Seminar Fall Quarter, 1964, Oregon State University, Jan. 1965.

23. The Effects of High Temperature on Aquatic Life, R. Patrick and L. W. Cadwallader, A. S. M. E. New York, Nov. 27, 1962.

24. Observations on the Response of Some Benthotic Organisms to Power Station Cooling Water: S. Markowski, J. Animal Ecology Vol. 29, p. 349, 1960.

25. The Cooling Water of Power Stations: A New Factor in the Environment of Marine and Freshwater Invertebrates; S. Markowski, J. Animal Ecology, Vol. 28, p. 243, 1959.

26. Faunistic and Ecological Investigations in Cavendish Dock, Barrow-in-Furness. S. Markowski, J. Animal Ecology, Vol. 30, p. 43, 1961.

27. Biology of Polluted Waters, Hynes, U. of Liverpool Press, 1960.

28. Effects of Cooling Water from Steam-Electric Power Plants on Stream Biota: F. J. Trembley, Lehigh U.

29. The Effect of a Heated Water Effluent upon the Macroinvertebrate Riffle Fauna of the Delaware River: C. C. Coutant, Proc. Penn Ac. of Science, Vol. XXXVI, p. 58, 1962.

30. Patuxent River Estuary Study with Special Reference to the Effects of Heated Steam Electric Station Condenser Water upon Estuarine Ecology: J. A. Mihursky, Hallowing Pt. Station, N. R. K., Aug. 1963.

31. Oceanography and Marine Biology Annual Review: H. Barnes, Editor. George Allen and Unwin, Vol. 1, 1963. Vol. 2, 1964 especially the contributions by Dr. O. Kinne "The Effects of Temperature and Salinity on Marine and Brackish Water Animals."

32. Effect of Salinity on Algae Distribution: L. H. Carpelan, Ecology Vol. 45, p. 70, Winter 1964.

33. The Epifauna of a California Siltstone Reef, W. E. Pequegnat, Ecology Vol. 45, p. 272, 1964.

34. Salt Water Disposal--East Texas Field: East Texas Salt Water Disposal Co. , 1st Ed. , 1953, 2nd Ed. , July 1958.

35. Aridity and Man: C. Hodge, Ed. Publ. No. 74, A. A. A. S. , Wash, D. C. 1963.

36. The Future of Arid Lands: G. F. White, Ed. Publ. No. 43, A. A. A. S. 1956.

37. Land and Water Use: W. Thorne, Ed. Publ. No. 73, A. A. A. S. 1963.

38. Symposium on Water Improvement: Denver, Dec. 1961, A. A. A. S.

39. Bioecology of the Arid and Semi-Arid Lands of the Southwest --Symposium: New Mexico Highlands University, April 1958, Publ. 1961.

40. Salinity Control in Irrigation Agriculture: C. A. Bower, (U. S. Salinity Lab. U. S. D. A. ) Proc. of F. A. O. -Government of Pakistan Salinity Seminar, 1965.

41. Oceanography--The Ten Years Ahead (1963-1972) Interagency Committee on Oceanography. Pamphlet 10, 1963.

42. Oceanography 1960-1970. Chap. 5, NAS-NRC 1959.

43. Restoring the Quality of our Environment: Report of the Environmental Pollution Panel--President's Science Advisory Committee, The White House, Nov. 1965.

44. The Annotated Catalogue on Water Publications of UNESCO, U. N. IAEA, WHO, FAO, WMO, AEF: National Agency for International Publications, Inc. , Sept. 1965, contains many relevant additional references, as do a number of the sources listed previously.

## 17. Extending Use of Available Supply — A System Approach To Power, Water, and Food Production

Carl N. Hodges, Solar Energy Research Laboratory, and
A. Richard Kassander, Jr., Director,
Institute of Atmospheric Physics, The University of Arizona

The expanding population problem of the world is extremely difficult to imagine, yet alone cope with. Professor Georg Borgstrom's
"The Hungry Planet" (MacMillan, 1965) gives us a very frighten-
ing picture of our problem. References to this are borrowed
rather freely herein. While it is dangerous to cite statistics out
of context from such a massive accounting, a few points might be
helpful.

In 1960 the world population passed the three billion mark. In
the first sixty years of this century the world's population has doubled, and we can look forward to a second doubling before year
2000. This amounts to the addition of almost a whole new United
States each third year or a new Soviet Union each fourth year.
Most of us can expect to live to face up to this.

If the minimum requirements of the entire present population
were to be met we would have to double our food production immediately. If we were to ration what the globe totally carries in food
in such a way that each individual received an equal share, this
would mean universal starvation.

In Asia, for example, only fifteen years from now there will
be a billion people in addition to the one and one-half billion there
now. This period is chosen for an example here because it represents a period of time in which birth control cannot be expected
to help much. If a standard were to be provided for these two and
one-half billion people comparable to the rather modest one of
present-day Japan--actually very low, judged in western terms--
Professor Borgstrom tells us that the following additional quantities of various key commodities would be required per year:

| | |
|---|---|
| 5000 | billion gallons of water |
| 90.4 | million tons of rice (world crop now 172 million tons) |
| 11 | million tons of wheat |
| 198.4 | million tons of vegetables |
| 66 | million tons of food fish (world catch now 35.3 mil- ion tons) |
| 14.3 | million tons of meat |
| 1 | trillion kilowatt hours |

Approximately half of the world's population is in Asia, so it
would seem profitable to examine what would be required to provide the standard of existence of Professor Borgstrom's table.
Let us assume for the purposes of this discussion that the world

crop of meat and grains could be expanded to meet the challenge. This seems feasible on the basis of the yields per acre in developed countries versus the underdeveloped. The very great discrepancy in terms of supply and demand is in the area of vegetables which represent approximately one-half of the total extra tonnage of food products to be required.

If, then, we limit this discussion to requirements for vegetables, power, and water production, divide the totals of the table by two million and make appropriate scale changes, we find that for each 500 people we will require 100 tons of vegetables per year, approximately 60 kilowatts of electrical generating capacity, and 2-1/2 million gallons of water per year (6850 gallons per day, 13. 7 gallons per person per day).

The University of Arizona's Solar Energy Laboratory has done a number of experiments that relate to these requirements and currently is attempting to combine the results in a system for the maintenance of living standards in coastal desert communities.

This effort started in 1959 when the Solar Energy Laboratory building was put in operation.  This 1500 square foot building is fully heated and cooled using solar energy collection equipment to store hot water for a radiant heating system and reversing the system at night to radiate heat to the night sky for cooling water for the building air conditioning system.

By 1962 a preliminary effort at using solar energy for desalting water was well under way (Figure 1).  This system is different substantially from previous efforts in that evaporation and condensation are performed separately from the water heating operation.  This permits multiple-effect operation resulting in greatly improved per-square-foot-of-collector productivities over earlier conventional solar stills.

Under support of the Office of Saline Water an experimental desalting plant was installed in Puerto Penasco, Sonora, Mexico, on the Gulf of California (Figure 2).  This is a cooperative effort with the University of Sonora.  The plant has worked very well and has produced over 5000 gallons per day from 10, 400 square feet of solar collector.  One gallon per ten square feet is considered peak production from a conventional solar still.

In the fall of 1965 this plant was equipped with a 60 kw diesel-electric generator with conventional waste-heat recovery equipment (Figure 3).  Operations to date have exceeded 6000 gallons per day operating the generator at 3/4 load.  This system can be operated with either parallel or series solar collector and generator waste-heat feed so that considerably increased output is possible during summer peak demands.

An interest in the general world food and water problem had

Figure 1.   Tucson pilot desalting plant and Solar
Energy Laboratory building.

Figure 2.   Puerto Penasco desalting plant now modified for operation with
diesel-electric system waste heat. Productivity on solar energy
alone exceeded 0.5 GPD per square foot of collector.

Figure 3. Diesel-electric generator and waste-heat collection equipment. The waste heat from this 60 kw generator supplying the Puerto Penasco desalting plant has produced over 6000 GPD of fresh water with the generator operating at 3/4 load.

Figure 4. Productivity of closed-system horticulture to be coupled to desalting system blowdown. Annual productivity exceeds 100 ton/acre in tomato crop.

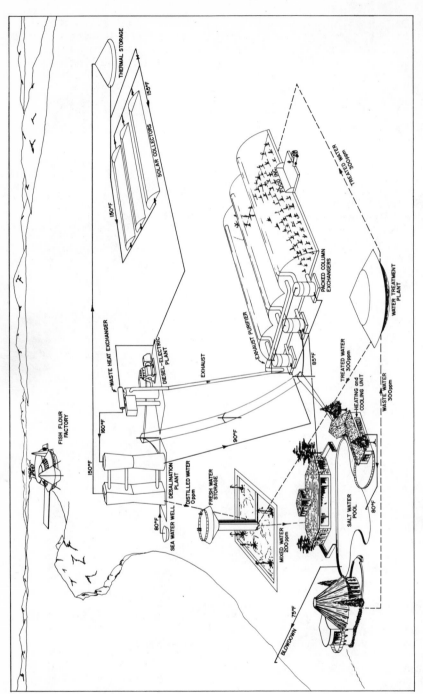

Figure 5. Idealized schematic of system for production of power, water, and food for coastal desert community.

*AN INTEREST IN THE GENERAL WORLD FOOD & WATER PROBLEM HAD*
led the Solar Energy Laboratory staff to speculate also on the possibilities of producing food, particularly with the use of sea water,
although it was not hoped that the plants could be grown in direct
contact with the sea water. It is well known that, for their nutri-
tion, plants require less than two per cent of the water they absorb and transpire to the atmosphere. It was felt that if they
could be grown in a fully enclosed environment, using simple vapor and humidity exchange mechanisms between sea water and
plant atmosphere, a productive horticulture could be maintained
on an extremely small quantity of fresh water. A number of different experiments have been performed testing this hypothesis.
It has been demonstrated that this is entirely feasible, the only
special requirement being the maintenance of carbon dioxide concentration in the closed atmosphere. Calculations indicate that
this can be easily handled from the diesel engine exhaust with sea
water scrubbing and a low temperature catalyst for removing objectionable gases from the exhaust. A number of different crops
have been tested and the feasibility of, for example, tomato productivity above the level of 100 tons per acre per year has been
demonstrated. (Figure 4)

The production rates cited are in very interesting correlation
with the numbers cited from Borgstrom. The thermodynamic and
practical consistency of 60 kw of power, 6850 gallons of fresh water per day, and 100 tons of vegetables per year for 500 persons
has been demonstrated. Preliminary economic estimates indicate
that this productivity can be had for less than $100 per person per
year with proper attention to amortization of capital investment
as well as maintenance and operating costs. Interestingly enough,
Professor Borgstrom also tells us that the present world average
of tilled acreage is 1.25 acres per person. The University of
Arizona system required 1 acre per 500 persons.

Figure 5 shows an idealized schematic of a suggested system
along the lines that have been described. Provision also has been
made for the use of sewage effluent in the greenhouse operation.
Obviously nuclear energy fits very well into such a system concept except that the carbon dioxide generation for food production
would have to be handled independently. Proposed power-water
ratios in nuclear plants are consistent with the numbers cited
here.

## Acknowledgements

The research described is a team effort with significant tech-
nical contributions from D. H. Frieling, J. E. Groh, G. Jimenez,
A. W. Johnson, J. J. Riley, and T. L. Thompson. Development
of the desalting system was supported principally by the Office of
Saline Water, as a cooperative project with the University of
Sonora, Mexico. Continued research combining food production
with power and water production is supported by the Rockefeller
Foundation.

# NUCLEAR REACTORS FOR WATER DESALTING

Angelo Giambusso,
Division of Reactor Development and Technology,
U.S. Atomic Energy Commission

## 18. Water-Cooled Graphite-Moderated Reactors*

R. L. Dickeman, General Manager, and W. J. Dowis, Consulting Engineer, Hanford Atomic Products Operation, General Electric Company

Over a period of nearly 20 years as prime contractor to the Atomic Energy Commission at Hanford, the General Electric Company has been associated with the design, construction, operation and maintenance of large, light-water-cooled, low-fuel-enrichment, graphite-moderated reactors specifically designed for the low-cost production of defense materials; some 120 reactor operating years are represented in this experience. It is my intent to discuss briefly facets of this experience which may bear constructively on the Commission's program to study, evaluate and develop large, low-cost multi-product nuclear complexes.

At the outset, I am sure we all recognize that the design of a nuclear complex represents a balance of conditioned trade-offs -- the net result of which is expected to be a plant complex which can be operated and maintained with high standards of nuclear and radiological safety, high reliability or plant factor and which produces the desired products at lowest cost over the amortized lifetime of the plant -- perhaps 35 years. Thus, many interrelated factors (technical, operating, economic and market) are brought into juxtaposition -- it will seldom prove prudent to concentrate in one area to the essential exclusion of others.

In mid-1963, when the N-Reactor was in an advanced stage of construction, the Atomic Energy Commission, Department of Interior and Federal Power Commission, through the Interagency Subcommittee, evaluated the use of nuclear heat from large reactors for desalting sea water; case 5 of this study is based on a 3500-megawatt graphite-moderated reactor of the general N-Reactor type. The three general types evaluated in this size range -- all considered to be current technology -- were the light-water-moderated and cooled; the graphite-moderated, light-water-cooled; and the $D_2O$-moderated, $D_2O$ or organic-cooled types. The graphite-moderated reactor plant design used in this study was evaluated from the accumulated background of N-Reactor design and construction experience; further, since N-Reactor is of the pressure tube type, it resembled in that respect a general class of reactors judged to have potential for construction in very large sizes. Thus, the combination of a range of technologies under demonstration in a 4000-megawatt elevated temperature, pressure tube reactor, coupled with actual design and

---

* Work performed for the Atomic Energy Commission under Contract AT(45-1)-1350.

construction experience, and imminent operating and maintenance experience, presented a number of measurement points useful in programmatic evaluations.

The N-Reactor, or New Production Reactor, is the Atomic Energy Commission's newest production reactor and the only production reactor specifically designed with a view toward recovery of energy values from the process heat. This plant was originally authorized as a convertible reactor -- that is, a reactor designed primarily for the economic production of defense materials but with provisions to facilitate the subsequent addition of electrical generating facilities, thereby establishing an economic potential for dual-purpose operation. Dual-purpose, in this case, refers to isotope production coupled with the recovery of electrical power from what would otherwise be waste heat. The complex was designed by General Electric and Burns and Roe; Kaiser Engineers was the constructor.

The reactor attained the design power rating in December 1964. The performance anticipated at the time of the Interagency Task Force Study has been fully realized -- in summary:

> The technological base is sound. This result is well established with the possible exception of specific aspects of material performance which require longer term experience for a conclusive verification of predicted performance.

> The capacity of all critical systems is at least equal to design expectation; a significant stretch in thermal capacity above the design rating is available.

> The thermal-hydraulic-nuclear coupling yields stable operating modes.

> The intrinsic performance of the metallic uranium fuel has exceeded first load expectations.

> Process parameters have been accurately predictable in all operating modes.

> Problems with conventional equipments in the heat dissipation complex have been vexing but tractable.

An 860-MWe generating facility being constructed by a complex of Northwest Utilities, incorporated as the Washington Public Power Supply System, will be completed later this year. Process steam, which is now being condensed, will be sold by the Atomic Energy Commission to the utilities and the dual-purpose mode of operation will, thus, be engaged.

## PLANT SCHEMATIC

The process is represented schematically as shown in Figure 1. The 4000 megawatts of thermal energy is removed from the reactor core through a pressurized, light-water-coolant system designed at 1825 psi and a coolant mass flow of 96 million pounds per hour at 300°C. The heat is transferred from the primary coolant system through boiling in a battery of 10 horizontal "U-tube" steam generators. Nominally 15 million pounds per hour of steam are generated and currently condensed in a battery of 16 dump condensers -- the Columbia River provides the ultimate heat sink.

Pertinent N-Reactor design parameters are tabulated in Appendix I; a broad perspective of the physical plant for a reactor of this type is gained by briefly examining the following figures. The block consists of 1800 tons of traphite in a structure 33 feet by 33 feet in section and 39 feet long. Boron carbide containing control rods penetrate from either side to provide operating reactivity control, flux shaping and safety control; an independent safety control system consists of ceramic balls containing samarium oxide held in top shield hoppers. The capacity of either syssystem, acting alone, is adequate to control all credible operating and safeguards-related reactivity transients.

The primary coolant system contains some 1500 tons of carbon steel; the system employs a headering and connector pipe arrangement to admit and remove the light-water-coolant from the pressure tube lattice cells. The piping arrangements are shown in Figures 2 and 3.

Later this year, some 13 million pounds per hour, or about 85 per cent of the available steam, will be exported to the Washington Public Power Supply System's electrical generating plant to drive two 430 MWe turbine-generator sets.

Of particular interest in the design of reactors of this type are the lattice cell construction module, the pressure tube, the graphite moderator, the primary coolant system and the fuel cycle; the salient features of each, as they are appraised from the N-Reactor design, construction and operating experience as well as the technological background, are briefly summarized.

## LATTICE CELL CONSTRUCTION MODULE

The basic reactor construction module is the lattice cell consisting of graphite moderator, Zircaloy-2 pressure tube, light-water coolant and fuel as shown in Figure 4. The nuclear core for N-Reactor consists of 1004 such cells -- each 8 by 9 inches in section and 39 feet long arranged in an octagonal array. Each cell is designed to generate and remove some five megawatts of thermal energy. Thus, reactor rating can be adjusted in the design phase through the power rating assigned each power-producing cell and, of course, the number of included building-block modules.

Generalized studies have indicated the technical and design feasibility of reactors of this type up to at least 10,000 megawatts in size; this extrapolation from the demonstrated N-Reactor capability of 4000 megawatts is not large and does not closely approach a limiting condition. Reactivity transients, stress levels in major components and the complexity of piping coolant to and from the individual pressure tube modules are all manageable from essentially current technology. We would, therefore, tentatively judge that economic, market and, perhaps, environmental considerations would establish size limits for plants of this type; additional definitive study is required to establish more conclusively both the technical and economic limits on ultimate size.

## ZIRCALOY PRESSURE TUBE

The assured integrity of the pressure tube is, of course, pivotal. The Zircaloy-2 pressure tubes provided in N-Reactor are 53 feet in length, 2.7 inches I.D., and 0.25 inches in wall thickness and, thus, are designed to accommodate the 1825-pound system pressure. The procurement, inspection and installation phases were executed to high quality standards without major difficulty. The Zircaloy-2 pressure tubes are joined to the carbon steel primary coolant system through mechanical rolled joints which have performed without problem. There are two chief potential long-term problem areas with Zircaloy pressure tubes -- both of which we believe can be controlled by tube design and control of the operating environment. The first is long-term physical deformation and the resulting impairment of integrity. We design to a deformation, or creep, limit of one per cent elongation over the expected life of the tube; within these limits, the ultimate strength, ductile failure characteristics and creep rate for given conditions appear to be preserved. Secondly, hydriding profoundly deteriorates the desired physical properties and must be avoided; we protect against hydriding through environmental controls which limit the concentration of nascent hydrogen and continuously deposit adequate levels of the protective $ZrO_2$ coating on the pressure tube surfaces. In both cases, dynamic balances are maintained and a primary assurance of long-term integrity is derived from conservative design and operating practice and periodic examination of the irradiated pressure tubes themselves. Studies of the change in physical properties with irradiation and chemical composition of the environment lead the reactor by several years of equivalent service and are continuing; however, the extension of specimen-level results to full reactor performance must be made with great care in this instance.

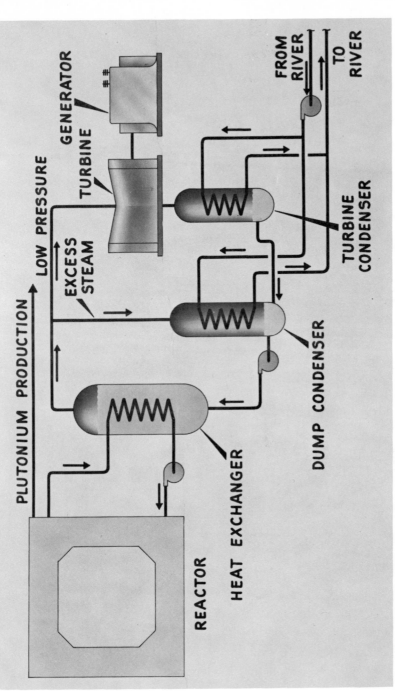

Figure 1. New Dual Purpose Plant Features

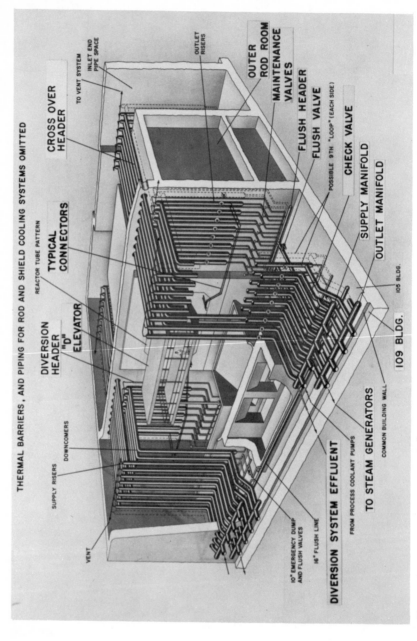

Figure 2.  N-Reactor Outlet Piping

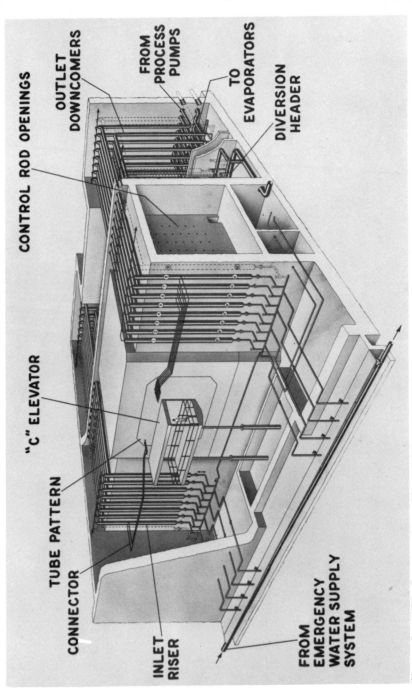

Figure 3. NPR-Reactor Inlet Piping

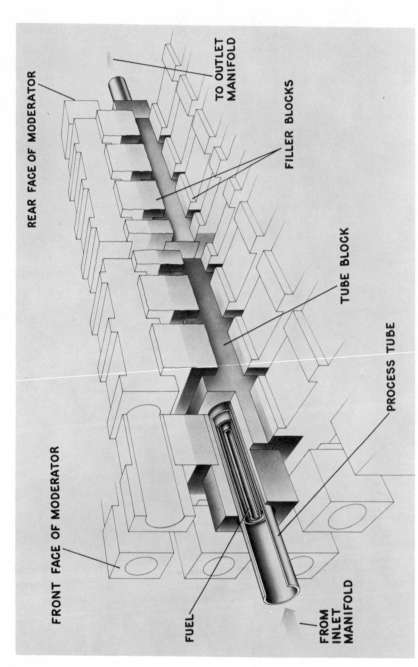

REAR FACE OF MODERATOR

TO OUTLET MANIFOLD

FILLER BLOCKS

FRONT FACE OF MODERATOR

TUBE BLOCK

PROCESS TUBE

FUEL

FROM INLET MANIFOLD

Figure 4. N-Reactor Process Tube Module

## GRAPHITE

The macroscopic behavior of graphite, even after 20 years, is difficult to predict as a long-term function of temperature and irradiation history. Effects at the crystal level, such as stored energy and lattice deformation, are quite well understood phenomenologically and quantitatively; however, the total long-term physical deformation of non-isotropic polycrystalline shapes is not. The observed physical changes are the product of competing mechanisms -- lattice expansion in crystals and stress growth and relaxation in fabricated shapes -- and the net accumulative effect is a function of graphite type, irradiation history and temperature. An extruded graphite bar, for example, will both expand and contract in the direction transverse to the extrusion axis at different stages in the irradiation service; only contraction has been observed along the extrusion axis.

Graphite is readily oxidized at elevated temperatures; for example, chemical reaction rates with $O_2$ become important at 300°C; $CO_2$ at 650°C and water vapor at 700°C. At the 10 per cent oxidation (weight loss) level compressive strength is reduced 50 per cent and is very low at the 20 per cent oxidation level. However, oxidation control through inert atmosphere blanketing (helium) is not difficult.

The main summary observation is that large graphite moderated reactors have been successfully operated for periods now exceeding 20 years without impairment of function. However, the physical changes accompanying irradiation service are a function of the intermediate and fast neutron flux levels, as well as irradiation temperature, and each design must, therefore, be evaluated in light of its particular process conditions; in general, straightforward design solutions are available to accommodate the long-term physical changes.

## CARBON STEEL

The primary coolant system piping in N-Reactor contains 1500 tons of carbon steel piping; the choice of carbon steel saved some $10 million over the use of stainless clad carbon steel in this application. Particularly sensitive fundamental considerations to be satisfied include adequate control of uniform and pitting corrosion and caustic embrittlement, control of crud accumulation and transport, and the development of techniques for chemically removing radioactive deposits from pipe surfaces should these result from fuel failure or other causes.

The carbon steel system has now been operated at elevated temperature and pressure for some 1.5 years with excellent results. Corrosion is controlled by maintaining a relatively impervious magnetite film on pipe surfaces, water conductivity at one megohm or greater, pH at nominally 10 through addition of anhydrous ammonia in water treatment, and $O_2$ levels at 5 ppb or less. Uniform corrosion rates are less than one mil per year, pitting is negligible, crud deposits on fuel element surfaces are barely detectable and radioactivity on pipe surfaces at shutdown are in the 50-200 mr/hr range -- all within design expectations.

Large scale chemical decontamination in N-Reactor has not been necessary and is expected to be an infrequent requirement. A process employing alkaline permanganate and sulfamic acid has been developed and utilized successfully in the Plutonium Recycle Test Reactor at Hanford; this process has also been successfully tested on a small scale in N-Reactor. A simpler process, utilizing sulfamic or oxalic acid, appears adequate if only carbon steel is involved.

## FUEL

The low cost production of defense products requires high neutron economy and low fuel cycle costs in a situation in which high fuel exposure capability cannot be utilized to advantage. The use of uranium metal is thereby quite strongly favored in this application; the optimum level of enrichment for N-Reactor in the plutonium production mode is approximately one per cent U-235 in uranium metal.

The fuel is of the nested tube design, contains 21.6 pounds of uranium per foot of loading and is clad in nominally 25 mils of Zircaloy-2. During the formulative stages of the fuel design in the 1957-58 period several aluminum alloys, SAP, Zircaloy-2 and stainless steel cladding systems were evaluated technically and economically; the selection of the Zircaloy-2 system has proven to be sound in our case. A major assist was the successful development of the coextrusion fabrication process. Large, hollow billets of uranium metal (several hundred pounds) are enveloped in Zircaloy-2 shells, the system canned in copper, evacuated, heated and extruded through a die and over a mandrel. This operation produces the element to final dimension, including the Zircaloy-2 clad, and concurrently produces the very important metallurgical bond between the uranium and Zircaloy cladding. The result is a metallurgically sound Zircaloy clad metallic uranium fuel produced by an economic process.

Studies of alternate fuel cycles have been performed for N-Reactor operated as a power rather than production reactor; the results are broadly typical of those which would obtain in an optimized graphite moderated, pressure tube dual-purpose plant. The cycles considered were $UO_2$ enriched in U-235; $UO_2$ enriched with Pu ($PuO_2$-$UO_2$); thoria enriched with U-235 ($ThO_2$); and uranium metal. The enrichment levels as a function of average fuel

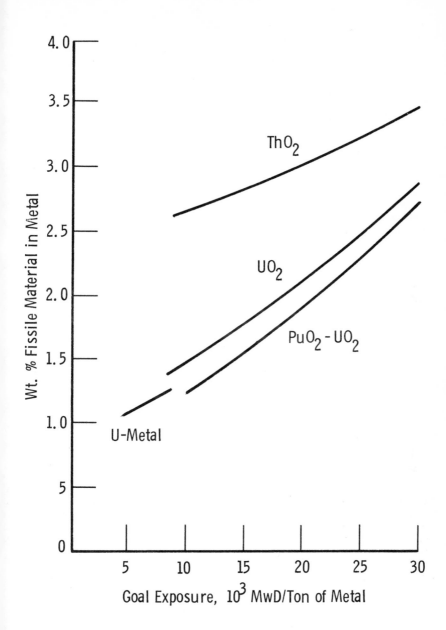

Figure 5.   Initial Enrichment vs. Goal Exposure

discharge exposure have not been truly optimized but broadly
project as shown in Figure 5.  The neutron utilization for the uranium metal case is competitive with that presented by any of the
alternate cycles evaluated -- largely the result of improved thermal neutron utilization and utilization in situ of the plutonium
produced.  For example, in attaining an exposure of 8000 MWD/T,
slightly over half the fissions have derived from plutonium produced in the fuel; at 8000 MWD/T some 75 per cent of the fissions
are from plutonium.  Additional study of the ability of graphite-
moderated reactors to sustain themselves on a plutonium economy
is indicated.

The costs of energy attributable to each fuel cycle are compared in Figure 6.  This analysis assumes industrial fuel fabrication and chemical reprocessing costs which are judged to be
reasonably achievable for the cycles evaluated, over the next two
decades, an 80 per cent plant factor and 7 per cent per annum as
the fixed charge rate on capital.  This study illustrates two points
of particular significance:

1.   Metallic uranium fuel irradiated to the 7-9,000 MWD/T
     exposure range becomes economically competitive with
     $UO_2$ fuel irradiated to the 20-25,000 MWD/T range.

2.   Plutonium enrichment is indicated to be quite competi-
     tive with U-235 enrichment in the case examining this
     parameter -- the $UO_2$ fuel case; rather small changes in
     the economic factors operative in these cycles could
     present an economic standoff.

The upper exposure limits for metallic uranium fuel in a
pressurized water coolant environment are not known.  There are
two main technical problems.  First, uranium metal corrodes
rapidly upon exposure to cooling water under power reactor conditions; thus a cladding failure requires a reactor shutdown unless provisions for removing fuel while operating are provided.
Fuel charge-discharge during operation would appear to be feasible in a pressure tube reactor and has been exploited in the
Canadian program but has not been studied in the N-Reactor program.  Several fuel elements have failed in N-Reactor service,
primarily through fretting corrosion induced by extraneous materials, and have been detected and discharged without problem.

The second problem is swelling induced by stresses resulting from anisotropic expansion of the crystal structure and, also,
fission gas bubble nucleation.  The dimensional growth, and,
therefore, induced clad strain is a function of uranium temperature, accumulated exposure level and level of applied physical
restraint.  Fuel elements in which no sophisticated provisions
to minimize the impact of swelling were applied have exceeded
5000 MWD/T without problem.  An excellent base from which to

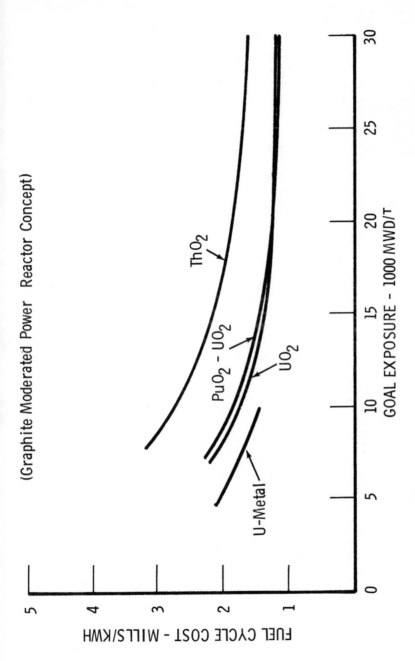

(Graphite Moderated Power Reactor Concept)

FUEL CYCLE COST - MILLS/KWH

GOAL EXPOSURE - 1000 MWD/т

ThO$_2$

PuO$_2$ - UO$_2$

UO$_2$

U-Metal

Figure 6.   Projected Fuel Cycle Cost

launch efforts to penetrate the potentially economically competitive range of 7, 000-9, 000 MWD/T is thus now established.

## ENERGY COSTS

The 3500-megawatt pressurized water-cooled, graphite-moderated reactor evaluated as case 5 in the Interagency Task Force Study included only minor second-generation modifications from the N-Reactor; it is thus a proven technology case and does not reflect sizable potential gains that additional study should reveal.  Modifications from N-Reactor included:

1.  A vertical rather than horizontal pressure tube orientation.

2.  Modest efforts to simplify and compact systems.

3.  $UO_2$ fuel to reflect the demonstrated exposure capability.

4.  Standard containment.

The results are set forth in Table I.

### TABLE I

Product Costs -- Water-Cooled, Graphite-Moderated
Reactor for Saline Water Conversion

| 3500 Mw Plant | Unit Cost |
|---|---|
| Electric Power, Net - 640 MW(e) | 3. 1 Mills/KWH |
| Thermal Energy to Still - 6. 76 x $10^{13}$ Btu/Yr | 9. 5¢/M Btu |
| Water Production Rate -     300 MGD | 25¢/1000 Gal |
| 8300 Mw Plant | |
| Electric Power, Net - 1590 MW(e) | 2. 6 Mills/KWH |
| Thermal Energy to Still - 15. 8 x $10^{13}$ Btu/Yr | 8. 9¢/M Btu |
| Water Production Rate -     600 MGD | 23¢/1000 Gal |

The table includes estimates of the unit cost of electric energy and thermal energy to the brine heater.  The costs of water are essentially those derived by the Interagency Task Force from reactor data we supplied.  Interagency Study ground rules, including 7 per cent fixed charge on capital, are applied.  These results, we emphasize, are derived from proven technology and demonstrated large reactor performance and, thus, do not reflect a large effort to optimize a second generation plant for the saline water conversion application; also, a larger shift of energy to generation of electric power would, under the ground rules employed, reduce the cost of energy to the desalting plant.

In summary, we set forth the following observations:

1.  The pressure tube, water-cooled, graphite-moderated reactor is judged to be potentially competitive in sizes above 4000 thermal megawatts.  This is almost certainly the case with low-cost (municipal or public) financing. Additional studies to reduce capital costs would be expected to be fruitful and thus expand the conditions under which this type of plant would be attractive.

2.  The demonstrated performance of the N-Reactor, including its design and technology, at the 4000 thermal megawatt level supports the thesis that very large nuclear plants are now technically and operationally feasible -- at least to the 10,000 megawatt level.  Size will then be determined by economic, market and environmental considerations -- that is, by the forces operative in the market place with due regard for health and safety.

3.  A single measure by which one can assess a reactor-type superiority for desalination purposes is not evident. Capital, fuel, operating and maintenance costs; product flexibility; level of technical risk; and versatility in accommodating to the economic and other changes certain to evolve during the operating life of the plant operate integrally in establishing superior values.

4.  A more sophisticated assessment of the ultimate potential of the water-cooled, graphite-moderated type will require a) a design-scoping study to establish the capital savings possible in a second generation plant of this type which is fully optimized for dual or multi-product operation, and b) additional study of the fuel cycle.  The graphite-moderated, pressure-tube reactor lends itself to nuclear superheat and the scoping studies we have performed on this type of reactor do indicate substantial potential for further energy cost reductions.  This notwithstanding, the experience with several areas of broadly applicable technology, and the design, operation and maintenance of the 4000 megawatt N-Reactor and the associated equipments, may be of some value to the Commission's advanced reactor program.

## APPENDIX I

## N-REACTOR PARAMETERS

| | |
|---|---|
| Thermal Rating | 4000 MW(t) |

**Moderator**
| | |
|---|---|
| Material | Graphite |
| Size | 39 x 33 x 33 ft. L. W. H. |
| Weight | 1800 Tons |
| Lattice | 8 x 9 in. W. H. |
| Process Channels | 1004 Horizontal Positions |

**Process Tubes**
| | |
|---|---|
| Material | Zircaloy-2 |
| Size | 2. 7 in. I. D. x 1/4 in. Wall x 53 ft. long |
| Weight | 150 Tons |

**Fuel**
| | |
|---|---|
| Material | Metallic Uranium |
| Clad | Zircaloy-2 |
| Geometry | Tube-in-tube |

**Nuclear Control**
| | |
|---|---|
| Control and Safety | 87 Side Entry Rods, Boron Carbide Absorber |
| Backup Safety | 108 Top Entry Ball Channels - Balls of Samarium Oxide in Aluminum Oxide Matrix |

**Shielding**
| | |
|---|---|
| Thermal | Cast Iron and Boron Steel |
| Biological | Ordinary and Heavy Aggregate Concrete |

**Primary Cooling System**
| | |
|---|---|
| Coolant | Light Water |
| Pipe Material | Carbon Steel |
| Pipe Weight | 1500 Tons |
| Design Conditions | 1825 psig - 600 F |
| No. of Coolant Loops | 6 Parallel Loops |
| Steam Generators | 12 Units - 16000 $Ft^2$ Each |
| Primary Pumps | Injection Shaft Seal |
| Pump Drives | 9100 HP Steam Turbines |

**Secondary Steam Loop**
| | |
|---|---|
| Design Pressure | 600 psig |
| Alternate Sinks | 16 - 8200 $Ft^2$ Dump Condensers 2 - Turbine Generators, 800-860 MW(e) Capacity with Condensers |

**River System**
| | |
|---|---|
| Capacity | 4 - 100, 000 gpm Pumps |

## NOTES

1. RL-NRD-173 PT1, Alternate Fuel Cycles for Power-Only Operation of N-Reactor, N-Reactor Department, September 30, 1965.

2. An Assessment of Large Nuclear-Powered Sea Water Distillation Plants, March 1964, A Report of an Interagency Task Force, Office of Science and Technology.

3. HW-78291, NPR-Type Reactor for Sea Water Distillation, N-Reactor Project Staff, July 17, 1963.

4. HW-83081, Design and Evaluation Studies of Nuclear Reactors for Desalination, Staff -- Reactor Design Analysis, July 1, 1964.

5. Hanford's New Production Reactor, Staff on N-Project, May 1963 (Rev.).

6. HW-73130, Hanford Graphite Superheat Reactor (HGSR) Design Study and Evaluation, N-Reactor Project Section, January 1964.

# 19. Organic-Cooled D$_2$O-Moderated Reactors — An Approach To Large-Scale Dual-Purpose Plants

Chauncey Starr, President, Atomics International;
Simcha Golan, Project Manager, Atomics International; and
Donald Graf, System Engineer, Combustion Engineering*

## INTRODUCTION

Large desalting plants require large blocks of energy. Furthermore, the controlling factor in the economics of large evaporative desalting plants is the cost of energy used to heat the brine. Also, as energy plants grow in size, fuel costs become the primary factor in selecting the type of energy source for providing this heat. This is why current light-water reactors are generally more attractive than fossil plants in large plant sizes, and why low fuel cost nuclear heat sources such as the heavy-water reactor and fast breeder are of special interest for future large power and desalting applications. As will be shown below, the heavy-water-moderated, organic-cooled reactor, or HWOCR, is particularly adapted to meeting future large-scale desalting requirements because of a unique combination of design and operating characteristics.

## SALIENT FEATURES

The HWOCR combines the desirable nuclear characteristics of heavy water as the moderator with the desirable economic characteristics of organic coolant.

As shown in Figure 1, the HWOCR energy-producing complex consists of banks of pressure tubes which are manifolded together to common headers for passage of the organic coolant. The heavy water is contained in a calandria tank which is insulated from the hot organic pressure tubes by a gas thermal barrier in the annuli between the pressure tubes and the calandria tubes. The organic coolant absorbs the heat released from the fissioning fuel contained within the pressure tubes (see Figure 2) and leaves the reactor at a higher temperature. The organic coolant then transports the reactor heat to steam generators and, after exchanging this heat to the working fluid, returns to the reactor to repeat the cycle.

By virtue of the pressure tube design utilized in this reactor concept, onpower refueling is facilitated. A remote refueling machine is provided at the top and bottom for bidirectional refueling in a computed preprogrammed sequence. The refueling

---

* ATOMICS INTERNATIONAL-COMBUSTION ENGINEERING-
A Joint Venture for Heavy-Water, Organic-Cooled Reactors

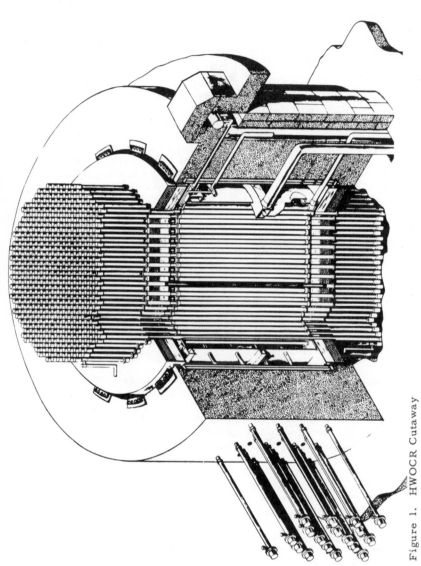

Figure 1. HWOCR Cutaway

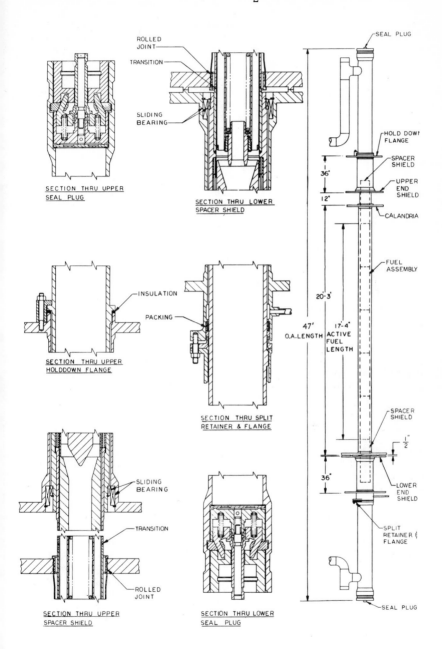

Figure 2. Pressure Tube

machines will index at both ends of a given pressure tube, re-
motely connect to the pressure tube, remove the pressure tube
end cap, inject new fuel simultaneously with reception of used
fuel, effect closure of the pressure tube extensions and the refueling machine snout, and index to the next position for refueling.
This concept provides optimum fuel management economies by
minimizing fuel inventory for burnup and the associated parasitic
absorption for control, and by alleviating the need for refueling
downtime, thus increasing availability.

By the use of noncorrosive, low-vapor pressure, organic
terphenyls as the primary coolant, carbon and low-alloy steel can
be used as a material for construction of the primary plant piping
and steam generators.  This considerably reduces the cost of the
primary coolant system as compared with water systems under
high pressure.

Since the organic coolant is basically noncorrosive, there are
very few metal ions in the coolant that become radioactive after
flowing through the core.  In addition, the induced activity in the
organic coolant is much lower than that of water because of its
$N^{16}$ content.  Consequently, the primary coolant of this plant has
extremely low radioactivity, as was demonstrated at the Piqua
plant.  Since the activity level of the coolant is of such low magnitude, shielding and containment need only be provided about the
reactor and the refueling equipment.  The steam generators and
main coolant pumps are located in a conventional auxiliary building adjacent to the containment building, and are connected by
primary coolant piping which has isolation valves on both sides of
the containment vessel wall.  Low capital costs result from such
an arrangement, with no sacrifice in safety.

The main coolant pumps, Figure 3, are horizontal single-
stage centrifugal units with vertical suction and discharge nozzles.
Each pump has a single impeller.  The pump driver is a steam
turbine which is connected to the impeller by parallel shaft reduction gears.

The main steam for the turbine generators is generated in
double U-tube, horizontal, natural circulation evaporator units,
similar to the ones currently in use at the NPR (see Figure 4).
The tube bundles and central cylindrical tube sheet are located at
the bottom portion of the shell.  Steam separation equipment is
located in the upper half of the shell above water level.  An economizer or preheat section is contained integrally with the evaporator.  The tube-supports act as baffles to separate the entering
feedwater from the boiling mixture in the shell.  The superheaters
use a similar arrangement, but are smaller in size.

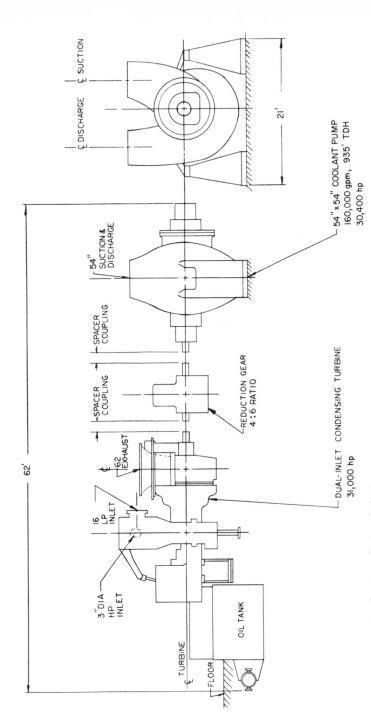

Figure 3. Main Coolant Pump & Drive

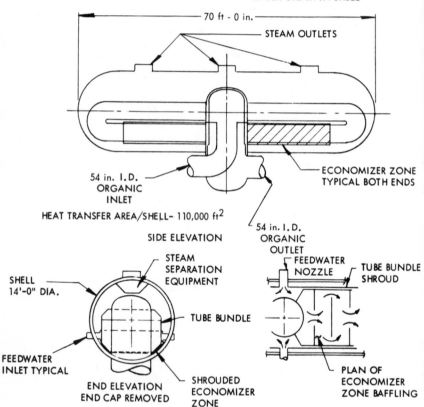

ORGANIC IN TUBES
WATER-STEAM IN SHELL

70 ft - 0 in.

STEAM OUTLETS

54 in. I.D.
ORGANIC
INLET

ECONOMIZER ZONE
TYPICAL BOTH ENDS

HEAT TRANSFER AREA/SHELL- 110,000 ft$^2$

SIDE ELEVATION

54 in. I.D.
ORGANIC
OUTLET

SHELL
14'-0" DIA.

STEAM
SEPARATION
EQUIPMENT

TUBE BUNDLE

FEEDWATER
NOZZLE

TUBE BUNDLE
SHROUD

FEEDWATER
INLET TYPICAL

END ELEVATION
END CAP REMOVED

SHROUDED
ECONOMIZER
ZONE

PLAN OF
ECONOMIZER
ZONE BAFFLING

Figure 4.   Steam Evaporator

## MAJOR ATTRIBUTES

### Modular Reactor Construction

As mentioned earlier, the HWOCR reactor is composed of many pressure tubes containing fuel through which the organic coolant flows in parallel. This arrangement and method of construction are adaptable to subdividing the reactor into reproducible portions, or modules, as shown in Figure 5. Therefore, the power of the reactor can be changed within wide ranges by simply adding or deleting modules. By considering the nuclear and mechanical aspects of core size, the module was defined to consist of a row of 13 pressure tubes with their pigtails. Since the modules can be placed end-to-end as well as in line, two modules end-to-end form a basic size of 26 channels. A square array of such a 26-tube matrix produces 3000 MWt. Larger reactors would be designed and engineered by figuratively separating the two halves of the above-described square reactor; inserting therein, two at a time, additional modules; and rounding off the corners of "loafing" fuel channels. Therefore, the plan view of a reactor larger than 3000 MWt would have the shape of a parallelepiped with semicircular ends.

### High Availability

Because of the pressure tube design and the low coolant vapor pressure, the HWOCR is particularly adaptable to on-line refueling, the overall availability factor of the plant is limited only by the requirements of the energy-consuming portions such as turbine overhauls and evaporator maintenance. In addition to proviing for high availability, on-line refueling minimizes the inventory of fuel required thus lowering the fuel cycle cost.

### Unsurpassed Fuel Management Flexibility

With the pressure tube design, on-line refueling capability, excellent neutron economy, simplicity of fuel geometry, and the complete compatibility of the organic coolant with all fuel materials, the HWOCR is unequalled in flexibility of fuel choices and optimization of fuel management.

The excellent neutron economy permits the use of natural or enriched uranium, or even thorium, depending on economics. The chemical compatibility of the organic coolant permits the use of any desired fuel form, including uranium and thorium metal fuels. The HWOCR can become an efficient plutonium supplier in an expanding fast breeder economy or it can efficiently recycle this plutonium. It further has the capability of utilizing the thorium cycle. With the pressure tube design and on-line refueling,

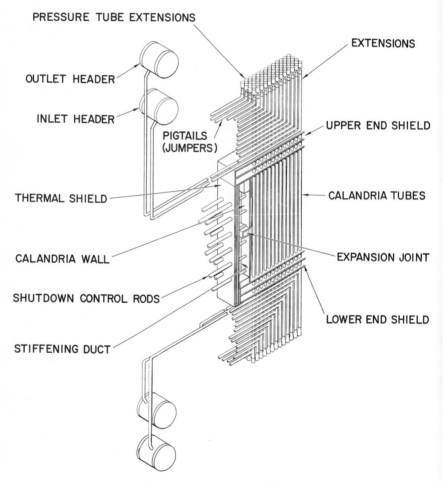

Figure 5.   HWOCR Pressure Tube Module

the HWOCR can readily convert from one fuel type to another on a timely basis and with minimum loss in plant availability. This unequalled flexibility with regard to fuel cycle provides for long-term base load operation of the plant since the HWOCR can adapt its fuel cycle to the most economic conditions of the time in addition to the obvious fuel conservation benefits.

## CONSIDERATIONS AS RELATED TO DUAL-PURPOSE APPLICATION

The application of nuclear energy to combination power-water plants is of particular interest in those areas where very large requirements exist for both power and water. There are areas in this country and overseas where such requirements exist today, as evidenced by the currently proposed MWD and Israeli desalting projects. The southwestern section of this country is a prime example for consideration of a dual-purpose plant to produce one billion gallons of water per day and 3500 MWe of power as indicated to the House Interior Committee this year. [1]

There are several important considerations which differentiate between the most desirable energy source characteristics for dual-purpose application and power-only applications. First, the combination of power and water in a single installation permits the consideration of much larger energy sources than would otherwise be required for power-only applications. This simple consideration favors those energy sources which provide relatively large reductions in capital cost per unit power with increased size.

Second, in a dual-purpose plant the energy-consuming portion represents a much larger fraction of the total investment than in a power-only plant. This places a special premium on an energy source with high availability and low fuel cost, the latter being required to justify economically base-load operation of the heat source at its maximum availability.

Third, the portion of the energy plant related to water production will normally carry much lower fixed charge rates than large power-only plants. The investor-owned utility power plants have fixed charge rates which range from 10 to 14 per cent. The fixed charge rate for water plants range from 4 to 7 per cent in the large public water systems. This, of course, favors a high capital cost-low fuel cycle cost energy source over a low capital cost-high fuel cost energy source. The net effect of these first three considerations is to favor an energy source with good scale-up characteristics, low fuel cycle costs, and high availability.

Fourth, the energy plant should be extensively base-loaded over its full life. To justify loading the plant in this manner, its incremental energy cost must be at least as low as that of any other power plant in the grid.   In this regard, it is desirable that the energy source have a high degree of fueling flexibility with regard to fuel type and form, to take full advantage of improved technology and changing market prices for uranium and plutonium.

Fifth, the efficient operation of a flash-type evaporator is very sensitive to slight changes in operating conditions.   Consequently, on startups, considerable time can be spent in balancing the evaporator plant for optimum operation.

To minimize such operational problems, the energy source should have high reliability so as to provide a steady steam supply to the water plant.   High reliability can be achieved through a preventive maintenance program which in turn requires ready access to all critical components while the plant is on-line.   Finally, in view of the high probability of minor leaks in the brine heaters, the steam supply system must be sufficiently resistant to sudden chloride concentration buildup so as to avoid unnecessary plant shutdown.   In this regard, the elimination of stainless steel from the steam supply system is desirable.

As noted from our earlier discussion, the above requirements are in fact the salient design features and operating characteristics of the HWOCR, thus indeed qualifying it as a potentially most attractive heat source for large dual-purpose applications.

## TYPICAL HWOCR DUAL-PURPOSE PLANT

### Plant Description

We have described the HWOCR concept and, by discussing its advantages, shown why this reactor is being developed and why it should be constructed.   Let us now apply such a plant to the previously mentioned needs of the southwestern United States-Mexico area, as was indicated to the House Interior Committee.

In developing this plant for these needs, we have used preliminary engineering data developed by the AEC-sponsored HWOCR program under contract AI(38-1)-430 and information developed in connection with the MWD[2] and Israeli[3] desalting projects.

The plot plan for our proposed plant is shown in Figure 6.   As noted, this 1 BGD, 3400-MWe net dual-purpose plant will utilize two 8250-MWt HWOCR units in parallel, each sharing in common the reactor fuel facilities, the heavy-water-moderator process plant, and the waste disposal plants.   The steam which is developed in this nuclear heat source will power five 800-Mwe backpressure turbines which exhaust steam at 25 psia to the brine

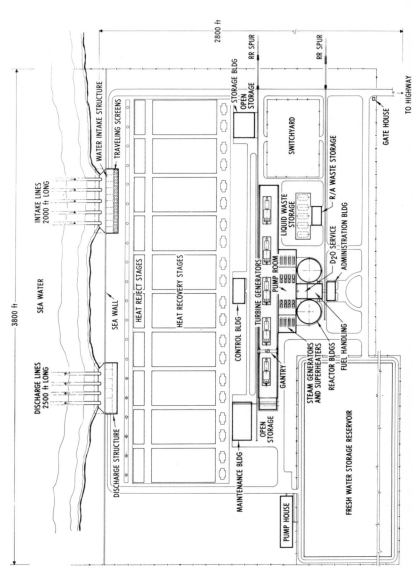

Figure 6. Plot Plan, One Billion Gallons per Day and 3400-MWe (net) Dual-Purpose HWOCR Plant

heaters often 100-MGD multistage flash-type evaporators. Intake
pumps are arrayed in two banks at standard crib house installations. Sea water requirements are met through five 24-foot intake lines and four 24-foot outflow lines extending into the ocean.
Product water is collected in a local reservoir from which it is
pumped to the distribution system. It is of interest to note from
this plot plan that a site of 3800 by 2800 feet would be required for
this plant which is equivalent to 244 acres. It is recognized that
such a plant would be built on a schedule commensurate with growing electrical energy and water requirements. The proposed arrangement was selected to meet a two-phase construction schedule
over a six- to seven-year period, and the construction costs for
this plant have been estimated accordingly. Detailed design of
such a plant can be initiated by 1974.

The reactors of 8250-MWt size can be built with eight headers
on each reactor providing coolant distribution through the core.
The reactor headers are connected in parallel to a reactor inlet
mix tank and reactor outlet mix tank through 54-inch low-alloy
steel pipe (see Figure 7). Four individual heat transfer loops are
arranged in parallel for each reactor. Each loop consists of a
main coolant centrifugal pump, a steam generator, and a superheater. The superheated steam is manifolded from all eight heat
transfer loops and distributed to the five back-pressure turbines
for maximum plant flexibility and availability.

A heat balance for this plant is shown in Figure 8. The calculated on-site auxiliary power requirements for this plant are
about 600 MWe which, when deducted from the gross output of
4000 MWe, leaves 3400 MWe as salable power. A portion of this
power would, of course, be used for transporting the product water to its point of use. The turbine generator complex employs
five back-pressure machines exhausting at 25 psia; the steam at
240°F provides the heat required by the desalting plant. Provision is also made for 10 per cent main steam bypass around the
turbines for maintaining 100 to 110 per cent heat duty to the brine
heaters at reduced power generation. The amount of steam by-
passed is determined by pressure reducing stations at each brine
heater set to maintain a constant backpressure of 25 psia.

The reactor plant characteristics are summarized in Table I.
The reactor is of the parallelepiped shape with semicircular ends.
It is built up from standard modules which have been figuratively
inserted between the cleaved halves of a circular 3000-MWt reactor. There are 76 (38 rows) complete modules with 52 incomplete modules making up the semicircular ends. The pressure
tubes are 4 inches in diameter and are 45 feet long from end to
end (see Figure 2). A central portion of about 22 feet is composed of Sintered Aluminum Product (SAP). Transition joints
connect the SAP sections to stainless steel extension tubes. Axial
support for the assembly is provided by flange-mounting the upper

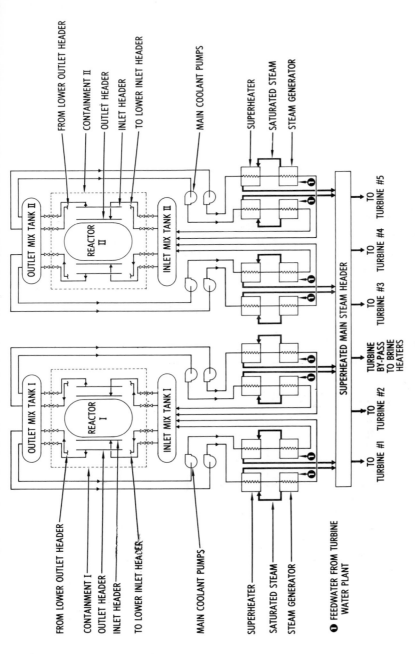

Figure 7. Nuclear Island for One Billion Gallon per Day 3400 MWe Net HWOCR Dual-Purpose Plant

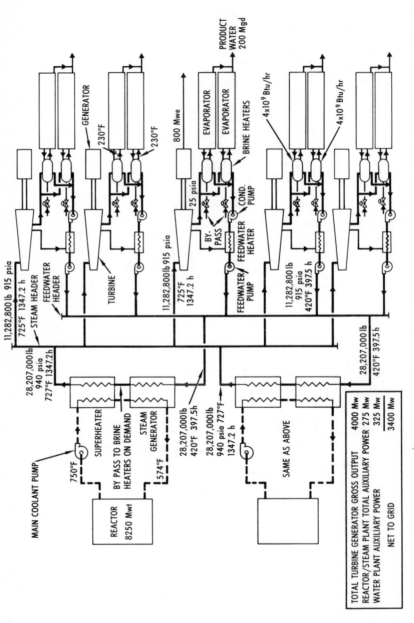

Figure 8. Heat Balance - 1 Billion Gallon per Day 3400 MWe HWOCR Dual-Purpose Plant

extension piece to the upper end shield.  The lower extension
piece, as it extends through the lower end shield, is provided with
a packed gland both for maintaining a seal and to serve as a radial
bearing.  This packed gland allows vertical expansion and contraction of the fuel channel assembly to take place with temperature cycling.  One other radial bearing is located in each of the
shields to isolate the reaction loads caused by pigtail expansion
from the thin-walled process tubes.  In addition, each extension
piece is provided with antirotational keys to resist torsion loads
from the pigtails.

The coolant flow enters and exits through pigtails which connect to a tee on the extension tubes.  Using a "tee" connection
places the connecting weld in a vertical position near the end of
the tubes, thus making it more accessible.  All of the pigtail connection nozzles are at the same relative location on the extension
pieces.

Each tube has a refueling-machine-actuated, end-closure
seal mechanism at both ends.  These closure mechanisms are
operated by a series of push-pull movements by the refueling
machines, to perform the on-power refueling functional requirements of (1) connecting, (2) disconnecting, and (3) handling and
storage.  The closure mechanism is comprised of a system of
cams, latches, and springs designed to exert a load on a metal
seal disc at the end of the tube and lock it in place.

The fuel column consists of five 43.2-inch-long fuel elements
with 43.2-inch-long spacer shields located above and below the
fuel.  A spring arrangement in the shield plugs permits changes
in the length of the fuel from thermal expansion.  In addition, this
assembly is provided with one of several standard orifices to control the flow in the channel according to its position in the reactor
core.  The orifice is replaceable for flow adjustment.

TABLE I

Reactor Plant Characteristics

| | |
|---|---|
| Thermal Rating (Mwt) | 8,250 |
| Total Number of Process Tubes | 1,424 |
| Calandria Length (ft) | 61 |
| Calandria Width (ft) | 24 |
| Process Tube Length (ft) | 45 |
| Reactor Inlet Temperature (°F) | 574 |
| Reactor Outlet Temperature (°F) | 750 |
| Coolant | Santowax OM (10% HB) |
| Number of Loops | 4 |
| Main Coolant Pump Capacity | |
| (each of four) (gpm) | 160,000 |
| Main Coolant Pump Drive Horsepower | 31,000 |
| Steam Generator Heat Transfer Area (ft$^2$) | 110,000 |

Latch assemblies mounted in the upper and lower carbon-steel extension pieces position and support the fuel column. The assemblies are spring-loaded, cam-operated devices which actuate latches by a series of coordinated movements of the refueling machines.

The calandria is 61 feet long by 24 feet wide. A reinforced concrete biological shield 6 feet thick is placed around the periphery of the moderator tank. Therefore, a reactor of this power level exclusive of headering occupies an overall space of 73 by 36 feet. The containment for each of these reactors will be 190 feet in diameter. The steam generators, superheaters, and main coolant pumps are located outside the containment in the steam generator building. (See Table I for a tabulation of reactor plant characteristics.)

Extrapolation of the HWOCR reactor concept to the 8250-Mwt size can be done with relatively modest engineering development because of the modular design approach. Special design of the calandria is required in that it becomes a flat-sided pressure vessel that must be adequately cooled without increase in heavy water inventory. The support is accomplished by providing light water-filled partitions on the exterior sides to give the calandria adequate support. Control of the reactor by a computer which utilizes approximately 75 zones of control is no more difficult than for a smaller reactor using fewer zones of control.

Vendors of process equipment indicate their capability for making pumps and heat exchangers in the size ranges listed in Table I.

The desalting plant portion is similar to the design proposed for the MWD project. The principal characteristics for this plant are noted in Table II, and its general arrangement is shown in

TABLE II

Desalting Plant Design and Performance
Characteristics

| | |
|---|---|
| Capacity (MGD) | 1000 |
| Number of Modules | 10 |
| Performance Ratio (lb/1000 Btu) | 8.7 |
| Number of Stages | 45 |
| Evaporator Surface (90-10 Cu-Ni)(ft$^2$) | 55 x 10$^6$ |
| Heater Surface (70-30 Cu-Ni)(ft$^2$) | 4.3 x 10$^6$ |
| Sea Water Flow (gpm) | 4.4 x 10$^6$ |
| Pumping Power (Mwe) | 325 |
| Top Brine Temperature (°F) | 230 |
| Sea Water Temperature (°F) | 65 |
| Concentration Factor | 2.0 |
| Heat Transfer Coefficient (Btu/hr-ft$^2$-°F) | 505-600 |
| Brine Recirculation Rate (lb/ft of stage width) | 10$^6$ |
| Tube Velocity (ft/sec) | 6.5 |
| Evaporator Structure Material | Steel |

Figure 6. The plant characteristics were derived with the aid of a digital computer program which solves the material and energy balances, "specifies" the major plant parameters, and estimates capital and production costs.

## Plant Economics

A summary of the economic analysis for this plant is shown in Table III. As mentioned earlier, the plant produces a billion gallons per day of fresh water and 3400 MWe of salable power. The annual production is predicated on the plant availability and capacity factor analysis shown in Table IV. This analysis indicates that as a result of on-line refueling, the steam supply system would be available 97 per cent of the time. After allowing for the 3 per cent loss in heat source availability, the turbine generating and desalting facilities can operate only a maximum of 94 per cent of the time. However, to allow for normal operational limitations outside the plant which limit power distribution, the average capacity factor for the turbine generating facilities was set at 90 per cent. No such considerations apply to product water distribution, hence justifying 94 per cent as the capacity factor for the desalting facilities. It should be noted from Table IV that this combination of operating factors for power and water production requires only an average capacity factor of 93 per cent for the steam supply system, which is quite plausible when compared

TABLE III

Summary of Economics

Plant Output

| | |
|---|---|
| Reactor Power (Mwt) | 2 x 8250 |
| Gross Electrical (Mwe) | 5 x 800 |
| Net Electrical (Mwe) | 3400 |
| Product Water (MGD) | 1000 |

Annual Production

| | |
|---|---|
| Electricity at 0.90 PF ($10^9$ kwh) | 27 |
| Product Water at 0.94 PF ($10^9$ gallons) | 344 |

Investments ($10^6$\$)

| | |
|---|---|
| Nuclear Steam Supply | 260 |
| Power Conversion | 170 |
| Water Plant | 500 |
| Total Depreciable Plant | 930 |
| $D_2O$ at \$20/lb and Initial Core | 120 |

Annual Cost ($10^3$\$)

| | |
|---|---|
| Depreciable Capital at 5.5% | 51,200 |
| Fuel and $D_2O$ Inventory at 3.5% | 4,200 |
| Plant Operation and Maintenance | 19,300 |
| Fuel Expense at \$8/lb $U_3O_8$ | 24,900 |
| Total | 99,600 |

TABLE IV

Plant Availability Analysis

|  | % Outage | % Availability | % Capacity Factor |
|---|---|---|---|
| Reactor Refueling (on-line) | 0 | | |
| Steam Supply--Unscheduled | 1 | | |
| Steam Supply--Scheduled | 2 | | |
| Total Steam Supply | 3 | 97 | 93 |
| T-G Plant--Unscheduled | 1 | | |
| Turbine Overhaul* | 2 | | |
| Total Electricity Supply | 6 | 94 | 90 |
| Desalting Plant--Unscheduled | 2 | | |
| Desalting Plant--Scheduled* | 1 | | |
| Total Desalting Plant | 6 | 94 | 94 |

*These are incremental to steam supply scheduled outage since they can be programmed as concurrent operations.

with the estimated availability of 97 per cent. It should be evident that the above favorable operating factors stem directly from the on-line refueling capability of the HWOCR. This increased availability from such capability is clearly demonstrated from published statistics of on-line fueled British reactors.

The total investment for the plant is estimated at $1050 million of which about $120 million represent nondepreciable capital for heavy water and fuel inventories. This investment is exclusive of the costs of land, power distribution and water conveyance facilities.

The total cost to own and operate the plant, namely the annual production cost, is estimated at about $100 million. The assumed capital fixed-charge rates of 5.5 per cent against depreciable capital and 3.5 per cent against nondepreciable capital are those assumed for the MWD project. It should be noted that even at these low fixed-charge rates, capital charges account for more than half of the total production cost.

The plant operation and maintenance costs include $7.8 x $10^6$ for the energy plant portion and $11.5 x $10^6$ for the water plant portion. The energy plant's operation and maintenance cost portion includes $2 x $10^6$ for nuclear insurance, $1.2 x $10^6$ for heavy water and organic makeup, $3.5 x $10^6$ for maintenance supplies, and $1.1 x $10^6$ for personnel. Organic makeup costs are minimized through the use of a coolant recovery unit which converts the high-molecular compounds in the organic coolant back to useful coolant. The feasibility of the process has been established, and work is currently in progress for the installation of such a unit at the Piqua plant.  The water plant operation and maintenance cost portion includes \$5 x 10$^6$ for maintenance materials and interim replacements, \$1 x 10$^6$ for personnel, and \$5.5 x 10$^6$ for chemical treatment.  The latter is based on studies by ORNL for on-site production of sulphuric acid.

The fuel replacement cost is estimated at 5.5 cents per million Btu based on \$8/lb ore cost, \$25/kg separative work cost, and a fissile plutonium value of \$9/gm.  These assumptions reflect conditions anticipated during the early years of plant operation around 1980.  Fuel cycle cost levels for later years would depend primarily on the relative changes in plutonium market value and uranium ore prices.  Successful development of fast breeders will increase the relative plutonium value, whereas rapidly increasing ore demand anticipated after 1990 will cause ore prices to rise.  Both of these trends favor the HWOCR because of its excellent neutron economy, thereby improving its fueling cost advantage compared to light-water reactors.  This would assure base-load operation for the plant during later years.

The two products of a dual-purpose plant are fresh water and electricity, with the cost of water depending on the market value for power.  Since this value depends on many factors relating to the nature and location of this power market, it is impossible to predict a specific cost for water at this time.  The cost relationship between these two products which provides the necessary revenue to cover all production costs can be determined as shown in Figure 9.  This figure shows, for example, that if power can be sold at the busbar for 2.0 mills/kwh, then the cost of water at the site boundary will be about 13 cents per 1000 gal.  Conversely, if water is valued at 10 cents per 1000 gal, a marginally useful cost for agriculture, then the cost of power is about 2.4 mills/kwh. It appears from this analysis that with further anticipated improvements in desalting technology and with the depletion of low-cost water sources, water produced from future large HWOCR dual-purpose plants could indeed be justified for agricultural use.

## CONCLUSION

Development of the HWOCR concept is proceeding on schedule. Avenues of approach being used to solve the problems in this development are leading toward successful results.  All areas of investigation are providing positive answers which make it appear reasonable to plan for early construction of a demonstration plant.

The studies done to date indicate the practicability of extrapolating the HWOCR plant to very large sizes.

The economic analysis confirms earlier studies[4] on the potential economic attractiveness of the HWOCR to large-scale, dual-purpose applications.  This economic attractiveness stems from the HWOCR's inherent design and operating features such as low fuel cycle costs, on-line refueling capability, and ease of extrapolation to very large sizes.

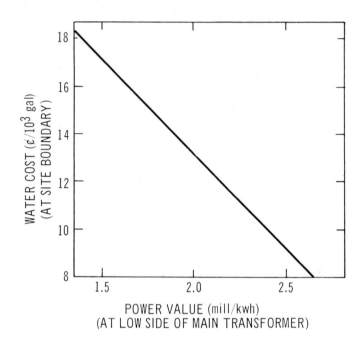

Figure 9.   Cost of Water Versus Power Value


## NOTES


1.   Water Desalination Report, Vol. II, No. 9 (March 9, 1966).

2.   Engineering and Economic Feasibility Study for a Combination Nuclear Power and Desalting Plant prepared by Bechtel; TID-22300.

3.   Study of Large Desalting Plant for Israel:  Nathan Arad; presented as paper No. SWD/49 at the First International Symposium on Water Desalination, Washington, D. C. (October 3-9, 1965).

4.   Application of Nuclear Energy to Large Scale Power and Desalting Plants, by Messrs. Siegel, Golan, and Falcon; Proceedings of American Power Conference, 27th Annual Meeting, Volume XXVII (1965).

# 20. Fast Breeder Reactors[*]

P. F. Gast and L. E. Link, Reactor Physics Division, Argonne National Laboratory

Early interest in fast reactors was generated by their ability to breed. At the present time, fast breeders have already acquired a considerable development history whose description is outside the scope of this paper. However, one significant event in that history was the preparation of four design studies of a 1000-MWe ceramic-fueled fast breeder reactor with sodium cooling. [1, 2, 3, 4] These studies were published in January 1964 and have furnished base points for recent studies of the use of liquid-metal-cooled, fast breeder reactors, LMFBR's, in desalting applications.

Current interest in breeders continues to be based to a large degree on their ability to produce more fissile material than they consume. A number of studies [5, 6, 7, 8, 9] have indicated that supplies of low cost uranium ore would eventually be exhausted if the projected growth in nuclear power capacity in the United States were satisfied entirely with converter reactors, with a consequent decline in the competitive position of nuclear power as compared with fossil fuels. Although this crisis lies a considerable number of years in the future, breeder reactors will be of aid in avoiding it only if they begin to form an important part of the total nuclear power capacity at dates considerably in advance of the arrival of the crisis itself. Such reactors will have to compete in the economic field with current and advanced types of converter reactors at a time when the price of fissile material will not be higher than it is today and may perhaps be lower.

The breeder reactor does hold the promise of certain economic advantages which would enable it to successfully compete even under those postulated conditions and the research and development program of the USAEC has the objective of reducing these potential advantages to practice.

Those factors which promise to make the fast breeder reactor a good energy source for electric power production will also make it a good energy source for dual purpose plants producing electric power and desalted water by an evaporative process. It would, of course, also be directly applicable to those advanced types of desalting process which use either electrical or mechanical power directly.

*Work performed under the auspices of the U. S. Atomic Energy Commission.

A meaningful economic comparison between a selected breeder design and, for example, a light-water converter reactor is precluded at the present time by the great difference in the state of technological development of the two reactor types. In this paper we intend rather to discuss those reasons for believing that such a comparison, when it could be meaningfully made, sometime in the future, would turn out favorable to the fast breeder. We will also describe some current fast reactor design concepts, the important problems faced by designers, the current status of the development program, and possible solutions to some of the outstanding design problems.

## POTENTIAL ADVANTAGES

An important potential advantage of the breeding process is the greatly extended reactivity lifetime of the fuel. Fuel exposures in breeder reactors will be limited only by the physical stamina of the fuel element, and there is reasonable expectation of life-times in excess of 100, 000 MWD/ton. In converter reactors, on the other hand, increased fuel lifetime requires increased initial enrichment of the fuel. For example, studies at the Pacific Northwest Laboratory of Battelle[10] have indicated that, in a boiling water reactor, minimum fuel cost would be obtained with exposures between 25 and 30, 000 MWD/ton and that for a representative set of conditions the fuel cost would be 2 mills/kwh with private utility financing or 1. 7 mills/kwh with municipal financing. In fast breeders, estimated fuel costs can be obtained from the results of the 1000 MWe studies and their more recent revisions. A comparative analysis of these results[11] gives fuel costs ranging from 0. 3 to 1. 0 mills/kwh in various designs under private financing conditions or costs of 0. 3 to 0. 8 mills/kwh with municipal financing.

An important factor in the variations between designs is the nuclear performance. This is also the main factor in determining the merit of a design as a conservator of fissile material. The use of doubling time as a figure of merit for the nuclear performance of breeders has achieved wide popularity. However, it is possible to obtain more directly interpretable measures of nuclear performance rather simply. As an illustrative example of the disadvantage of use of doubling time alone, we mention the case of two breeder designs each of the same power output and each having the same doubling time, but in which one has a significantly larger inventory than the other. From the conservation standpoint, an electric power system containing the second type of reactor will require a larger investment of fissile material in order to attain the self-sustaining growth stage. From the standpoint of the individual reactor operator the larger investment in plutonium inventory represents a greater amount of capital at risk in the event of a change in plutonium price during the reactor's lifetime.

As an economic measure of nuclear performance, we prefer to use simply the plutonium cost, which is the cost of carrying the plutonium inventory minus the returns realized from the sale of excess plutonium produced. Figure 1 presents a contour plot of these costs as a function of the specific inventory, that is, the kilograms of fissile plutonium per megawatt electric, and a generalized breeding gain. This is the breeding gain referred to unit energy output by taking account of the fact that some fissile material is destroyed without producing fission and also that some some fissions are produced in fertile material. The breeding gain may also be corrected for losses of plutonium in the reprocessing and refabrication cycle. The solid lines in Figure 1 were obtained using a price of $10/gram of fissile plutonium and a 10 per cent annual charge on working capital. Three representative breeder designs are plotted on the figure. In plotting the points we have used an estimated system inventory including material

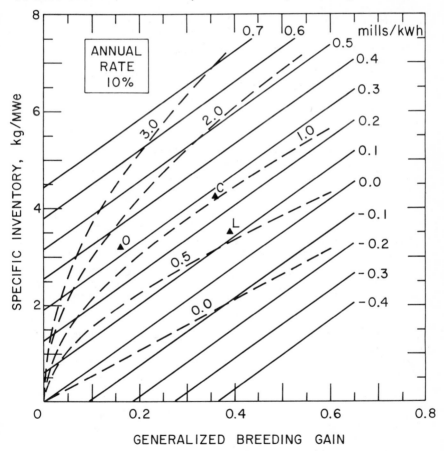

Figure 1. Nuclear Performance from Economic Standpoint

in the reactor and in the reprocessing and fabrication pipeline supporting the reactor. Cost figures obtained will therefore be somewhat different from those given elsewhere[11] since inventory charges during reprocessing and fabrication are normally included as a component of the cost for those particular steps in the fuel cycle. The three designs plotted are: an oxide-fueled reactor of 1000 MWe capacity and of a conservative design from a safety standpoint (O); a carbide-fueled reactor of the same capacity and a somewhat more optimistic design (C); and a large reactor of 10,000 MWt capacity designed expressly as an energy source for desalting application (L).

To obtain a quantitative measure of the conservation merit of breeder designs, the plutonium which must be supplied to a postulated growing breeder reactor system until it becomes self-sustaining has been computed.[12] Contours of equal conservation merit are shown as dashed lines in the figure. The parameters labeling the dashed curves are the plutonium requirements in arbitrary units. Thus, a smaller number indicates a better conservation performance. It will be seen that for moderate and high breeding gains there is a general correspondence between economics and conservation; but that for reactors designed with small breeding gains conservation performance will be poorer even if the specific power is increased so as to remain economically competitive with higher breeding designs, under present price conditions.

Figure 2 is representative of the situation which would exist with municipal financing in which the annual charge on working capital might be 5 per cent. Here a much larger improvement in specific power is required from an economic standpoint to offset a decreasing breeding gain. However, reactor designs able to achieve such an increase will also rank high from a conservation standpoint. Note also that the O and C reactors which had comparable plutonium costs in Figure 1 now have a difference of about 0.1 mills/kwh. In the medium and high breeding gain range, designs with equal plutonium costs may have considerably different conservation merit. In this economic situation, conservation merit then becomes a separate factor to be considered in design choices.

Costs of fuel fabrication and chemical reprocessing make an important contribution to the total fuel cycle costs. However, they do not usually enter strongly into economic choice between designs since they fall within a rather narrow range. This is a reflection of the fact that, in the present state of technology, fuel designs tend to fall within a rather narrow range of dimensions, to use similar cladding materials, and to make the same assumptions with respect to reprocessing and fabrication process costs.

There is understandably a paucity of information on the capital costs of large fast-breeder reactors. Cohen and O'Neill[13] have estimated a cost of $125/kw for a sodium-cooled breeder of 1000 MWe capacity. This is a penalty of perhaps $25/kw as compared with a boiling-water reactor of the same capacity. On the other hand, Amorosi[14] has estimated that for sizes in excess of perhaps 500 MWe the sodium-cooled fast reactor should be no more expensive than a pressurized water reactor. Studies at ORNL, discussed later in this paper, indicate about $115/kw for a 1000 MWe plant.[29, 30] Twenty-five dollars per kilowatt represents a penalty of 1/2 mill/kwh with private financing and about half that much with public financing, which when combined with the fuel cost advantages leaves an interesting competitive margin of better than 1/2 mill/kwh in favor of the fast breeder reactor. If expectations of lower uranium ore and enrichment costs are realized, then fuel costs at the lower end of the range of estimates would be needed to achieve this competitive advantage.

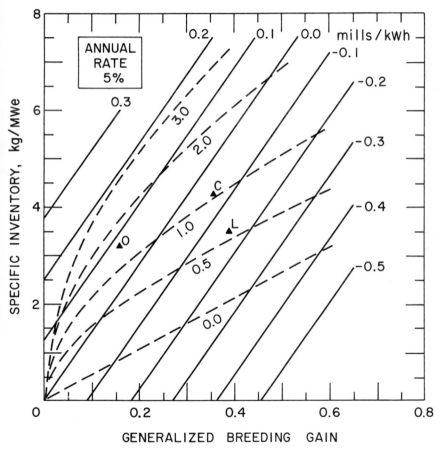

Figure 2.   Comparative Requirements Under 5 per cent Municipal Financing

These potential economic advantages were reflected in the results of the study sponsored by the Office of Science and Technology, [15] which concluded that large dual purpose desalting plants postulated for construction in 1980 could produce water and power at somewhat lower costs when powered by fast breeders than when powered by reactors of other types.

## FAST REACTOR DESIGN CONCEPTS

Sodium, [16] gas, [17, 18] and steam [19, 20] are being considered as fast reactor coolants. The program of the USAEC has placed heavy emphasis on sodium because of its excellent characteristics as a heat transfer medium. To date, published studies of fast breeders for desalting application have been confined to those using sodium as a coolant. Correspondingly the remainder of this paper will confine itself to sodium-cooled designs.

In the design of large sodium-cooled reactors fueled with plutonium and uranium the reactivity behavior in the event of sodium boiling is a paramount consideration. A reactivity increase results from the hardening of the neutron spectrum when sodium atoms are expelled. In small reactors this increase is less than the reactivity drop due to increased leakage, resulting in a net negative effect. In large reactors, however, some special design features must be employed to obtain sufficient leakage to hold the net sodium voiding effect within workable bounds. Unfortunately, these special features may reduce the breeding gain and in some cases may also adversely affect the average specific power. Thus designs of large fast breeders are compromises between these conflicting requirements.

Approaches that have been taken to this design problem are given below. Figure 3 shows a large thin-core design extensively studied by the General Electric Company. [13] In this design, usually called a pancake core, the small vertical dimension is used to enhance core leakage. In the General Electric version of this design, beryllium has also been introduced into the core at selected fuel locations in order to soften the neutron spectrum. This produces an enhanced Doppler effect which is available to compensate accidentally added reactivity and its permanent presence reduces the magnitude of the spectral hardening attendant upon the sodium loss.

In Figure 4, core leakage is enhanced by dividing the total core volume among a number of small modules, each surrounded by its own breeding blanket and separated from the other modules by a graphite reflector. In this particular version, studied by Westinghouse, the core consists of seven modules. The modular approach has also been used in designs by Atomics International [21] and by ANL. [22]

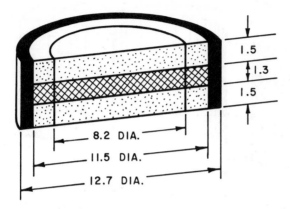

Figure 3.   Thin Core Design by General Electric

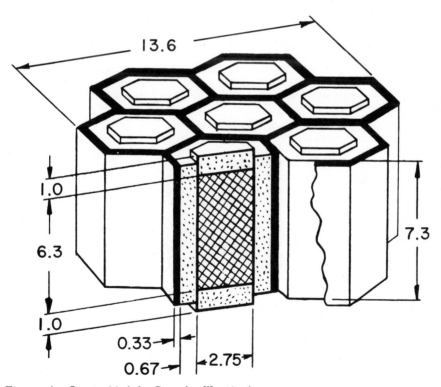

Figure 4.   Seven-Module Core by Westinghouse

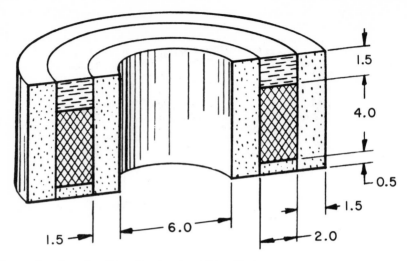

Figure 5.   Annular Ring Design by Allis-Chalmers

In the design shown in Figure 5, the enhanced leakage is achieved by forming the core into a thin annular ring surrounded by breeding blankets.  Each of these concepts has its own particular advantages and disadvantages and at the present stage no one of them can be designated as the leading contender.  The reader is in fact invited to speculate on other core shapes which might achieve the same ends.

Another approach to making sodium void effects more negative has recently been explored by Loewenstein and Blumenthal.[23] In U-233-Th fueled fast breeders, calculated sodium-voiding effects are generally more negative than for corresponding Pu-U-238 systems.  Thus, use of U-233-Th fuel in the neutronically important central region of a fast breeder core can produce a considerable effect, in the negative direction, on the reactivity change resulting from sodium removal.  Some penalty in the form of decreased breeding gain would result, but nuclear performance may be better than that in single fuel designs having comparable voiding effects.

In the area of fuel materials, significant development work has been done on oxides, carbides, and metals.  More information is currently available about the behavior of the oxides because of the extensive successful experience with this material as a thermal reactor fuel.  The carbides are of interest because of their higher density and thermal conductivity.  Developmental samples of oxide and carbide fuels have attained exposures of 100,000 MWD/ton.  However, demonstration of consistent reliable attainment of this exposure in practical fuels remains for the future. Recent irradiation experience[24] has demonstrated that metallic fuels with reasonable fuel element designs can be considered seriously for burnups up to 10 atom%. Nitrides, sulphides, and phosphides are also receiving consideration as possible fuel materials but relatively less information is presently available about their preparation and behavior.

The technical feasibility of constructing and operating a sodium-cooled power plant system is now being demonstrated by the operation of EBR-II and the Fermi plant. In a recent review, Goldman and Minushkin[25] state that sodium technology has been developed sufficiently to permit the design of coolant systems whose reliable operation can be assured at temperatures up to 1000°F. Serious failures and operating difficulties have occurred in the reactors which have been built and operated, but the speed with which they have been overcome has indicated an encouragingly advanced state of development. For the interested reader, Goldman and Minushkin present an extensive list of references to publications in this area.

The development of the technology required for future sodium systems to operate at temperatures of 1200 to 1400°F is under way. Additional work is projected in the area of sodium pumps, large valves, large piping installations, and basic mechanisms for sodium service.

In the safety area, studies analyzing postulated nuclear accidents of various types have been conducted by Atomics International,[21] General Electric,[13] and Westinghouse.[26, 27] It is possible to imagine sets of circumstances which could lead to very large reactivity additions. For example, one such chain is: loss of coolant flow to the entire core with simultaneous failure of the safety control system; voiding of the sodium from the core; then fuel meltdown and core compaction. Calculated energy releases for accidents of this extreme type run from a few hundred to a few thousand megawatt seconds, depending upon assumptions as to the details of initiation and the course of events during the accident. At the present time more information is needed about the rates of sodium ejection that might conceivably be achieved in flow stoppage accidents.

## 10,000 MWt STUDY

The Argonne National Laboratory has recently completed, at the request of the Oak Ridge National Laboratory, a feasibility study of a nuclear steam supply system utilizing a very large sodium-cooled fast-breeder reactor. The secondary sodium circuit and steam generator design was subcontracted to Westinghouse Electric Corporation.[28] According to the ground rules adopted for the study, steam conditions were to be chosen on the basis of power only production. However, the electrical generating equipment was outside of the scope of the study. The study used as a starting point the 1000 MWe designs previously mentioned.

The approach used was to make a conceptual design and based on this design to make a feasibility determination. Because of the limited scope of the study in time and manpower, it was not possible to strive for optimization. Fuel cycle costs were estimated as a guide in core design but selection of design conditions, materials, and components was based on engineering judgment. Emphasis was placed on those aspects of the system which might cause some limitations on extrapolation to larger sizes. Some items which would be required in a complete design were not covered, either due to apparent insignificance, or because it was expected that they would become standardly available as the result of development of 1000 MWe plant designs. As a basic ground rule it was assumed that commercially competitive 1000 MWe designs existed at the time of design of this very large plant. The date for construction of the 10,000 MW plant was therefore assumed to be after 1980. Table I presents a summary of the design characteristics.

The neutronic and thermal designs of the reactor were closely linked. The thermal design was based on reasonable expectations for fuel development to satisfy the required thermal performance. The neutronic design was based on holding the sodium-voiding effect within workable bounds while achieving a satisfactory breeding ratio. An annular shape was chosen for the reactor, as shown if Figure 6. The mean core diameter is about 22 feet. The core fuel is uranium-plutonium carbide; the clad is 304 SS with helium bonding. Axial blankets also are uranium carbide while the radial blankets utilize a uranium zirconium alloy also clad in 304 SS. Control of the reactor is achieved by 84 poison rods whose drives are mounted on the reactor vessel cover.

Figure 7 shows the reactor arrangement. The reactor is contained in a cylindrical vessel with sodium inlet and outlet lines entering above the reactor core level, thus preventing accidental

TABLE I

Very Large Fast Breeder Summary Data

| | |
|---|---|
| Gross Reactor Power | 10,000 MW |
| Net Plant Output (power only) | 3,880 MWe |
| Sodium Inlet Temperature | 720°F |
| Sodium Outlet Temperature | 1050°F |
| Steam Pressure | 2400 psia |
| Steam Temperature | 900°F |
| Type of Fuel in the Core | (U + Pu)C |
| Type of Core | Annular |
| Volume of Core | 16,700 liters |
| Reactor Fissile Pu Weight | 10,500 Kg |
| Reactor Breeding Ratio | 1.4 |
| Fissile Material Doubling Time | 7 years |
| Linear Heat Rate (avg) | 16.8 Kw/ft |
| Core Burnup (avg) | 110,000 MWD/MT |
| Interval Between Refuelings | 1/2 yr |
| Equilibrium Fuel Cycle Cost | 1/4 mill/KwHr |

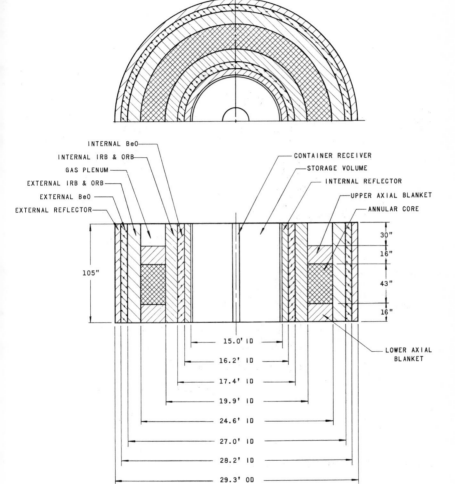

Figure 6.  Simplified Reactor Section

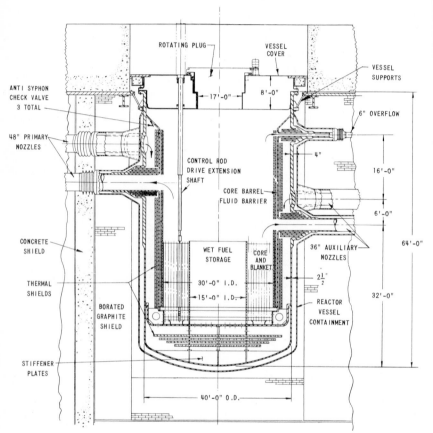

Figure 7.   Reactor Vessel Assembly

draining of the vessel. The 14-foot diameter region interior of the inner radial reflector provides a space for storage of irradiated and fresh fuel. Figure 8 shows this arrangement in perspective. Recharging is accomplished by a mechanism having a radial arm operating through a rotating plug in the vessel cover. Fuel is transferred in either direction between the reactor and the storage area with the reactor shut down. After reactor operation is resumed irradiated fuel subassemblies are removed from storage through the rotating plug and placed in a transfer cask for shipment to a processing plant. The storage area is then replenished with fresh fuel for the next recharging cycle.

The location and arrangement of the reactor and other primary loop components within the containment vessel is shown in Figure 9. The reactor coolant circulates in six primary loops, each containing a 140,000 gpm pump and an intermediate sodium-sodium heat exchanger. Intermediate sodium loops transfer the heat to six once-through steam generators located in three buildings outside the containment sphere. The steam generators use Incoloy 800 tube material and supply steam at the throttle of 2400 pounds 900°F. Live steam reheat to 660°F is used rather than a sodium reheat cycle. Steam is delivered to three sets of turbine generators in the turbine hall as shown in Figure 10.

Safety problems faced in the design are basically the same as those encountered in the design of a 1000 MWe reactor. A negative power coefficient of reactivity provides stability during normal operation. The design adopted makes incredible the total loss of sodium from the reactor. Containment of the reactor and the six primary loops is provided by a 240-foot diameter spherical shell which also contains an emergency shutdown cooling loop.

Fuel cycle costs were estimated in order to aid in the development of the design. With a 90 per cent annual plant factor, 5 per cent charge on working capital, and $10/gram fissile plutonium, the fuel cycle cost is 1/4 of a mill/kwh. No complete capital cost estimate was made. However, certain equipment items were costed on an installed basis. Sodium to sodium heat exchanger, secondary sodium pumps and drives, secondary sodium piping, and steam generators were estimated at $10 to $12 per net kwe. A brief analysis of the refueling operation indicated that the plant availability as limited by refueling is 95 per cent.

In the future more detailed examinations of very large fast reactors may result in a more suitable selection of design conditions, that is, those which give a lower energy cost. Such examinations may modify the following conclusions but will probably cause no significant changes. These conclusions are:

1. The 10,000 MWt sodium-cooled fast-breeder reactor is feasible within the context of the ground rules of the

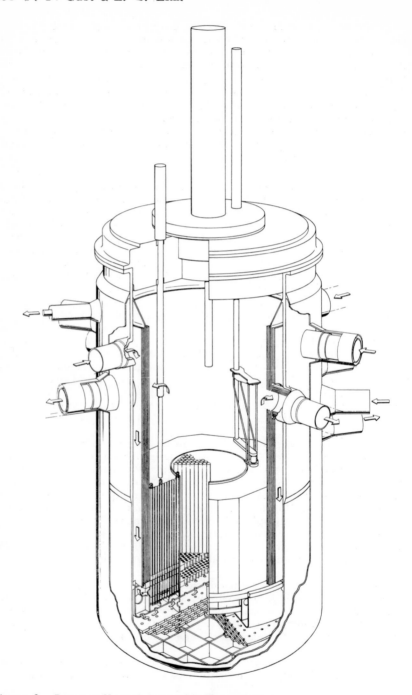

Figure 8.   Reactor Vessel Assembly Perspective

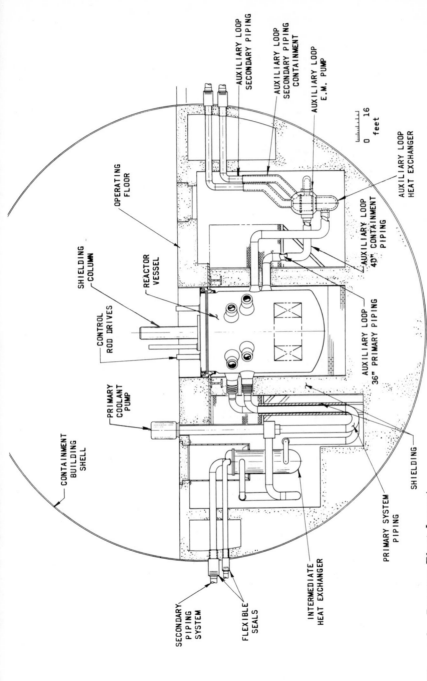

Figure 9. Reactor Plant Layout

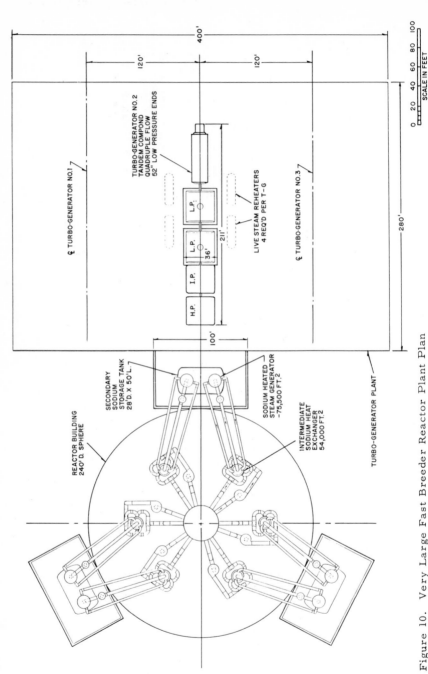

Figure 10. Very Large Fast Breeder Reactor Plant Plan

REACTOR BUILDING
240' D. SPHERE

SECONDARY
SODIUM
STORAGE TANK
28' D. X 50' L.

SODIUM HEATED
STEAM GENERATOR
~75,500 FT.²

INTERMEDIATE
SODIUM HEAT
EXCHANGER
54,000 FT.²

TURBO-GENERATOR PLANT

℄ TURBO-GENERATOR NO. 1

TURBO-GENERATOR NO. 2
TANDEM COMPOND
QUADRUPLE FLOW
52" LOW PRESSURE ENDS

LIVE STEAM REHEATERS
4 REQ'D PER T-G

℄ TURBO-GENERATOR NO. 3

H.P.  I.P.  L.P.  L.P.

36'
21'

400'
120'
120'
280'
100'

0  20  40  60  80  100
SCALE IN FEET

study. The equipment sizes and duties are not excessive by comparison to the probable requirements of 1000 MWe designs. Although no complete capital costs were estimated, it seems likely that some normal type scaling law for the influence of size on sodium-cooled fast breeder costs would apply. However, no knowledge of scaling effects was gained from the study.

2. Fuel performance for this concept is in line with other fast breeder studies using carbide fuel, considering the estimated fuel cycle cost and doubling time.

3. Successful development of fast breeders of 1000 MWe size will provide the technological base for very large fast breeders with no major further R&D program required.

## FAST BREEDERS WITH LOWER TEMPERATURE

In situations where a large quantity of low-cost heat is required for desalination, and the need for power is relatively low, the high temperature characteristics of a high efficiency electric power production system may have less economic importance. Also, lower design temperatures for the reactor and the primary sodium coolant system give rise to a number of advantages. Temperature restrictions on the cladding and fuel performance are reduced. The sodium operates at a greater distance below its boiling temperature and, in accident situations, more negative reactivity is available from the Doppler effect between operating temperature and fuel melting temperature. Lower operating temperatures also permit use of lower cost equipment in the reactor systems, and development problems associated with proving component reliability in the 1000 to 1200°F range are bypassed. Prompted by these considerations, Olson, Carlsmith and Hoskins at ORNL[29, 30] have investigated the design features and economics of a low temperature sodium-cooled fast breeder reactor for desalting applications. A reactor power of 3500 MWt was chosen. The reactor consisted of 12 modules with stainless steel clad oxide fuel for the cores and stainless steel clad metal in the radial blankets. The average coolant temperature at the reactor outlet was 800°F. Table II provides a brief summary of other reactor characteristics.

The reactor was incorporated as a heat source in four types of plants: 1) a process heat only plant producing heat as steam at 260°F; 2) a plant producing process heat and 230 MW of electric power for internal consumption only; 3) a dual purpose plant producing process heat and 420 MW of excess electric power for sale; and 4) a central station power plant producing 1000 MW of Electric power. According to the accompanying cost analysis, the dual purpose plant could produce process heat at a cost of 4.7¢/ million Btu at the brine heater, whereas the cost was twice that much for the water-only plant. As is usual in these studies, the revenue from power sold from the dual purpose plant was determined by the cost of power produced by the power-only plant. It is interesting to note that with municipal financing the cost of power produced by the power-only plant was no higher than the cost from a sodium-cooled fast breeder reactor plant operating at a reactor outlet temperature of 1200°F.

In the water-only plant, the 260°F steam was produced directly from the 800°F sodium coolant. In a plant designed specifically for this type of operation it would be possible to go to still lower reactor temperatures and a heat cost of less than 9¢/ million Btu might then be achievable.

## CONCLUSIONS

From this review of fast breeder reactors in a desalting context, it is concluded that:

1.  The potential economic advantages of fast breeder reactors as heat sources for central station power plants extend also to their use as heat sources in dual purpose, water and power production plants.

2.  The planned AEC development program for fast breeder reactors is expected to provide the technology for building such plants in sizes up to 2500 MWt by the 1980's.

3.  Following upon the successful completion of such a program one might expect that still larger sodium-cooled fast breeder reactors would come about as an evolutionary process and that nuclear power plants utilizing such

TABLE II

Low Temperature Fast Breeder Summary Data

| | |
|---|---|
| Gross Reactor Power | 3,500 MW |
| Net Plant Output, Power Only | 1081 MWe |
| Sodium Inlet Temperature | 500°F |
| Sodium Outlet Temperature | 800°F |
| Steam Pressure, power and dual purpose | 700 psig |
| Steam Temperature, power and dual purpose | 495°F |
| Type of Fuel in Core | $(U + Pu)O_2$ |
| Type of Core | Modular |
| Fissile Specific Power | 565 kw/kg |
| Volume of Core | 9,300 liters |
| Reactor Breeding Ratio | 1.59 |
| Maximum Linear Heat Rate | 17.3 kw/ft |
| Core Burnup (avg) | 100,000 MWD/T |

reactors will be available when electrical systems can accommodate the output.

4. Fast breeder reactors also merit consideration as energy sources in plants having low power-to-water ratios. Low temperature design may permit capital cost reductions which, when combined with low fuel cost, would make them competitive with more traditionally low temperature energy sources.

## NOTES

1. Allis-Chalmers Mfg. Co., Atomic Energy Division, Milwaukee; Atomic Power Development Associates, Inc., Detroit; and Babcock and Wilcox Co., Atomic Energy Division, Lynchburg, Va. "Large Fast Reactor Design Study," ACNP -64503, Jan. 1964.

2. Combustion Engineering, Inc., Nuclear Division, "Liquid Metal Fast Breeder Reactor Design Study," CEND-200, Jan. 1964.

3. General Electric Co., "Liquid Metal Fast Breeder Reactor Design Study," GEAP-4418, Jan. 1964.

4. Steck, R. B. (Comp.), "Liquid Metal Fast Breeder Reactor Design Study, Final Report," WCAP-3251-1, Westinghouse Electric Corporation, Jan. 1964.

5. Faulkner, R. L., and McVey, W. H., "Fuel Resources and Availability for Civilian Nuclear Power, 1964-2000," 1964 Geneva Conference P/256.

6. Dietrich, J. R., "Efficient Utilization of Nuclear Fuels," Power Reactor Technology 6, No. 4, 1-53, 1963.

7. Young, Gale, "The Fueling of Nuclear Power Complexes," Nuclear News 7, No. 11, 23-30, Nov. 1964.

8. Smith, E. E., and Wright, J. H., "Future Energy Needs and Nuclear Fuel Use," Atomics 18, No. 3, 22-26, May/June, 1965.

9. Class, H., "Uranium Resources," Nuclear Engineering 10, 415, Nov. 1965.

10. Deonigi, D. E., Horton, P. A., and McConiga, A. F., "Minimized Fuel Cycle Cost for a Simulated Boiling Water Reactor, Part I," AEC Report BNWL-105, April 1965.

11.  Pursel, C. A. , and Link, L. E. , "1000 MWe Sodium Cooled Fast Breeder Reactor Studies, " Proceedings Fast Breeder Reactors Conf. , London, May 17-19, 1966, sponsored by Brit. Nuc. Eng. Soc.

12.  Gast, P. F. , "Evaluation of Breeders from a Conservation Standpoint, " ANS Transactions 7, 530, Nov. 1964.

13.  Cohen, K. P. , and O'Neill, G. L. , "Safety and Economic Characteristics of a 1000 MWe Fast Sodium-Cooled Reactor Design, " in Proceedings of Conference on Safety, Fuels, and Core Design in Large Fast Power Reactors, Argonne National Laboratory, Oct. 11-14, 1965.

14.  Amorosi, A. , Private Communication, Jan. 10, 1966.

15.  "An Assessment of Large Nuclear Powered Sea Water Distillation Plants, " a report of an Interagency Task Group, Office of Science and Technology, March 1964.

16.  Literature on sodium cooled fast reactors is voluminous. c. f. reference 11 for a recent summary. Also, Proceedings of Conference on Safety, Fuels, and Core Design in Large Fast Power Reactors, Argonne National Laboratory, Oct. 11-14, 1965, for recent individual design reports. Hereafter referred to as Proc. S. F. and C. D.

17.  Fortescue, P. , et al. , "Safety Considerations and Characteristics of Large Gas-Cooled Fast Power Reactors, " in Proc. S. F. and C. D.

18.  Dalle-Donne, M. , "Comparison of He, $CO_2$, and Steam as Coolants of a 1000 MWe Fast Reactor in Proc. S. F. and C. D.

19.  Kiefhaber, E. , and Ott, K. , "Survey Parameter Study of Large Steam-Cooled Fast Power Reactors, " in Proc. S. F. and C. D.

20.  Webb, R. , and Schluderberg, D. , "Steam Cooling for Fast Reactors, " in Proc. S. F. and C. D.

21.  Eggen, D. T. , et al. , "Feasibility Study of a 1000 MWe Sodium Cooled Fast Reactor, " NAA-SR-11378, Atomics International, June 1965.

22.  Link, L. E. , et al. , "A Large Metal-Fuel Fast Reactor Study, " in Proc. S. F. and C. D.

23.  Loewenstein, W. B. , and Blumenthal, B. , "Mised Fuel Cycle Fast Breeder Reactors, Nuclear, Safety, and Materials Considerations, " in Proc. S. F. and C. D.

24.  Machery, R. E., et al., "Metal Fuels for Fast Reactors," in Proc. S. F. and C. D.

25.  Goldman, K., and Minushkin, B., "Sodium Technology," in Reactor Technology, Selected Reviews-1965, L. E. Link (Ed.), pp. 321-425.

26.  Wright, J. A., et al., "Conceptual Design and Prelimi-nary Accident Analysis of a Sodium Cooled, Carbide Fueled Large Modular Fast Reactor," in Proc. S. F. and C. D.

27.  Gunson, W. E., et al., "Transient Response of Coupled Fast Reactor Cores," in Proc. S. F. and C. D.

28.  Gast, P. F., and Hub, K. A. (Eds.), "Feasibility Study of Nuclear Steam Supply System using 10, 000 MW Sodium Cooled Breeder Reactor," ANL-7183, Jan. 1966.

29.  Olson, R. C., Carlsmith, R. S., and Hoskins, R. E., "A 3500 MWt Low Temperature Sodium Cooled Fast Breed-er Reactor for Desalination," ORNL-TM-1143, June 10, 1965.

30.  Carlsmith, R. S., Olson, R. C., and Hoskins, R. E., "Use of Low-Temperature Fast Reactors for Desalination or Power," ANS Transactions, 8, 157, June 1965.

# 21. High-Temperature Gas-Cooled Reactors
## For Large Dual-Purpose Plants*

T. A. Johnston and R. B. Minogue, General Atomic Division of General Dynamics

A major factor in maintaining rapid economic growth in the United States and, indeed, in all nations, is an adequate supply of fresh water. In recent years, an increasing amount of effort has been devoted to general studies of the many alternate methods of augmenting natural supplies to meet these requirements. The results of this work clearly indicate that even with the present state of the art, the production of fresh water by the distillation of sea water can be effectively coupled with power generation in large nuclear dual purpose plants at costs which are economically competitive with other sources in many situations.

While it is possible to identify the promise of large nuclear dual purpose plants, it is not possible at this juncture to make a specific judgment as to the particular class or classes of reactors most attractive for this application principally because experience on such plants is lacking. It is possible, however, to list the basic features which should characterize a reactor well-suited to this application.

In large nuclear dual purpose plants, the four major water production cost components normally identified are the water plant capital investment, on-site pumping power, operating and maintenance costs and the steam charge. Of these four items, only the steam charge and the pumping power charge have a first order dependence upon the characteristics of the reactor. Since the cost of steam generally represents between 30-40 per cent of the total cost, any significant reduction in this area is important. The electrical pumping power cost, since it generally represents 10 per cent or less of the total charge, is of lesser importance. Thus, it can be reasoned that to be attractive, the nuclear system should have basic features which tend to minimize both the capital and operating portions of the steam charge over plant lifetime without compromising electric power production costs. These features would include:

* This work was supported in part by the U.S. Atomic Energy Commission under Subcontract No. 2543, Prime Contract W-7905 -eng-26 for the Nuclear Division of Union Carbide Corporation, Oak Ridge, Tennessee.

1.  Extensibility to large single unit sizes with a corresponding reduction in unit capital cost.

2.  Low fuel cycle costs and fuel cycle cost stability.

Obviously, a number of other secondary factors such as the product balance, siting requirements, etc., are also of interest, particularly where a specific project is involved; however, it is believed that the above features are generally those of greatest importance.

In this paper, we would like to discuss each of the above in relation to the High Temperature Gas-Cooled Reactor (HTGR).


## HTGR SYSTEM

The HTGR is an advanced converter reactor characterized by helium gas as the primary coolant, graphite as the neutron moderator and structural portion of the fuel elements, and a uranium-thorium fuel cycle. These basic elements were selected to be compatible with high temperature operation and a high thermal and nuclear efficiency. With reactor cooling gas temperatures in the range of 1400°F, steam can be generated at temperatures of 1000°F or higher and at pressures desirable for modern high temperature steam turbine generators.

The fuel for the HTGR system is in the form of uranium and thorium dicarbide particles coated with single or multiple layers of pyrolytic carbon which are contained in graphite fuel rods. Because of the absence of a metal cladding within the reactor, the parasitic loss of neutrons is minimized, resulting in high conversion of thorium to uranium-233. Both the graphite and the coated fuel particles are capable of withstanding high radiation doses without significant structural effects, making possible fuel lifetimes of six years and longer. The combination of high conversion ratio, high thermodynamic efficiency and long fuel life provides the prospect of low fuel cycle cost from the HTGR system.

The 40,000 kw(e) prototype HTGR plant is at Peach Bottom, Pennsylvania, on the system of Philadelphia Electric Company. The plant is designed for a bulk helium core outlet temperature of approximately 1400°F and throttle steam conditions of 1000°F at 1450 psi. The prototype plant contains the core in a steel reactor vessel. Hot helium gas passes to and from the reactor vessel to the steam generators through two external loops.

Development of large scale HTGR's has been underway since 1960 and has resulted in designs of reactors having essentially the same primary system operating conditions as the prototype, but of more efficient and compact design. This results from the incorporation of advanced design features including the use of an integrated primary system including the reactor core, steam generators, and helium circulators all contained within a prestressed concrete reactor vessel (PCRV). This integral design minimizes the helium piping and inventory, eliminates the need for a steam generator pressure shell, reduces component shielding and allows a major reduction in the plant's physical size per unit of capacity.

Figure 1 schematically shows the arrangement of such an integrated HTGR system. Helium gas coolant passes upward over the fuel elements absorbing their heat from them. The helium at a temperature of about $1400^\circ F$ is ducted to steam generators, shown here schematically beside the core, to produce superheated or supercritical steam at $1000^\circ F$ or greater. The cooled helium flows to steam driven helium circulators.

The steam produced will pass to the turbine plant which is conventional in all respects, except that in advanced HTGR systems, the cold reheat steam from the high pressure turbine passes to the steam turbine drive portions of the helium circulators prior to reheat. Intermediate and large size plant net thermal efficiencies of 40-45 per cent can be anticipated.

For use in dual purpose plant application, the conventional turbine would be replaced by a back pressure turbine with the steam exhausting to the brine heater of an evaporative desalination unit and then to the feed water cycle.

## EXTENSIBILITY TO LARGE SINGLE UNIT SIZE

The national program has pointed to the ultimate need for developing large, 3,500 to 10,000 MWt, reactor systems both to supply the requirements for hundreds of millions of gallons of fresh water daily and to take advantage of the decline in unit cost normally associated with increased size. As a part of the continuing effort in this regard, the AEC has sponsored a number of studies to investigate limitations or special problems which might result from attempting to scale up the capacity of various nuclear reactor types. As part of this AEC program, General Atomic has recently completed a study for Oak Ridge National Laboratory of the technical feasibility of scaleup of single unit HTGR reactors to 5,000 MWt and 10,000 MWt. This study was not directed at an overall optimization of an entire dual purpose plant, but rather concentrated upon the design and construction limitations which might exist in an HTGR nuclear steam supply system of the type originally investigated under the AEC supported 1000 MWe TARGET* design study. The recent study also adopted the TARGET design study steam conditions of 3500 psia, $1050^\circ F$ with a single reheat to $1050^\circ F$.

* This work was supported under U. S. Atomic Energy Commission Contract AT (04-3)-167, Project Agreement No. 17.

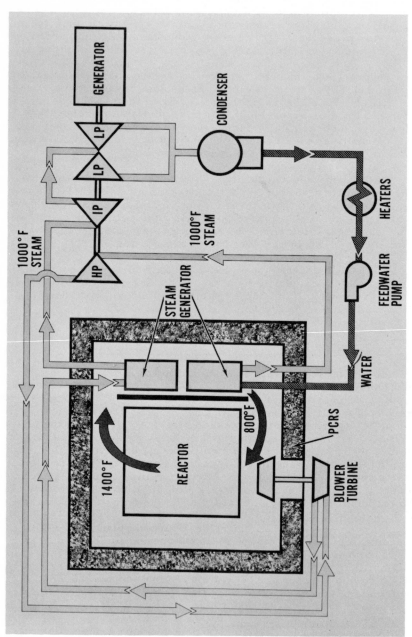

Figure 1. Schematic Flow Diagram for HTGR System

The conceptual reactor arrangement considered in the large plant program is shown in Figure 2. The reactor is of the integrated type in which the entire primary coolant circuit is contained within the PCRV. In this arrangement, the steam generators and helium circulators are placed under the core and reflector assembly. The core and reflector assembly is designed for upflow of gas through the core and downflow of the heated outlet gas through passages in the graphite block side reflector to the modular steam generators and then to the circulators. This design places most of the ducting and other structures in contact with cool inlet gas. The control rod drives are located in water cooled nozzles penetrating the PCRV above the core. These nozzles are also used for refueling.

The core and reflector assembly is contained within a steel core barrel and supported by a grid structure mounted on brackets on the PCRV wall and columns rising from the PCRV floor. Under the grid structure is a steel plenum for the cool gas leaving the circulators and entering the core.

In the 5,000 MWt design, the six steam generators and helium circulators are located beneath the core. Twice this number were considered for the 10,000 MWt.

The control rod drives are of a winch type in which two control rods are suspended from cables vertically within the reactor core. The rods are simultaneously moved by winding or unwinding of the cables from two counter-rotating drums. AC motor drives are used, and an electromagnetically operated gravity release scram is provided.

The helium circulators are driven by means of steam turbines. In the basic design, the helium flows from the lower plenum and is driven by axial flow compressors through diffuser sections to the plenum beneath the reactor core. The steam comes from the cold reheat line of the high pressure turbine and slows from the circulator turbines to the reheaters.

The PCRV as shown is a monolithic concrete structure in the shape of a 12-sided right prism with a cylindrical cavity. It has a steel liner which functions as a leakage barrier. The major penetrations are located in the top and bottom heads of the vessel and all penetrations are lined with steel sleeves anchored to the concrete and attached to the steel liner. The inner surface of the liner is covered with laminated metallic insulation in the region around the core and on the floor and above the core with low conductivity graphite.

Cooling coils and anchors are attached to the outer surface of the liners and are embedded in the concrete as it is poured. Also cast in the concrete are steel tendon tubes into which are inserted the steel cables used for prestressing. Structural requirements of the vessel dictate thick walls and placement of the tendons in

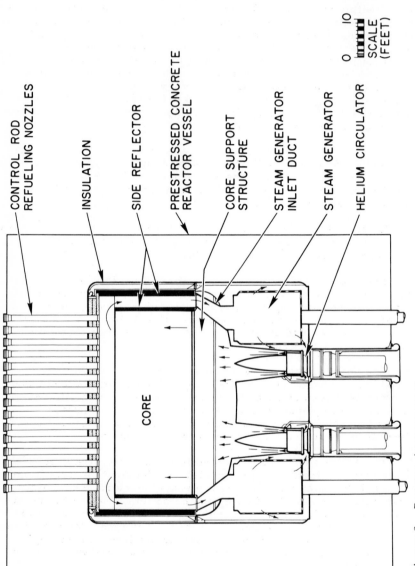

CONTROL ROD
REFUELING NOZZLES

INSULATION

SIDE REFLECTOR

PRESTRESSED CONCRETE
REACTOR VESSEL

CORE SUPPORT
STRUCTURE

STEAM GENERATOR
INLET DUCT

STEAM GENERATOR

HELIUM CIRCULATOR

CORE

0   10
SCALE
(FEET)

Figure 2.  Reactor Arrangement

the outer regions of the concrete. This places the tendons in a zone where both radiation and temperature are low. The tendons are accessible for adjustment or replacement.

The 5, 000 MWt vessel is approximately 100 feet high and 87 feet across the flats with an interior cavity approximately 62 feet in diameter and 57 feet high. The corresponding internal dimensions for the 10, 000 MWt vessel are approximately 81 feet and 60 feet. Although such sizes would present difficulty using conventional steel pressure vessels, they are well within the present state of the art for PCRV's.

Major design and development work on prestressed concrete is underway in the U.S. as well as abroad. In fact, in France and Britain this technique has been extensively applied to reactor vessels. In France, two reactors with prestressed concrete vessels are in operation (one since 1959 and one since 1960) and two more are nearing start-up. In Britain, four such reactors are under construction. One of the French reactors and all of the British reactors are of the integrated design wherein the concrete structure houses the entire primary system. All eight of these reactors are gas-cooled.

The utilization of prestressed concrete pressure vessels for the high temperature gas-cooled reactors has been studied at General Atomic since 1961 with both AEC and private support. This work includes an extensive effort on analytical code development, experimental work on elastic and concrete models, as well as the development of HTGR, and Gas Cooled Fast Reactor (GSFR) designs incorporating this concept. The first use of a PCRV in the United States will be for the 300 MWe Fort St. Vrain Power Station to be built for Public Service Company of Colorado by General Atomic Division as a part of the AEC Power Reactor Demonstration Program.

Figure 3 illustrates the relative sizes of several of the European vessels and the conceptual structures considered in the study of 5, 000 and 10, 000 MWt reactors. As can be seen, the latter vessels are generally in the same size range as those being constructed in Europe and well within the present state of the art. The Fort St. Vrain vessel, which is also shown, is substantially smaller in size.

In addition to the structural considerations mentioned above, the feasibility of large HTGR's has also been studied from the stand-point of fuel element configuration, xenon stability, component sizes and other similar factors and although not reported here, it was concluded that in all these respects the TARGET type HTGR design can be economically and practically scaled-up to sizes as large as 10, 000 MWt.

The technical feasibility of scaling-up in size a reactor is a major factor in determining its applicability to large dual purpose

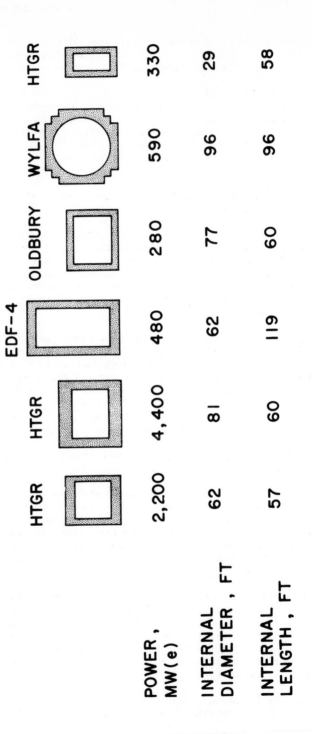

|  | HTGR | HTGR | EDF-4 | OLDBURY | WYLFA HTGR | HTGR |
|---|---|---|---|---|---|---|
| POWER, MW(e) | 2,200 | 4,400 | 480 | 280 | 590 | 330 |
| INTERNAL DIAMETER, FT | 62 | 81 | 62 | 77 | 96 | 29 |
| INTERNAL LENGTH, FT | 57 | 60 | 119 | 60 | 96 | 58 |

Figure 3.  Size Comparison of Prestressed Concrete Reactor Vessels

plants. Consideration must also be given, however, to limitations or additional costs which may arise in the turbine plant as a result of the selection of any particular reactor type. The importance of this side of the plant can be visualized by noting that a 10,000 MWt HTGR is capable of producing 4,450 MWe as a single purpose unit, or approximately 2,600 MWe with 900 MGD of fresh water as a dual purpose plant in which the full flow from a back pressure turbine exhausts to the distillation plant.

The effect on the turbine plant equipment resulting from the selection of a particular reactor type can be illustrated by consideration of the turbine itself. The turbine size is effected by the throttle steam conditions which are available. Thus a turbine designed for use with an HTGR producing steam at 3600 psi and 1050°F with reheat to 1050°F would be more compact than a turbine designed to use saturated steam where for equal output a 50 per cent greater steam flow would be required. The more compact turbine would be expected to have a lower unit cost as well as leading to a smaller and proportionally less expensive turbine hall.

## CAPITAL COST TRENDS

Previously reported studies of a single purpose 2240 MWt HTGR plant (TARGET) have shown favorable capital costs of between 100 and 110 $/kw(e). The preliminary cost studies of large 5,000 and 10,000 MWt reactor plants indicate a significant downward trend in cost with increasing size. For the nuclear steam supply system alone a reduction of approximately 20-25 $/kw(e) appears possible in going to the 5,000 MWt size with an additional saving of 5-10 $/kw(e) in scaling up to 10,000 MWt. These cost savings when taken with those which might be anticipated in other portions of the plant should provide for a substantial reduction in the steam charge to a water plant.

This large reduction in unit capital cost is not unexpected, since the use of prestressed concrete reactor vessels provides the reactor designer with a substantial degree of freedom in the design of the plant system and components. For example, no restriction in the unit size of steam generator vessels is imposed. In addition, the use of PCRV's eliminates any major step increase in cost such as would be associated with the change from shop fabrication to field fabrication of the primary system vessel.

## FUEL CYCLE COST

The second factor of importance in determining the suitability of reactors for large dual purpose plants is a low fuel cycle cost along with protection against large increases in these costs over the anticipated plant lifetime. As indicated previously, the HTGR is designed for the uranium$^{235}$-thorium$^{232}$ fuel cycle with uranium$^{233}$ recycle and has the potential of high conversion ratios and low fuel cycle costs.

In the large plant study consideration was given to nonvented fuel elements of the TARGET configuartion which are 4 1/2 inches in diameter and 20 feet long with an active fuel length of 15.5 feet. This resulted in "pancake" type core geometries having equivalent core diameters of 46 feet and 65 feet respectively for the 5,000 and 10,000 MWt cores. As expected, the larger core provides some reduction in the radial leakage, however, overall the improvement in this regard is small and the fuel cycle costs for both size units would be expected to be comparable.

The study considered fuel elements of all-graphite design as well as elements containing BeO. Previous studies have shown that all-graphite designs generally provide the lowest fuel cycle costs while the BeO containing cores can be optimized to provide the highest conversion ratios. In certain cases thermal breeding appears possible in the BeO-graphite cores.

The studies were based on partial fuel replacement each year, and average core lifetimes of 3 to 6 years.

For the large sized units General Atomic estimated that with all-graphite cores equilibrium fuel cycle costs in the range of 0.75 to 0.80 mills/kw(e) are possible with private ownership of the fuel. Under public ownership the fuel cycle cost decreases by about 0.15 mills/kw(e). These estimates were based on uranium ore costs of $8/lb, separative work costs of $30/kg, and a value ratio of $U^{233}$ to $U^{235}$ of 14/12. Other cost factors were estimated using assumptions as to the size and status of the technology during the 1985 period. Conversion ratios of 0.7 to 0.8 are typical for the all-graphite designs.

## FUEL CYCLE COST STABILITY

Reactor systems must be examined in the context of the entire need for nuclear power and the market conditions under which they will have to operate many years in the future. In general, technological advances can be expected to take place during this time which will reduce those portions of fuel cycle costs associated with fabrication, shipping and reprocessing. These advances are particularly to be expected for thorium cycle systems, such as the HTGR, if the technology of reprocessing and refabrication for thorium systems is subject to the same degree of intense study and development applied to $U^{238}$ systems in former years. However, over this same period many experts have predicted an increase in ore costs. Fortunately, in the case of the HTGR, because of the excellent conversion ratio and the high specific powers which can be achieved, the dependence upon the cost of raw materials and, in particular, the cost of uranium ore can be minimized. This is illustrated in Figure 4. It shows the small effect on HTGR fuel cycle cost from changes in ore costs

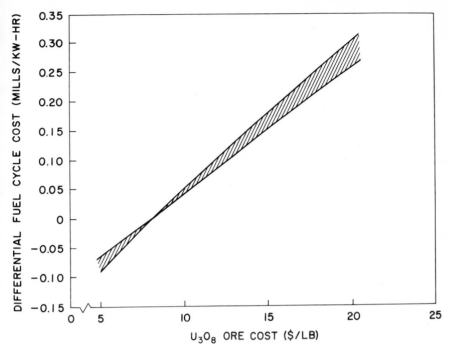

Figure 4. Effect of Ore Cost on HTGR Fuel Cycle

in the range from \$5/lb to \$20/lb of $U_3O_8$. As indicated, a four-fold change in ore cost results in less than a 0.4 mill/kwh change in fuel cycle cost.

## CONCLUSION

The results of the conceptual design study of large HTGR nuclear steam supply systems, incorporating an integrated primary coolant system within a prestressed concrete reactor vessel, show no apparent limitations in scaleup to the 5,000 MWt or 10,000 MWt size. The study also indicated low fuel cycle costs and favorable capital cost trends for these systems. Taken with other considerations, it can be concluded that the HTGR system is well suited for application in large dual purpose power/desalination stations.

# 22. Boiling Water Reactors

G. White, General Manager, Atomic Power Equipment Department,
General Electric Company

The water reactors have now reached the point where they are considered on an essentially equal footing with fossil-fired units by customers about to purchase power plants. The industry is benefiting from the substantial accumulation of experience from many units now in operation or under construction. During 1965, commitments totaling some five million kwe of various water reactor power plants were made, thus bringing the total capacity in design, in construction, and in operation to nearly ten million kwe. To give some feel to these numbers, it might be pointed out that the rate of nuclear commitments this past year equals or exceeds the total rate of additions of power plants in the U.S. in the early 50's. This trend is expected to continue as shown in the forecast of Figure 1.

The Dresden 1 plant outside Chicago has now generated over five billion kilowatt-hours (electrical) and has experienced a forced outage rate of under 1.7 per cent over the four-year operating period 1962-1965. Design and construction of the twin (800 MWe) Dresden 2 and 3 units is now underway using the same site. The design of these units represents a marked advancement over the first Dresden unit. These units are now estimated to be competitive with other power sources using fuel costing under 20¢/MBtu. Major areas of advancement include the use of a single cycle design, jet pumps, and steam separation within the reactor vessel. These and other advances have resulted in a far simpler, more compact plant providing more economic operation. A comparison of the configurations of the Dresden units is shown on Figure 2.

The overall arrangement of the Dresden additions is shown on Figure 3. In this figure, the pressure suppression containment system for the reactor is readily apparent. This also represents an advancement over earlier reactor containment systems. It is designed to absorb energy released under postulated circumstances of a major system failure, thereby rapidly returning the containment pressure to near atmospheric and thus minimizing the potential for leakage of contained materials.

A schematic diagram of the single cycle reactor system as employed in current plant designs is shown on Figure 4.

The nuclear fueled core, generating heat within the reactor

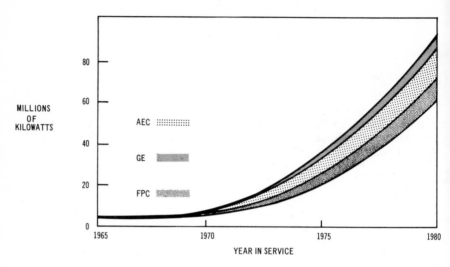

Figure 1. Installed Nuclear Capacity Forecasts

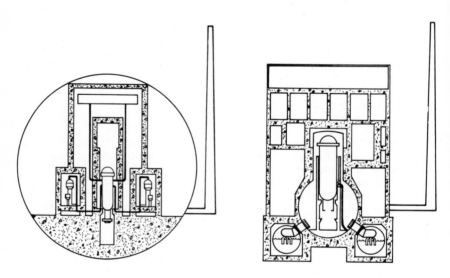

Figure 2. 1955 Dresden 1                1965 Dresden 2

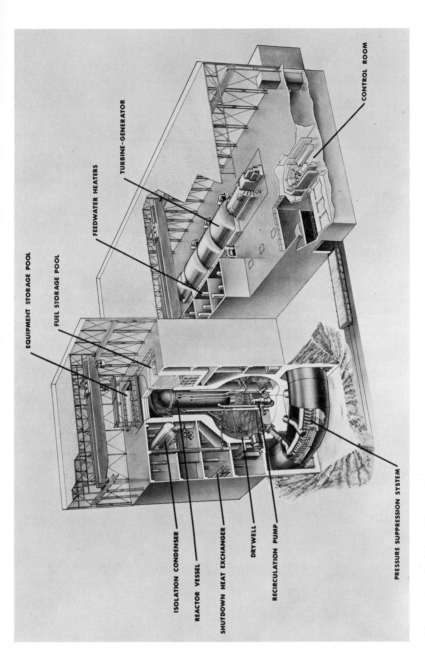

Figure 3. Boiling Water Reactor

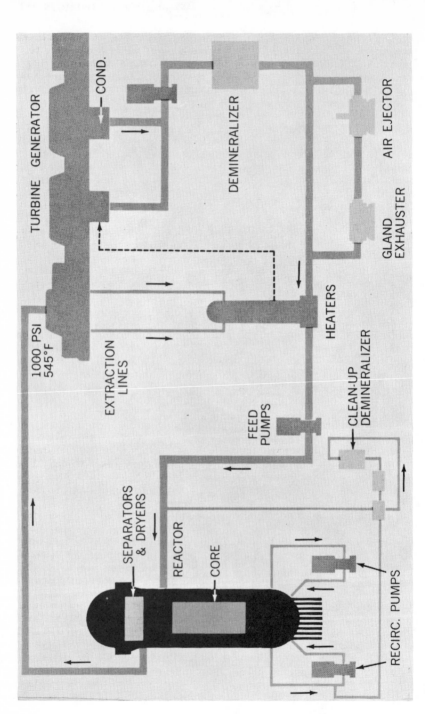

Figure 4. Single-Cycle Reactor System

vessel, boils water, producing saturated steam which then passes through internal steam separators and dryers and on directly to the turbine. The steam enters the high-pressure turbine casing at about 965 psi and 545°F. Steam leaving the high-pressure casing passes through moisture separator units prior to admission to the lower pressure casings.

The main condenser provides feed system deaeration and is followed by a full flow demineralizer system through which all condensate, extraction, and makeup flow must pass prior to the feed heaters. The condensate demineralizer system removes corrosion products produced in the turbine, condenser, and the shell side of the feedwater heaters. It also protects the reactor against condenser tube leaks and removes impurities which may enter the system in the makeup water. A second demineralizer system, the cleanup demineralizer, circulates reactor water for the removal of corrosion products originating in the reactor and reactor auxiliary systems. The power cycle uses a conventional regenerative feedwater system. The feedwater temperature and the number of feed heaters are selected in accordance with normal power plant considerations of power plant performance and economics.

In all BWR systems above the 50-100 MWe range, it has been customary to achieve the required heat transfer and to maintain the proper steam void content through the use of external recirculation loops. Current designs reduce the number of external loops required through the use of jet pumps installed within the reactor vessel.

A cutaway view of the reactor vessel and the associated internals is shown on Figure 5. The vessel is fabricated from low alloy steel internally clad with modified Type 304 stainless steel and complies with the ASME Nuclear Pressure Vessel Code. The Dresden Unit 2 vessel will be approximately 68 feet in height, with a 21-foot internal diameter and a 6-3/8-inch wall thickness.

The nuclear fuel is held in a modular array between the core support plate and the upper support grid. Cruciform-shaped control blades are positioned between the fuel assemblies by bottom-entry locking piston control dirves. The movement of the control blades below the core is guided by control rod guide tubes, each of which also serves to support a group of four fuel assemblies.

Water discharged from the separators and dryers in the upper part of the reactor vessel is joined by the incoming feedwater and flows downward in the downcomer annulus between the shroud and the vessel wall. A portion of this flow exits the vessel through the coolant outlets and is pumped back in to serve as the driving flow for the jet pump circulators (see Figure 6). Variable speed pumps in the recirculation loops allow variation of the recirculation rate as a means of power level control over a 30 per cent

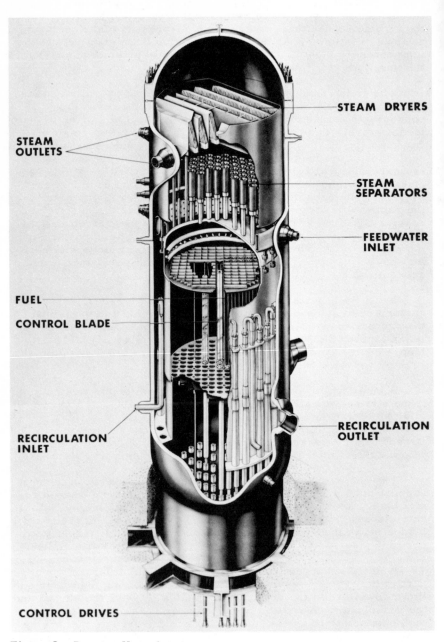

STEAM DRYERS

STEAM
OUTLETS

STEAM
SEPARATORS

FEEDWATER
INLET

FUEL

CONTROL BLADE

RECIRCULATION
OUTLET

RECIRCULATION
INLET

CONTROL DRIVES

Figure 5.   Reactor Vessel

range without movement of the control rods. The jet pump application and recirculation flow control system are innovations responsive to the objective of system simplification and load following capability.

In arriving at the core design of a BWR of a given output, a "modular" or "building block" method is used. Each fuel assembly, as illustrated by Figure 7, is uniform in size with a 7 x 7 rod array of slightly enriched $UO_2$ pellets with Zircaloy-2 cladding. The fuel rods are 0.570 inch in diameter with an active fuel length of 12 feet. The core is built up of modules consisting of one control blade and four fuel assemblies.

BWR nuclear boiler systems are built up of these modules to produce reactor capacities over the range of 500 to 1000 MWe or higher ratings. Generally, the reactor height remains fairly constant while the vessel diameter varies. With this modular design, many of the advantages often associated with the extrapolatibility of the tube-type reactors to very large sizes have been achieved.

This modular concept of core synthesis leads automatically to standardization of design and size of the fuel assemblies, control blades and control rod drives -- facilitating the move to larger size plants.

### FUTURE ADVANCEMENTS OF THE BWR

Continued evolution of the boiling water reactor concept is anticipated over the next several decades and the following factors are typical of those expected to be significant in this continued advancement:

> Larger unit sizes
> Higher power densities
> Field constructed pressure vessels

The U.S. power industry has witnessed a steady growth in the size of power production equipment in the past; nuclear units show every evidence of furthering this trend in the future. These trends are illustrated by Figure 8, together with a current estimate of the future rate of unit size increase for central station power plants; it neglects any special considerations regarding possible large-scale desalting plant projects.

BWRs offer scope for size increase to meet these trends, and thus are well beyond the 1200 MWe single unit installations which presently represent the upper limit to which design detailing efforts have been carried to date. The BWR's strongly negative local power coefficient from the boiling process exists throughout the core regardless of the magnitude of core dimensions. This is a major asset in the avoidance of a tangible upper limit to BWR

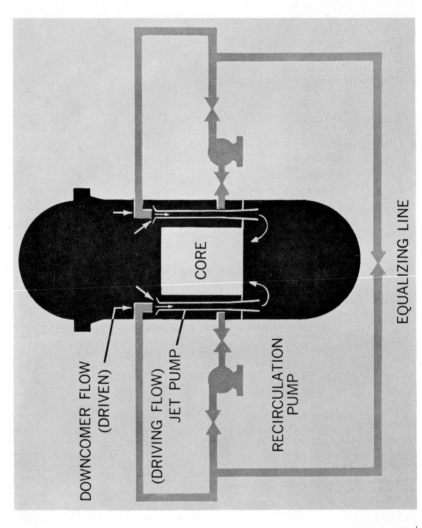

Figure 6. Jet Pump Recirculation

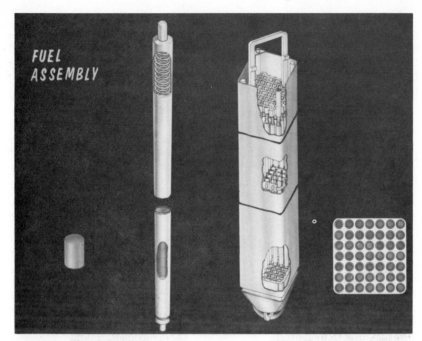

Figure 7.   Fuel Assembly

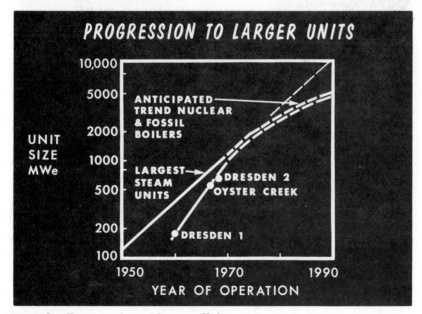

Figure 8.   Progression to Larger Units

unit size, as it serves to ensure stability and controlability of the power distribution even in the largest size units. In consequence, other aspects of the plant design have been evaluated with regard to potential size economies or limitations. Throughout these appraisals, it has been realized that increased rating with only minor equipment adjustments is one of the prime sources of economy. In consequence, a major effort is continuing on increase of the power density of the BWR core.

Power densities of up to 1700 kw/ft$^3$ of core (60 kw/liter) have already been demonstrated in the Big Rock Point plant of Consumers Power Company under a joint development program with the Atomic Energy Commission. Given a certain cost level for the uranium in the core and a unit cost of fabrication of the fuel and other equipment, there is an optimum value for the power density. The BWR power density trends of Figure 8 fall close to these optimum levels under the changing circumstances of uranium price and ownership and of equipment fabrication cost, etc.

The above advancement in power density, coupled with continued plant simplification and increasing unit size, will all help in the achievement of maximum performance economy. The size increase may in time strain capabilities for use of shop-fabricated steel pressure vessels. The two longer term approaches to circumvent these limits are now under active study by General Electric. One approach involves field assembly of a steel vessel and the other field construction of a prestressed concrete structure.

One of the proposed phases in the on-site construction of a field-fabricated vessel is illustrated on Figure 9. In total, the concept involves transporting formed steel plate to the site where assembly, welding, and stress relieving are carried out in several phases with the help of a centrally located construction crane. Various high accuracy machining operations on the major components of the vessel are also carried out on site following final stress relief of the component. The field erection of steel vessels may open up some potential sites otherwise unsuitable for nuclear power plant installation due to vessel transportation limitations. Furthermore, there is a possibility of reducing the plant construction schedule by several months through adoption of this technique.

A longer term pressure vessel development effort now under study by General Electric's Advanced Products Operation is directed toward application of the prestressed concrete vessel technology now extensively applied to European gas-cooled reactors. One possible arrangement of this type of vessel is illustrated on Figure 10. Through its use, all practical limits on the size of BWR units due to vessel design appear to be removed. This development may be some years off yet; however, present steel vessel manufacturing facilities appear suitable for construction of vessels for BWR ratings up to at least 1500 MWe, and the aforementioned plans for introducing higher power density designs will

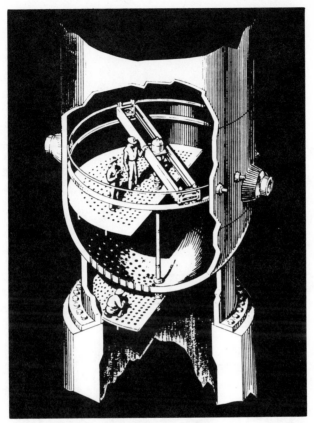

Figure 9.   Field Constructed Pressure Vessel

further extend this capability to 2500 MWe or more.   Such unit
sizes may well exceed the needs of the market for some years to
come,  except possibly for dual purpose desalting units.

## BWR DESIGN PARAMETERS FOR
## DESALTER SERVICE

Dual purpose installations employing back pressure turbines
continue to appear the most promising for the overall economy and
lowest fresh water production costs.   In such an installation using
a BWR, the steam expands from about 965 psia at the throttle to
the 10 to 40 psia required by the water plant.   The steam turbine
cycle would normally be non-reheat for dual purpose applications
just as in most current central station BWR plants.

A typical dual purpose system of this type is illustrated schematically on Figure 11.   The design parameters called out on the
illustration are typical of those computed for a 300 MWe plus 50

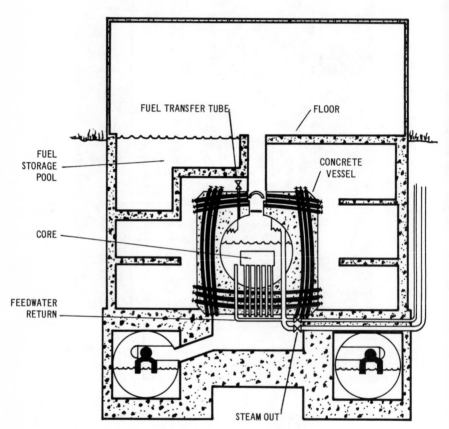

Figure 10.  Prestressed Concrete Pressure Vessel

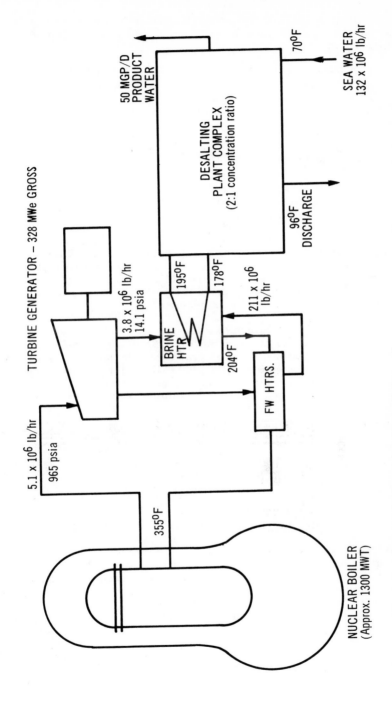

Figure 11. Dual Purpose BWR Desalting Plant Schematic

MGD dual purpose installation. Some of the main parameters open for design considerations in such a plant have been identified on the illustration are are:

|   |   |   |
|---|---|---|
| a. | Production ratio | 1/6 MGD per MWe net |
| b. | Reactor steam pressure | 1000 psia |
| c. | Turbine exhaust pressure | 14. 1 psia |
| d. | Condensate return temperature | 204°F |
| e. | Regenerative feed heat temperature | 355°F |
| f. | Desalting plant performance ratio | 5. 3 lbs/1000 Btu |

While the data shown on the dual purpose plant schematic are for a 50 MGD/300 MWe plant, higher ratios of water to power production are fully practical. Higher water to power ratios tend to result in higher initial brine temperature, but for typical present-day economic assumptions, there is very little change in the unit cost of the products over a substantial range. Currently, there is an upper limit on this economically achievable ratio of water to power of 1/2-1 MGD per MWe of net power generation capability. This corresponds to the point at which a maximum brine temperature of 250°F is reached.

The condensate return temperature from the desalter to the power plant and then to the BWR's full flow demineralizer tends to be fixed by the turbine exhaust pressure. In some designs, this turns out to be in excess of the 140°F limit for currently used resins. Under such circumstances, use of the high temperature "Powdex" resin is planned, thus avoiding potential design limitations on system optimization.

Regenerative feedwater heating of the returned condensate has been found from various studies to have a value in these dual purpose plants virtually identical to that for single purpose power units. Thus, again BWR system design is little different from that of the units now under design or going into service in the near future.

Lower rates of water production for any given steam temperature to the brine heater can be achieved by use of an extraction instead of a back pressure turbine. Figure 12 shows the associated variation of gross power that can be generated as a function of per cent extraction for various extraction temperatures. On the diagram, zero extraction corresponds to full condensing operation and the power is taken as 100 per cent. One hundred per cent extraction corresponds to back pressure operation and the variation of gross power generation with condensing steam temperature is thus also apparent from Figure 12. Intermediate percentages of extraction at any temperature also give less reduction in the power generation than full extraction.

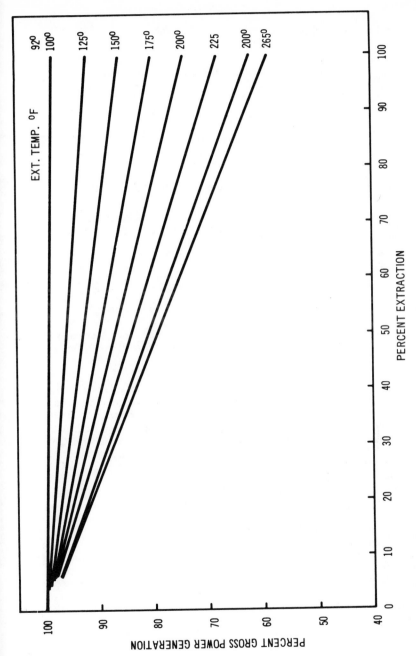

Figure 12. Per cent Gross Power as Function of Extraction at Various Temperatures for 365°F Feedwater Temperature

TABLE I

Effect of Introducing BWR Condensate
Into Sea Water Circulation Through Brine Heater

| Equilibrium Conditions | No Leakage | 1% Leakage | |
|---|---|---|---|
| | | 1 day decay | 1 day decay |
| (All Isotopes Except Tritium) | | $c \times 10^{-12}$ | $c \times 10^{-12}$ |
| From Ocean Salts | 471 | 471 | 471 |
| From Condensate* | --- | 15 | 1,500 |
| Total | 471 | 485 | 1,971 |
| MPC (Continuous Use) | 10,000 | 10,000 | 10,000 |

| Tritium | No Leakage | 1% Leakage |
|---|---|---|
| | $c \times 10^{-6}$ | $c \times 10^{-6}$ |
| From Ocean Water | .0014 | .0014 |
| From Condensate | --- | 17 |
| Total | .0014 | 17 |
| MPC (Continuous Use) | 3,000 | 3,000 |

*Condensate activity level of $2 \times 10^{-5}$  c/cc after 1 day decay and
corresponding to the multiple defect condition experienced during
experimental stainless steel clad fuel operation in Dresden.

The final aspect of the design noted previously is an entirely
new one special to the nuclear desalting field, namely assurance
of adequate separation between the nuclear heat source and the
desalted water product.  This is an area that has now been studied
at some length and discussed with the staff of the AEC and OSW.
One of the more significant aspects of this study is the fact that
the direction of leakage across the heat exchange surface separating the two systems, if such should occur, can be made to be
from the water plant to the nuclear plant.  Furthermore, even if
reversal of this leakage direction is postulated, the consequences
are still not significant.  The conclusions reached leave no doubt
as to the adequacy of the separation barriers inherent to the mul-
tiflash evaporation process regardless of other barriers present
within the nuclear plant itself.  To illustrate this point, data presented on Table I show the negligible change in product water activity under the postulated but uncredible circumstances of a failure of the brine heater tubing resulting in leakage from the reactor
system of one per cent of the total reactor steam flow into the
water plant and continued operation of the latter at full load.
These data are shown for the equilibrium condition which only
arises after the various activity concentrations have built up during the course of several hours of continued leakage.

# 23. Pressurized Water Reactors for Desalting Applications

J. C. Rengel, General Manager, A. R. Jones, Manager of Advanced Development, and W. H. Comtois, Atomic Power Division, Westinghouse Electric Corporation

In examining the PWR as applied to the desalting program, the reactor as a class will be considered rather than any specific design. Three areas will be touched on in this paper. They are:

a) The PWR and its qualifications for the desalting application;
b) Certain overall plant considerations that are of interest; and
c) A look at some possibilities for the future.

The PWR technology is the result of nearly two decades of intensive development, design and operation on several fronts. These include the Navy, the small military, the merchant ship Savannah and the electric utility programs. The PWR that has been developed for the electric utility application will serve equally well as an energy source for desalting.

## THE PRESSURIZED WATER REACTOR

The Pressurized Water Reactor, fueled with slightly enriched (2-3 per cent) uranium in the oxide form, moderated and cooled by ordinary water has a very considerable pedigree of technology and operating performance. There is no substitute for successful experience as an assurance of reliability and availability. These are at least as important in water production as in electrical generation, possibly more so.

A schematic diagram of the PWR Nuclear Steam Supply System is shown in Figure 1. It consists of a pressure vessel containing the heat-producing core, one or more steam generators with an equal number of circulating water pumps, a pressurizer and connecting piping. The number and size of steam generators and pumps is varied to meet the requirements of the application in the most economic manner. It is in the steam generator that the heat produced by the reactor is transferred from the reactor coolant to produce steam which is completely free of radioactivity and which is then supplied to the electric and water producing facilities. (The freedom from radiation permits visitors to the Yankee Atomic Electric Plan, Row, Massachusetts, to be conducted throughout the entire turbine-electric plant without limitation.) This accessibility allows low-cost operation and maintenance which is of obvious economic value. Six electric utility PWR's are continually adding to the experience record and by 1970

they will be joined by twelve or more PWR systems now under
construction or on order. (See Table I. ) The number of plants
now being built and under consideration makes it possible to
standardize the major components and thereby effect savings in
cost. These savings extend through the engineering, equipment
manufacture, plant construction and fuel fabrication. There is
ample evidence that cost reductions will continue to be forthcoming. It is to be expected that these will be gradual rather than
spectacular, but significant, nonetheless.

## APPLICATION TO WATER PRODUCTION

Turning now to the utilization of a PWR for the production of
water, a typical arrangement of the major systems which com-
prise a combination plant producing both water and electric power
is shown in Figure 2. The Nuclear Steam Supply System (NSSS)
the Power Generating System, and the Desalting System are
shown. In this arrangement, the last few rows of turbine blades
and the condenser of the usual turbine-generator are replaced by

TABLE I

PWR Plants (Spring 1966)

| NAME | OWNER | MW |
|------|-------|-----|
| SHIPPINGPORT | U. S. ATOMIC ENERGY COMMISSION / DUQUESNE LT. CO. | 150 |
| YANKEE | YANKEE ATOMIC POWER CO. | 185 |
| INDIAN POINT NO. I | CONSOLIDATED EDISON CO. OF NY | 255* |
| SAXTON | SAXTON NUCLEAR EXPERIMENTAL CORP. | 5 |
| BR-3 | CENTRE D' ETUDES NUCLEAIRE, BELGIUM | II |
| ENRICO FERMI | ENTE NAZIONALE PER L'ENERGIA ELETTRICA, ITALY | 272 |
| CHOOZ PLANT | SOCIETE D'ENERGIE NUCLEAIRE DES ARDENNES FRANCE / BELGIUM | 258 |
| SAN ONOFRE | SOUTHERN CALIFORNIA EDISON / SAN DIEGO G & E | 450 |
| HADDAM | CONNECTICUT YANKEE ATOMIC POWER CO. | 616 |
| KBWP | KERNKRAFTWERK BADEN-WURTTEMBURG PLANUNG, GERMANY | 282 |
| ZORITA | UNION ELECTRICA MADRILENA, SPAIN | 160 |
| BEZNAU | NORDOSTSCHWEIZERISCHE KRAFTWERKE, SWITZ. | 350 |
| BROOKWOOD | ROCHESTER GAS & ELECTRIC CO. | 450 |
| TURKEY POINT NO. 3 | FLORIDA POWER & LIGHT CO. | 760 |
| INDIAN POINT NO. 2 | CONSOLIDATED EDISON CO. OF N. Y. | 873 |
| ROBINSON NO. 2 | CAROLINA POWER & LIGHT CO. | 700 |
| (SITE NOT SELECTED) | WISCONSIN ELECTRIC POWER CO. | 450 |
| PALISADES | CONSUMER'S POWER CO. | 770 |

* INCLUDES OIL-FIRED SUPERHEATER

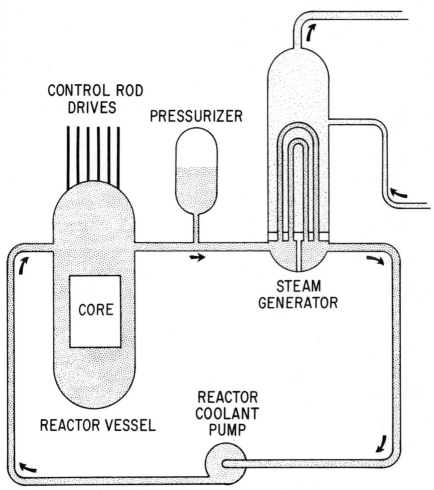

CONTROL ROD DRIVES

PRESSURIZER

CORE

STEAM GENERATOR

REACTOR VESSEL

REACTOR COOLANT PUMP

Figure 1. Nuclear Steam Supply System

the brine heater of the Desalting System. The steam supplied by the NSSS passes first through the turbine where some of its energy is converted to electric power. The steam from the turbine is exhausted to the brine heater where it is condensed and returned as feedwater to the NSSS. The heat of condensation increases the brine temperature to its maximum design value prior to beginning the multistage flashing process. In Figure 3, a schematic diagram of a combination plant arranged to use steam extracted at a suitable low pressure point in the turbine to heat brine is shown. The use of two turbo-generators with the upper one exhausting to a conventional condenser and the other to the brine heater is shown in Figure 4. This latter arrangement permits very large production capacity and is similar to the cycle which has been recommended for use in the proposed Metropolitan Water District plant in Southern California.

The range of electric water production capacity possible with a plant roughly of the size commercially available today is shown in Figure 5. If this reactor, whose rating would be just under 3000 MWt were to be utilized in a single purpose electric plant, its gross electric output would be approximately 1000 MWe. The upper portion of the figure above 600 MW electrical output is the operating zone within which water production can be increased at the expense of electrical production by extraction or multi-shaft turbine arrangement, i.e., the cycles of Figures 3 and 4. At 600 MW electrical production, the cycle changes to the full back pressure arrangement of Figure 2. Below 600 MWe, more and more steam bypasses the turbine. Finally, if no electric power were being generated and all the reactor heat utilized for water production, on the order of 300 million gallons per day is possible. The band indicates the effect of varying the heat performance of the water plant from 80 to 120 Btu/lb.

Thermal rating required for a wide range of power and water capacity combinations can be roughly estimated from Figure 6. Those combinations which fall to the left of the line labeled "full back pressure" require that steam from the nuclear steam supply system be by-passed around the turbine and throttled directly to the brine heater. Those combinations falling to the right are of the extraction or multi-shaft cycles.

With such a range of technical considerations, coupled with an even more complex set of economic variables, it is small wonder that some confusion exists over the exact economic state of the industry today. We strongly feel that this will only be resolved by very detailed evaluation of specific cases and by the building of a number of units. That has certainly been the situation in the electric utility application. A few of the results and conclusions we have reached in our studies of desalting plant potential based on the application of existing PWR technology and multi-stage flash evaporation, as discussed by Mr. Gaunt (Chapter 11) may be of interest. While these data are not firm in the quantitative sense,

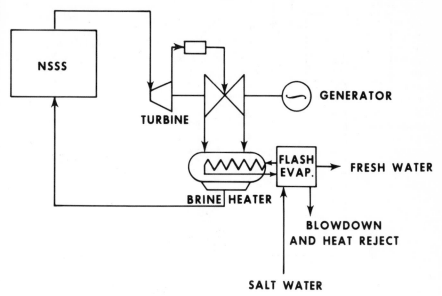

Figure 2. Back-Pressure Nuclear Power-Desalting Cycle

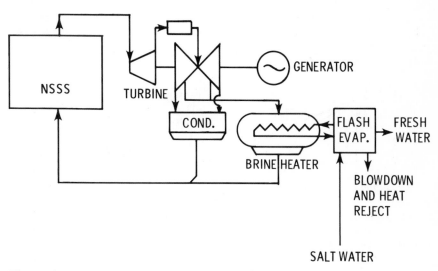

Figure 3. Extraction Power - Desalting Cycle

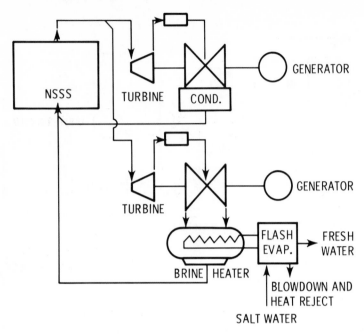

Figure 4.   Multi-Shaft Power - Desalting Cycle

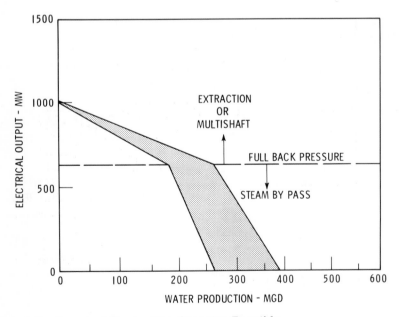

Figure 5.   Range of Production Capacity Possible

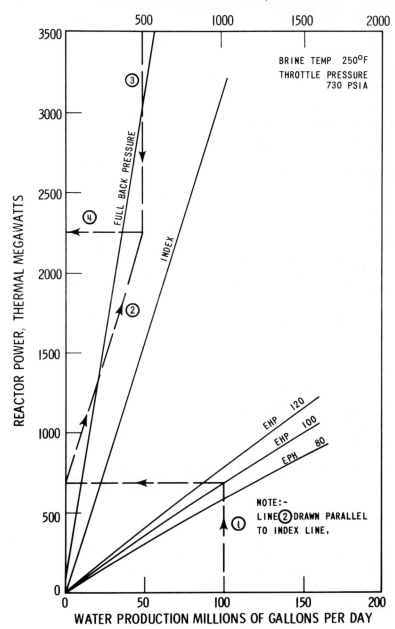

Figure 6. Nomograph for Estimating Reactor Rating

they illustrate trends correctly. We are convinced that with today's technology, water can be produced for less than 30¢/1000
gal. in a large dual purpose plant. In a water only unit it might
be as much as a factor of 2 higher.

The effects of size and fixed annual charges on the cost of
steam supplied to the turbine throttle are shown in Figure 7.

The effects of size and fixed annual charges on the cost of
steam supplied to the brine heater of the water plant are shown in
Figure 8. These are based on an electric energy credit of an
electricity only cycle of the same output. Both size and fixed
annual charge effects are markedly reduced. The conclusion to
be drawn is that there are indeed real opportunities for effective
and mutually beneficial cooperative ventures between investor-
owned and public bodies.

If we calculate water costs based on the increment above for
an electric plant that would produce the desired electric power
only, we get a certain set of water and power costs. See Figure 9.
Now assume these are represented by the point on the line shown
in Figure 10. If we wish to change the relative credits the point
will move along the line. Now the slope of the line is determined
by the product ratio. * If the product ratio is low, the line is very
flat. In other words, the method of cost distribution is most important where a large quantity of electricity is being considered.


THE FUTURE

As we look to the future and attempt to assess the probable
course of events we are inevitably forced to conclude that the water reactors such as the PWR will account for essentially all of
the "work-horse" installations at least through 1980. The research and development effort followed by prototype and demonstration plants, needed for any so-called advanced concept is
simply going to require that kind of time schedule. During these
15 or so years many gradual and possibly some not so gradual
changes can be expected in the PWR. Fuel costs will come down
drastically due to increased manufacturing and processing
throughput, increased burnup and new technology. Capital costs
will come down slowly, subject to the pressures of escalating
unit and labor costs. Unit sizes will continue to increase, probably reaching 2000 MWe or 6000 MWt ratings in this period. The
details of component changes may come about in several ways.
Reactor vessels are a case in point. Vessels for 1500 MWe plants
have been reported by Gaines and Porse[1] to be feasible for in-
shop fabrication. 2000 MWe units are also probably in the cards.
Transportation to site, for coastal desalting application should

*Product Ratio = Power Production/Water Production

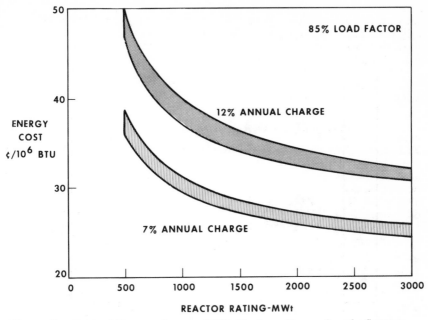

Figure 7.　Cost of Energy from a PWR Nuclear Steam Supply System

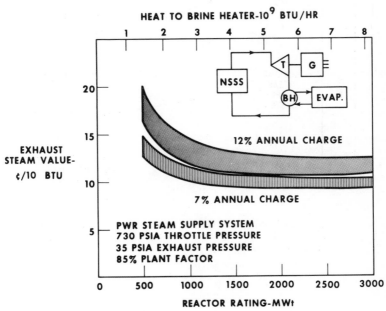

Figure 8.　Cost of Heat from a Full Back Pressure Cycle

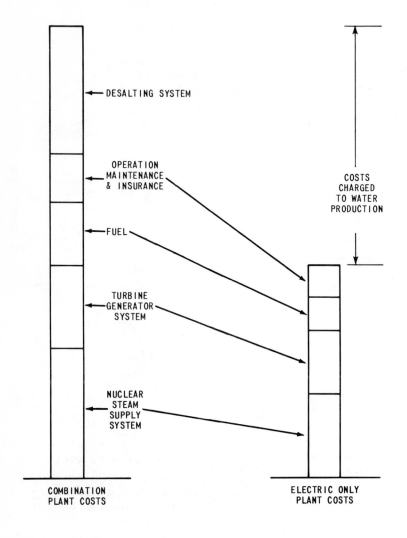

DESALTING SYSTEM

OPERATION
MAINTENANCE
& INSURANCE

FUEL

TURBINE
GENERATOR
SYSTEM

NUCLEAR
STEAM
SUPPLY
SYSTEM

COSTS
CHARGED
TO WATER
PRODUCTION

COMBINATION
PLANT COSTS

ELECTRIC ONLY
PLANT COSTS

Figure 9.  Graphical Representation of the Method used to Determine
Water Production Costs in a Combination Plant.  Both
Plants have the Same Net Electrical Generating Capacity

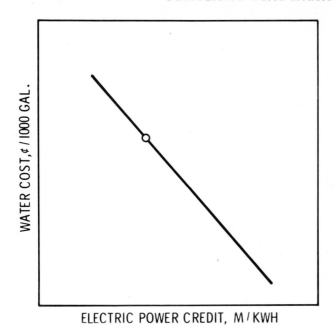

ELECTRIC POWER CREDIT, M / KWH

Figure 10.   Typical Variation of Water Cost for Arbitrary
              Electric Power Credit

pose no problem.   For inland sites, it may be.   Therefore work
is already underway on field fabrication techniques.

Another very interesting possibility is the use of prestressed
or more correctly post-tensioned concrete vessels.   A possible
vessel layout, which we have examined, that looks very interesting for 6000 MWt and up installations is shown in Figure 11.

We cannot resist taking a little peek into the long range future,
say to 2000 AD.   Our ideas of a self-sufficient energy center concept combine a 12,000 MWe electric power, 1000 MW gas turbine
peaking, 5000 MWe PWR and 6000 MWe fast breeders coupled with
a billion gallon/day desalting plant.   This complex would operate
on an equilibrium feed of 14.2 tons/yr of depleted uranium, of
which there is plenty, and produce an excess of 1.4 tons/yr of
plutonium.   The base load portion of the system demand would be
supplied by the fast breeder reactors since their incremental fuel
costs are extremely low.   The intermediate portion of the load
duration curve would be supplied by the PWR units, which have
lower capital costs but higher fuel costs when compared to the
breeders.   The PWR also provides excellent ease and flexibility of
operation so that the PWR produced steam will be switched as required from the production of electricity to the production of water

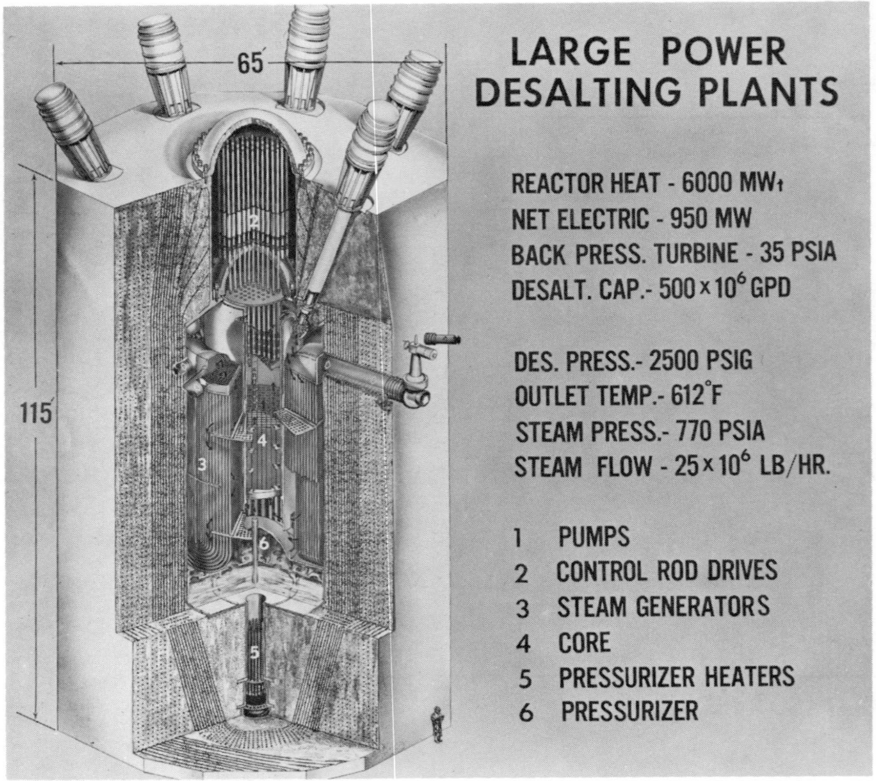

Figure 11. Large Power Desalting Plants

In a situation enjoying favorable financing, say six per cent fixed annual charges, this system could produce desalted water for 10 to 15 cents/1000 gal.

Thus we see ample evidence of a most promising future for the PWR in the production of both electricity and water.

## NOTES

1.  Proceedings of the Third International Conference on the Peaceful Uses of Atomic Energy, Geneva, 1964, Vol. 8, p. 464-472, Paper no. 227.

# SYSTEMS FOR
# WATER DESALTING

Howard S. Coleman, Dean
College of Engineering
The University of Arizona

## 24. Agricultural Water by Nuclear Desalination And Technical Routes to Its Achievement*

R. Philip Hammond, Director, Nuclear Desalination Program,
Oak Ridge National Laboratory

The application of nuclear energy to the task of desalting sea-water has changed in a few short years from a dream of a few to an important activity, with dozens of firms and hundreds of engineers busily engaged. The Metropolitan Water District of Southern California is proceeding with negotiations to construct the first major nuclear-powered desalting station in the United States. This station will complete the transition of nuclear desalination from dream to reality. There is no question but that an increasing number of cities around the world will find this kind of plant their best choice for meeting new water demands.

As important as this development is for the future well-being of cities, it becomes insignificant in comparison with the impact which a successful application to large-scale agriculture would have on the destiny of mankind. If only a tenth of the world's need for new food supplies in the next 30 years were met in this way, the growth of desalination reactors would rival or exceed the growth rate for electric power reactors. In a previous article[1] I have explored the general feasibility of providing nuclear desalination plants as major agricultural sources. In this report I present some newly available information which leads to a somewhat more specific definition of the problem itself and of the nature which a successful solution will have. It must be made clear at the outset, however, that not all the elements of the solution are available, nor is it even clear that they can be found. My purpose in this report is essentially threefold: to define the nature of the technical achievements which are missing, to underline their difficulty, and to add my voice to those who are attempting to show how urgent it is that we seek the goal in spite of its difficulties.

### THE CRISIS IN FOOD SUPPLY

In a country which historically has been concerned mainly with problems of food surplus, it is difficult to make the imminence of a catastrophic worldwide shortage of food seem very real or very near. Yet experts in demography and food production and an increasing number of political and scientific leaders are taking up the cry. Indeed, the facts are plain and their meaning inexorable

* Research sponsored by the U. S. Atomic Energy Commission under contract AEC W-7405-eng-26 with the Union Carbide Corporation.

to anyone who takes the trouble to look at them.  I quote from a
recent address[2] by the Hon. Frank Carlson, U. S. Senator from
Kansas:

> . . . the impending world crisis of mass starvation. . . is
> coming about at such an amazing pace that our national attitude
> and agricultural policies which, for 30 years, have centered
> upon ways to deal with crop surpluses, must be abruptly and
> unmistakably changed.  Abundant evidence -- supported by
> cold facts -- undeniably points to a world calamity, the true
> impact and effects of which are terrifying to consider.

The statistics of the increase of population and the growing
deficiency of food are readily available [3, 4, 5, 6, 7, 8, 9] and I will
not repeat them here.  Their import can be summarized in a few
statements:

1)  The world at present produces less food than an adequate
    minimum diet requires.
2)  The world has a very youthful population, and it is rapid-
    ly getting younger, so that the doubling of the population
    within about 35 years seems certain, even allowing for
    the most optimistic success with birth control efforts.
3)  As a very minimum, the output of food must double, per-
    haps triple, within the next 30 years.
4)  In the past, food output has been increased primarily by
    cultivating more land, but this will no longer be possible.
    The warm, fertile, well watered land is essentially all
    under cultivation, and only less favored or marginal land
    is available.  To find enough for a doubling of the world
    food output is beyond hope.

There are many proposed solutions to the problem and serious difficulties or inadequacies with nearly every one of them.
The rapid dissemination of birth control information and materials is, of course, an important first step, but it is not enough.

Measures offered as partial or total solutions to the food problem itself include huge increases in world fertilizer output, attempts to control weather and rainfall, big projects to develop and
control water resources, development of methods of "farming"
the sea for fish, cultivation of tropical rain forests, adapting
plants to use saline water, development of edible algae (fed either
in the sea or by our petroleum resources), an all-out effort to increase the yield per acre on presently cultivated land, and, finally, bringing some of the immense areas of fertile arid land into
production using desalted water from the sea.

All of these methods have a certain amount of promise.  But
Dr. Roger Revelle, Director of the Harvard Center for Population
Study, in a recent address to the Washington Colloquium on Sci-
ence and Society, stated that there was serious doubt whether even

all of them together would be enough.  The main problem, he
pointed out, was time.  It takes time to develop new agricultural
techniques, to educate illiterate farmers, and to develop new
strains of high-yield crops which can withstand the fungus, insects, and other problems of agriculture in the underdeveloped
countries.  It will even take a considerable time to alert the developed countries to the significance and extent of the problem
and get them to commit the necessary resources to combat it.
And yet the exponential nature of population explosions gives us
very little time to initiate any counter measures.  We have, Dr.
Revelle indicated, only about 10 or, at most, 15 years to get anything we are going to attempt into full-scale action.  Any solution
which arrives after that time will be too late, since the pressures
of the explosion itself will be starting to be felt, and any rational
activities inside the underdeveloped countries may be impossible.

## FARMING ARID LAND WITH DISTILLED WATER

I shall not attempt to assess the various proposed measures
listed above, nor to relate the prospects for arid land cultivation
to the other methods; as Dr. Revelle says, all of them may be
needed.  The cultivation of arid land has the major advantage,
however, that presently available crop varieties and farming techniques of the United States arid West can probably be used.  The
use of desalinated water will itself dictate the preferred choices
of irrigation technique, but these will be adaptations of proven
methods.

In order to visualize the nature of such a route to major food
supplies, however, it is important to note the differences which
this type of agriculture would have from our usual farming methods.  The following list summarizes the salient points, most of
which were developed more fully in my previous article.

1) The land used must have essentially a year-round growing season in order that the investment in water supply,
water distribution, sprinklers, etc., can be used at high
load factor.

2) Crop utilization of water must be high to minimize the
consumption of desalinated water.  The U.S. Department
of Agriculture, Agricultural Research Service, has
shown that over 5000 pounds of grain (wheat and corn)
can be produced per acre foot of water applied, and their
experts have indicated that these results should be readily transferable to the field conditions which would obtain
in arid land irrigated with distilled water.  Compared
with present average yields of 1200 pounds per acre foot,
such efficiency would be equivalent to a 75 per cent cut
in the cost of water.

3) Sprinkler irrigation would be preferred.  In order to
achieve high efficiency of water use by the crop, water

application must be even and controllable. Sprinkler irrigation best meets these requirements, although for some crops and soils other methods would be acceptable.
4) The optimum amount of fertilizer should be used. The tests of high efficiency of water utilization by the Agricultural Research Service showed that when less water is wasted, less fertilizer is wasted also, since there is little percolation below the root zone. The fertilizer application must be made at the right time in the growth cycle so that the plant does not produce rank growth which would increase its demand for water without increasing yield.
5) With distilled water less drainage would be required. If properly conducted with high efficiency of water use, farming operations with distilled water should not require artificial drainage in most soils. The high purity of the water means that evapotranspiration will not increase the salinity of the soil, so that after any initial salinity is flushed out, the water table would not be expected to be greatly affected.

## DUAL-PURPOSE VS. SINGLE-PURPOSE
## WATER PLANTS

If nuclear desalination is to have a major role in world food production, it must be available in underdeveloped lands where agriculture is still the principal activity. This means that, while some electric power would be needed, the ratio of water to power ($\omega$) would have to be much higher than could be obtained from present power reactors using back-pressure turbines. Table I shows several types of reactors, their steam conditions, and the resulting values of $\omega$ (Mgd/Mwe), with 35-psia back pressure and performance ratio of 10.

If, as seems likely, it will be essential to achieve higher values of $\omega$, or even plants which produce no power other than their own requirements, there are two main routes which appear feasible. One route is to use the shaft energy of the back-pressure

TABLE I

Water-Power Ratio for Various Reactor Types

| Type of Reactor | Steam Pres. | Temp. | $\omega$ MGD/MWe(net) |
|---|---|---|---|
| Boiling Water | 965 psia | 540°F | 0.47 |
| Pressurized Water | 640 | 493 | 0.56 |
| Heavy Water Organic | 900 | 725 | 0.46 |
| Gas Cooled | 1450 | 1000 | 0.44 |
| Sodium Graphite | 3500 | 1000 | 0.21 |
| Fermi Fast Breeder | 576 | 760 | 0.69 |

turbine to drive some other kind of desalting process. The other route would be to develop evaporators capable of high-temperature operation and couple these directly to special low-temperature or process-heat reactors. These two approaches to a water-only or high ω plant are shown schematically in Figure 1. The low-temperature evaporator referred to is the technology we have now, in which the problems of scale formation and corrosion are fairly well understood up to a maximum brine temperature of about 250°F, which would require a turbine back pressure of about 35 psia.

The upper diagram shows that for the first route the same reactor could be used to produce energy for either a dual-purpose plant or a water-only plant having two types of water conversion. The conventional low-temperature evaporator utilizing the 35-psia steam from the back-pressure turbine is the same, but the shaft energy of the turbine drives (a) an electric generator to give a dual-purpose plant, (b) a high-pressure water pump for a reverse osmosis plant, or (c) a steam compressor or a freezing plant compressor.

The lower diagram shows a low-temperature process-heat reactor which delivers heat directly to a high-temperature (e.g., 325°F) evaporator. The low-temperature portion of this evaporator would, of course, be very similar to the low-temperature evaporator in the upper diagram.

Let us examine briefly what we would have to accomplish to develop a successful agricultural water plant with each of these approaches as compared with dual-purpose plants. As is clear from the diagram, the first route would use the same type of reactor, turbine, and low-temperature evaporator as the dual-purpose plant, but these components must be larger and cost less. The counterpart of the electric generator, however, does not exist in a suitably developed form for the purpose. Of the several possibilities, only the vapor compressor evaporator can so far be characterized sufficiently to permit economic projections and to define the scope of a development program. (The membrane and freezing processes, however, must not be neglected. When sufficient engineering data are available, they should be compared with the vapor compressor evaporator.) The heat transfer equipment used with a vapor compressor would represent the same general block of technology as the exhaust steam evaporator. The principal new element then is the compressor itself. Because of the plant which OSW has built at Roswell, the operating factors for such compressors are known. The development of several very large wind tunnels in this country and the compressor technology developed at the Oak Ridge Gaseous Diffusion Plants make it possible to assess the aerodynamic and engineering problems of developing a very large steam vapor compressor.

The second route requires two new blocks of technical progress -- the low-temperature reactor and the high-temperature

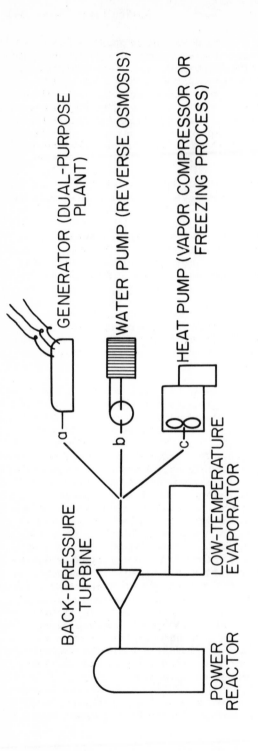

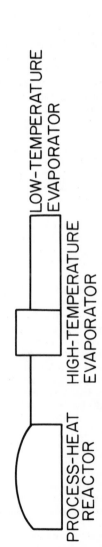

Figure 1. Schematic Diagrams of Alternative Routes to Single-Purpose Plants.

portion of the evaporator.  The high-temperature evaporator is a
relatively formidable technical problem, since it requires a method of controlling alkaline and sulfate scales which is effective up
to about $325^{\circ}F$ and costs very little to employ.  It also requires
suitable and inexpensive construction materials which will not cor-
rode at the elevated temperature.  The low-temperature or process-heat reactor would not have to explore new realms of materials technology, but could probably count upon making use primarily of information found in the course of power reactor development.  Yet it would still require a substantial development expense,
since the heat cost from such a reactor must be very low, and this
would necessitate detailed development and pilot-scale trials of
fuel manufacturing and processing methods.  A prototype reactor
would also be necessary.

At first glance it would seem easy to make a selection between these routes to water-only technology.  The cost of the vapor
compressor is a relatively small item in the cost of water, and
the main elements of its development to large size already exist.
The principal uncertainty is whether this route would ever produce cheap enough water, since it is clear that the water-only
station must not only use a more expensive form of heat than a
dual-purpose evaporator, but it must support the cost of the turbine and compressor to convert it for use.  Thus, with the same
cost for heat transfer surface, the vapor compressor plant can
only approach, but never equal, the economics of the dual-purpose
plant.

The process heat reactor matched to a high-temperature evaporator, though requiring a more difficult development, holds
strong promise of ending up with lower cost water than a dual-
purpose plant using a power reactor energy source.  There is not
enough information at the present time to make a correct choice
between these two routes.  The exigencies of the world food situation seem to compel that both be explored through some initial
phase.  The very short time available would make the vapor compressor route attractive in order that a pilot food-growing experiment could be set up as soon as possible.  On the other hand,
every decrease in the cost of water would mean enormous savings
of capital resources if the building of such stations became a major part of the battle for food production.  Thus the system of
lowest ultimate cost must be sought and developed within the 10 to
15 year time limit indicated by the food crisis.


## HOW MUCH CAN WE AFFORD?

Leaving for the moment the question of whether there is enough
time, we also need to discuss the question of how much the industrialized part of the world can afford to commit to such a battle
and whether there is hope of success short of ruin.  If the predictions of Dr. Revelle and the other experts are correct, no realistic limit can be set, for survival itself would be at stake.  Some

perspective, however, can be gained by putting the question in a way suggested by Gale Young, Assistant Director of Oak Ridge National Laboratory. He asks: "If arid land farming doubled the price of grain (i.e., water cost equaled present grain price), how many people could be provided for by the present U.S. defense budget?"

To answer this question, we can assume that the underdeveloped lands could provide the arid land, land preparation, and farm labor, and that our aid could be devoted to furnishing water and fertilizer. At 1000 pounds of grain per person (a semiadequate diet) and 2¢ per pound of grain (equal to present price), a $30 billion annual input would sustain 1.5 billion persons, which is the expected increase of population by about 1985. I consider this to be an encouraging result, since other countries and other measures could carry some of the burden. The $30 billion figure is less than ruinous, and there may be a substantial opportunity to lower the water cost for a pound of grain below that assumed above ($45 per acre-foot). Thus it would seem that making the deserts bloom might be a major factor in meeting the food crisis. It also appears that time, rather than financial resource, would be limiting.

## THE PRESENT ECONOMIC VALUE OF WATER
## IN AGRICULTURE

Another valuable source of perspective in grasping the magnitude and difficulty of achieving artificial water supplies which are technically and economically suited to the task is in leaving aside for awhile any consideration of crisis and determining how far we are from the goal in a purely commercial way. To do this we must estimate the present value of water for crop production and then relate this to present trends in desalinated water cost.

In my previous paper, cited above, I have shown that several methods can be used to show the range of prices that farmers of high-value crops can afford to pay for water. One extreme is shown by areas such as Israel, Egypt, etc., where local conditions make export crops profitable with water costing over $100 per acre-foot, especially if it can be blended with brackish water. Such cases need not concern us here, except to show that the market for agricultural water overlaps substantially the market for municipal and industrial water. In the United States the range of prices actually paid by private irrigators extends up to $45 per acre-foot.

The large western irrigation projects in the United States are arranged so that title to the land carries with it right to purchase project water at a determined price. The extent that land values in such areas have risen above the cost of preparing the ground provides a measure of the economic value of the water rights. Such a calculation indicates that Colorado River water is worth from $30 to $50 per acre-foot to an efficient irrigator in the Southwest, if his investment in land were only the cost of preparation. This checks well enough with the $45 figure mentioned above.

V. W. Ruttan in a recent study of the economic opportunity for irrigation projects in the United States [10] concludes that an average economic incentive (increased yield) for irrigating an acre of land is over $400 per acre in the Southwest and even higher in some parts of the eastern United States. Deducting the cost of preparing the land, etc., this would correspond to water values greater than $50 per acre-foot.

At the other end of the value range, the basic food grains, corn and wheat, are grown extensively in the West on irrigated land with water costing (incrementally) about $10-20 per acre-foot. These crops are usually part of a multicrop sequence, and perhaps the grain does not bear its full share of water rights cost.

The value of water noted above is (in the West) based on Colorado River water, whose high salinity requires extensive flushing and other waste. We have noted above that farming with distilled water could be accomplished with much less water per unit of food output, so the economic value of desalted water should be corrected to allow for this increased efficiency. Although the water consumption efficiency experiments would indicate the value could be more than doubled, I have added only 50 per cent to the value when used on grain crops and much less when used on high-value crops. Thus the range of economic value for distilled water might extend from $65 per acre-foot downward for high-value crops and from $30 per acre-foot and down for grains.

Provided that low-cost land is available, it would seem reasonable to expect that some use of water for agriculture would begin at $65 per acre-foot and substantial quantities would find a market at any price below $45. The production would be primarily high-value crops (which constitute about half the dollar value of all crops in the United States). At $30 per acre-foot or below, the market would be very large, would include basic food grains, and desalinated water could be considered a strong possibility for assisting in the world food crisis on a strictly commercial basis. This is a conservative assumption, since it is based on the present price of 2¢ per pound for grain. The relative value of food would, of course, be expected to rise in times of worldwide famine. A one-cent rise in price would increase the value of water used in its production by about $30 per acre-foot.

Water at $65 per acre-foot seems to be within the reach of present technology, since the projected cost of water for the MWD project [11] is nearly that low. But for $45 and $30 costs, some improvement in technology will be necessary. Let us now see what degrees of improvement are thus implied.

## COMPONENTS OF THE COST OF WATER

The cost of water as received by the farmer includes several components which we must identify and subtract in order to choose the types of energy source which may be suitable. These components include delivery cost, capital cost of the evaporator plant, operation and maintenance of the water plant, and heat cost. The only size plant which is considered in the following analysis is one billion gallons per day. This choice was made for two reasons: It is the largest size for which extensive design and cost studies have been made, and it is small enough so that all its water output can be consumed on farms within 20 miles of the plant, thus keeping delivery costs low.

### Cost of Distribution

At 90 per cent load factor, the annual output of a 1-BGD plant is one million acre-feet of water, which would provide 4 feet of water to an area of 250,000 acres. Let us assume that the water is to be distributed to such an area lying within a 400,000-acre semicircle (20-mile radius) surrounding the plant; the rest of the land is available for other purposes. The cost of distribution facilities would be about $45 million dollars, as shown in Table II.

This estimate was made using information furnished by the Bureau of Reclamation for lined, open ditches and appropriate other facilities. For head losses of about 50 feet and a capital charge rate of 4 per cent, the total annual costs for distribution would be about $2 million, or $2 per acre-foot of water. For our range of costs to the farmer of $30-$45 per acre-foot, we have an equivalent cost at the plant of $28-$43 per acre-foot.

### TABLE II

Cost of Distribution Facilities

| Facilities | Cost (in Millions) |
|---|---|
| Main Canals | $ 1.8 |
| Bridges | 1.4 |
| Pumping Stations | 10.0 |
| Transmission Lines | 0.9 |
| Turnouts, Gates, etc. | 0.4 |
| Lateral Canals (at $120/acre) | 30.0 |
| | $44.5 |

### Cost of Evaporators

In spite of the fact that no one has yet constructed a very large seawater evaporator, the costs of constructing such a plant can be estimated with reasonable accuracy, provided the fundamental process parameters are well known and these are preserved in the scaled-up plant. At Oak Ridge we have just completed for the

Office of Saline Water a study in depth of flash-type evaporators
in sizes ranging from 150 to 1000 MGD. For this study we utilized
accepted process characteristics, but introduced improvements in
plant arrangement, method of construction, and auxiliary systems
which we found were suited to the large scale of the installation.
The experience of the ORGDP staff in engineering of very large
plants contributed substantially to the soundness and ingenuity of
the design. The cost estimates in this study are very detailed and
should be attainable in the field by the time that anyone could undertake to construct a 1000-MGD plant. Today's bid prices would,
of course, be somewhat higher.

In order to illustrate the relationship between the cost of water and the cost of the heat supplied to the evaporator, we must
develop the cost of the evaporator system at various performance
ratios, since this parameter of the evaporator is always adjusted
to make the most economical choice for the cost of heat. As part
of the AEC program at Oak Ridge we are studying intensively certain aspects of the coupling economics. A computer code has been
developed which constructs an accurate model of the evaporator
design and which can optimize the plant for any given conditions,
making changes in 58 different parameters as it does so. The
code has been equipped with a cost storage library using the detailed information from OSW design studies.

For the purposes of this article I could have requested the
code to print out a curve showing the cost of water versus heat
cost, but this would probably be accpetable only to those readers
who were thoroughly familiar with the Oak Ridge code and the assumptions used in the calculation. Instead, I would like to start
only with information about the cost of certain components of the
plant and develop the cost of water vs. cost of heat curve in a
visible fashion.

### Cost of Components vs. R

Figures 2 through 5 show how the cost of eight major components or systems in the plant varied as the design was optimized
in turn for performance ratios (R) of 7 through 12, for a plant of
1000 MGD capacity. Separate cases were run for different maximum brine temperatures, but here I will refer only to the 250°F
cases.

The cost includes 22 per cent indirect costs, such as engineering, interest during construction, and contingency. The eight
major systems accounted for nearly all the cost of the plant; the
remainder was collected into a miscellaneous item.

It was found to be quite easy to fit the curves in Figures 2
through 5 with simple analytic expressions in R which gave an excellent match between R equals 7 and R equals 12. These expressions are listed in the second column of Table III. The sum of
these expressions, with only a minor rounding, gives the expres-

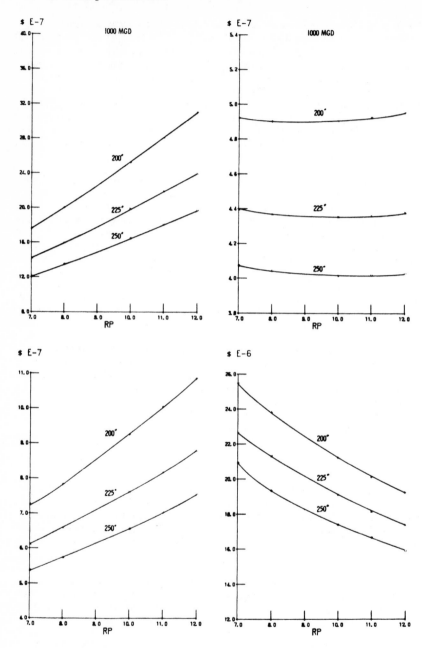

Figure 2. Capital Cost

    - Evaporator Area
    - Shell

Figure 3. Capital Cost

    - Pumps and Motors
    - Brine Heater

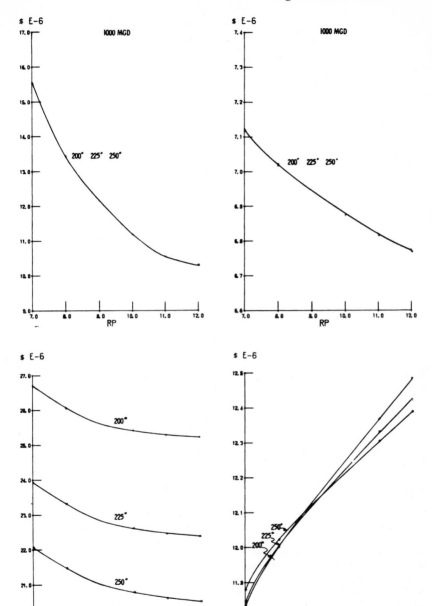

Figure 4.  Capital Cost

    - Water Intake
    - Valves and Piping

Figure 5.  Capital Cost

    - Chemical System
    - Deaerator System

TABLE III

Capital Cost (¢/dg) of Components

| Components | Present Flash* Evaporator System | Advanced System |
|---|---|---|
| Surface | $1.0 + 1.56R$ | $1 + .7R$ |
| Shell | $2.3 \cdot 0.43R$ | $2 + .3R$ |
| Pumps & Motors | $4.05$ | $4$ |
| Brine Heater | $\frac{8.3}{R} + 0.9$ | $\frac{8}{R} + 1$ |
| Water Intake | $\frac{8.7}{R} + 0.3$ | $\frac{8}{R} + 1$ |
| Valves & Piping | $\frac{2.5}{R} + 1.84$ | $\frac{3}{R} + 1$ |
| Chemical System | $\frac{.58}{R} + .63$ | $\frac{1}{R} + 1$ |
| Deaerator | $1.13 + .009R$ | $1 + .01R$ |
| Miscellaneous | $3.0$ | $2$ |
| Total | $15 + 2.00R + \frac{20}{R}$ | $14 + R + \frac{20}{R}$ |

* "Present Flash" costs, as noted before, represent present designs using "available" technology and are somewhat more advanced than current bid offerings.

sion at the bottom, which gives the cost of the whole plant with
good accuracy.

### Advanced Plants

Although the OSW's program for development of advanced
evaporators is just getting under way, it is already evident that
some remarkable improvements in the performance of heat exchangers and in the prevention of chemical scale may be in the
offing.  So that we do not imply that the entire burden for improvements in water cost must come from reactor improvements, we
must take some account of these advanced flash evaporators.  In
the third column of Table III, I have tried to estimate the way each
major component would be affected if improved heat transfer tubing of the types already being tested in our loops at Oak Ridge
were successful, and if scale-control means, such as carbon dioxide injection, could be worked out to eliminate the addition of
sulfuric acid.  Naturally, there is no assurance that the improvements will all be successful or that they will have the economic
effect which I have assumed in column 3.

Figure 6 shows a plot of the total cost expressions from
Table III.  The plot extends from R equals 3 to R equals 12, although we must remember that the information used extended only
between 7 and 12.  (Extrapolation to higher R is quite probably

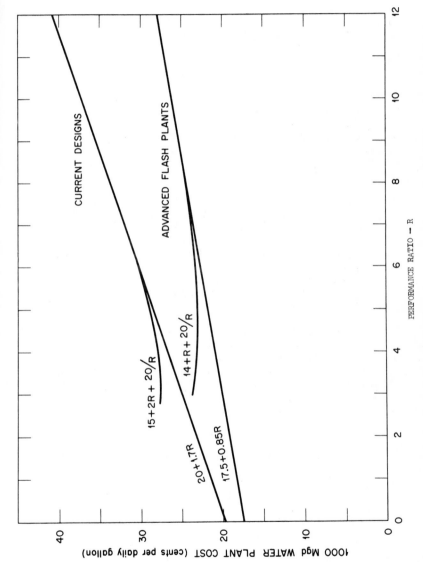

Figure 6. Capital Cost of a 1000 MGD Evaporator as a Function of Performance Ratio

valid. )  Over the range which we wish to use,  one can readily see
that the curve is,  in fact,  straight enough to permit the three-
term expression to be replaced by a linear equation without loss
of accuracy.

## Calculation of Water Cost

The ground rules used for the water cost calculation are as
follows:

1) Load factor equals 0. 9.
2) Fixed charge rate on capital (interest,  amortization,  and
   insurance) equals 5. 6 per cent.
3) Maintenance labor materials and supplies equals 1. 0 per
   cent of total construction cost per year.
4) Operating labor for a 1000-MGD plant will be 0. 27¢/1000
   gallon ($888, 000/yr) for a current plant and 0. 25¢ for a
   more automated one.
5) Sulfur, if used,  costs 1. 3¢/1000 gal of product.  (The
   cost of the plant includes an on-site acid plant. )
6) Pumping power will cost 1. 3¢/1000 gal of product for a
   current plant, 0. 7¢ for an advanced plant.  The decrease
   is primarily in the expected cost of power, although the
   amount used may go down also.
7) Miscellaneous costs equal 0. 13¢ and 0. 05¢, respectively,
   to round the sum of the operating costs to 3¢ and 1¢/1000
   gal.

The fixed charges and maintenance charges can be converted
easily to ¢/1000 gal of product by multiplying the construction
cost in cents per daily gallon by 0. 2, since 1 GPD is 0. 329 kilogal-
lon per year, and 0. 066/0. 329 equals 0. 20.  The cost of heat, H,
in ¢/MBtu can be converted to ¢/1000 gal by multiplying by $8.3/R$
since it requires 8. 3 MBtu to distill 1000 gallons, and R is the
number of times the heat is reused.

TABLE IV

Calculation of Water Cost

| Evaporator | Current Designs | Advanced |
|---|---|---|
| Capital Cost (¢/daily gallon) | 15 + 2R + 20/R | 14 + R + 20/R |
| Equivalent Expression | 20 + 1. 7R | 17. 5 + 0. 85R |
| Water Cost (¢/1000 gal) | 3 + 0. 2(20 + 1. 7R) + 8. 3 H/R | 1 + 0. 2(17. 5 + 0. 85R) + 8. 3 H/R |
| Optimum R | 4. 94   H | 7   H |
| Minimum Water Cost[*] | 7 + 3. 36   H | 4. 5 + 2. 38   H |

[*]R is eliminated by substituting the optimum R in the water cost
equation, which makes the second and third terms equal.

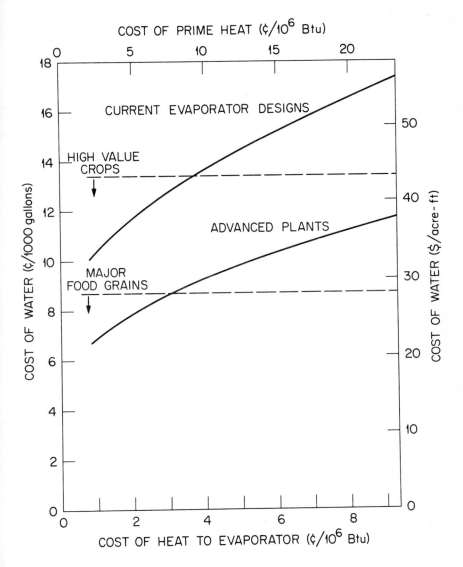

Figure 7.   Cost of Water as a Function of the Cost of Heat

The cost of water, then, can be calculated for any value of heat by the expressions in Table IV.

Figure 7 shows a plot of water cost from Table IV in ¢/1000 gal and in $/acre-ft versus the cost of the heat supplied to the evaporator (at about 260°F). The region between these curves covers a range of water costs which encompasses the agricultural market; the range of evaporator technology extends, as noted above, from essentially current (except for size) to hoped-for future advances. The range of heat costs shown covers an equally wide spread of technology progress. The reminder should be made that these curves apply only to 1000-MGD low-temperature evaporators. Smaller plants would produce more costly water, larger ones less costly water, at the same technological level.

## RELATION OF EXHAUST STEAM COST
## TO PRIME STEAM COST

The curves in Figure 7, using the bottom scale, are based on a steam supply at 255°F and would thus be appropriate for the exhaust steam portion of a vapor compressor type water-only station as discussed in Section 3. They would also be correct for a single-purpose, low-temperature reactor producing 255°F steam.

If the reactor can produce steam at a higher temperature at the same cost (and if the water plant can be designed for it), then the cost of water can be lowered, or, conversely, the same cost water can be made with a higher prime steam cost. In the direct coupled type of plant this would require a special high-temperature portion of the evaporator which has not yet been developed. In the vapor compressor type the high-temperature portion of the energy is converted into a larger quantity of low-temperature energy, so that the same evaporator technology can be used.

Defining the appropriate increase in prime steam cost which would just offset any increase in steam temperature above 255°F requires cost information about single-purpose water plants which does not yet exist. On an analytical basis, I have selected a projected vapor compressor water plant cost which permits a preliminary calculation of prime steam value relative to exhaust steam value as a function of temperature. The value used would be "optimistic" for a vapor compressor plant and "pessimistic" for a direct coupled plant.

When such a calculation is made for various energy sources, the prime steam is found to have a value in the range of 2 to 3 times the exhaust steam cost. For the most common nuclear systems the ratio is close to 2.5, which will do for our present discussion. Along the top of Figure 7 I have shown the prime steam cost which corresponds to the exhaust steam value with this assumption.

## PRIME ENERGY COST REQUIRED TO REACH
## AGRICULTURAL GOALS

If the opportunity for desalted water in agriculture begins as we have assumed at a water cost of $43 per acre-foot at the plant, Figure 7 shows that current evaporator technology will require a prime energy cost of less than 10¢/MBtu. With the advanced evaporator, however, the market is reached and well entered, even with a steam cost of about 25¢/MBtu, which is attainable with commercially available reactors under municipal financing.

For a large penetration of the agricultural water market, we have assumed above that $30/ft must be reached, or $28 at the plant. This cost appears attainable with the advanced flash plant at an energy cost of about 8¢/MBtu, according to Figure 7.

In summary, then, if one is optimistic about advances in the evaporator art, artificial agricultural water is definitely in the picture, regardless of any major improvements in the cost of energy. If, at the same time, one could see a way to expect energy costs below 8¢/MBtu, desalination would have a major impact on the market for water and for nuclear reactors. If one is skeptical about evaporator improvements, then a 10¢ energy source is necessary even for "openers" in the game. The difference between $45 water and $30 water would not be an important factor in its acceptability for municipal use, but in agriculture the difference is crucial. To produce this much improvement in the cost, we must reduce the cost of prime energy to about one-third of its present cost.


## CONCLUSIONS

In one sense it is premature to try to define the future role of nuclear desalination for agriculture, when no large city supply plant is yet operating. So far one plant is under construction (in the USSR), the Israel plant has been found feasible, and the MWD station has reached the final stages of negotiation. These pioneer plants are essential steps in development of a brand new resource, and all that I have said in this article is based on the premise that full support and emphasis is given to getting them built and operating successfully.

In another and overriding sense the utmost urgency should be given to seeking the possibilities of agricultural desalination. If watering the arid lands can become a factor in meeting the world food crisis -- the most crucial test which civilization has ever faced -- then time is already short. We must rapidly explore and compare this and other solutions to the problem, choose which routes are to be undertaken, and proceed with development at a pace far different from that which would be used for normal commercial development.

The basic technical information now available seems adequate for making desalted water supplies economically feasible for cities. This information must be converted into proven engineering practice by constructing and operating the first plants. For agricultural water supplies, there are important gaps in our technical ability. First, we must develop one or more approaches to a single-purpose plant, or one which produces only a little power. Second, we must hasten the development of low-cost, high-performance evaporators. Third, we must choose and develop nuclear reactors which can supply energy at much lower cost than present reactors. Finally, we must prove out our new information in experimental and prototype plants and prepare to scale them up to sizes far larger than would ever be needed for city water sources.

The difficulty of these tasks is not small. The element of urgency introduced by the food crisis adds greatly to the problem, especially for the reactors. If 20 years or so were available, the nuclear power industry would have matured, and a relatively easy spin-off to agricultural reactors could be taken. Without it, a parallel program aimed directly at the agricultural energy source may be needed.

## ACKNOWLEDGMENTS

The opinions expressed in this article are my own and do not represent any official statements of the Oak Ridge National Laboratory, the Atomic Energy Commission, or the Office of Saline Water. However, the technical data was based on work by members of the Oak Ridge Nuclear Desalination Program supported by AEC and OSW. Although many contributed, I am especially grateful for the assistance of R. A. Ebel and C. C. Burwell. The advice of Gale Young helped greatly in organizing the presentation.

## NOTES

1. R. P. Hammond,  Nuclear Desalting for Agricultural Water, Nucleonics, Vol. 23, No. 9, pp. 51-55, Sept. 1965.

2. Address by the Hon. Frank Carlson,  The Importance of Reclamation to Agriculture,  delivered to 34th Annual Meeting, National Reclamation Association, Kansas City, Missouri, Nov. 11, 1965.

3. A. M. Carr-Saunders,  World Population  (Oxford University Press, 1936).

4. United Nations,  The Future Growth of World Population,  U. N. Population Studies No. 28 (New York, 1958).

5. Frank W. Notestein,  World Population Determinants in the Future, Symposium on World Population and Food Supplies, American Society of Agronomy, spec. pub. No. 6 (Madison, Wisconsin, 1965).

6. Lester R. Brown,  Man, Land and Food,  Foreign Agricultural Economic Report No. 11 (U. S. Dept. of Agriculture, 1963).

7. Merrill K. Bennett,  The World's Food (Harper Bros., New York, 1954).

8. L. Goreux,  Long Range Projection of Food Consumption, F. A. O. Monthly Bulletin (June, 1957).

9. Lester R. Brown,  Population Growth, Food Needs and Production Problems, Symposium on World Population and Food Supplies, American Society of Agronomy, spec. pub. No. 6 (Madison, Wisconsin, 1965).

10. V. W. Ruttan,  The Economic Demand for Irrigated Acreage, (The Johns Hopkins Press, 1965).

11. Bechtel Corporation Report to the Metropolitan Water District of Southern California, Engineering and Economic Feasibility Study, Phases I and II, for a Combination Nuclear Power-Desalting Plant (June 15, 1965).

# 25. Water-Only Plant Studies

Richard L. Clark, Scientific Development Department, Bechtel Corporation

Much of the recent engineering work in the field of desalting has concentrated on large dual-purpose plants. Indications are that the costs of desalted water from such plants may be approaching those of developing new sources of natural water in certain areas. But in many parts of the world the water requirement, or the ratio of power to water demand, are not great enough to justify a large dual-purpose water plant. In some cases, it is difficult to integrate the water and power systems. As a result, most of the desalting plants in the world today produce water only.

In this paper several studies on the cost of desalted water are analyzed to investigate the technical and economic differences between dual-purpose and water-only plants. Recent investigations have considered a number of questions including, how much cheaper will water be from big plants, how does the plant capital cost decrease with size, how much cheaper is it to desalinate water in a dual-purpose plant which sells power as a by-product, how can present-day processes be scaled up to larger sizes, what kind of material should the plants be made of, and how long will they last ?

For large plants multistage flash distillation has received the most attention, but vertical tube multiple effect distillation has also been studied. Other conversion methods, such as freezing, membrane separation, etc. , are not presently developed to the point of large scale commercial operation on sea water. Questions common to all of these studies include what operating load factors can be achieved, how big can present-day plants be built without major engineering risks, what interest rate, amortization, insurance and taxes will be paid, what is the cost of energy to the plants and what is the optimum plant design ?

The results of all of these studies are in reasonably good agreement, permitting some broad conclusions to be drawn. First, the cost of desalted water is reduced from approximately $1 per thousand gallons at the MGD plant size, to somewhat between 30 and 50 cents per thousand gallons at the 50 MGD size, dropping below 30 cents per thousand gallons in dual-purpose plants producing 150 MGD. The predicted water cost becomes less than 20 cents per thousand gallons in BGD plants. It is generally conceded that desalted water costs below 10 cents per thousand gallons can only be achieved, without subsidy, by major advances beyond the present state-of-the-art, and then only in very large plants.

It may further be concluded that, in small plants, the most economical energy source is fossil fuel. But in large plants a nuclear reactor usually is the most economical source of heat. There is no sharp dividing line separating fossil fuel applications from nuclear applications because the choice depends upon the local fossil fuel cost, the plant financing arrangements, site availability and the possibility of dual-purpose operation. Finally, for the multistage flash process, the water plant investment per unit capacity drops from approximately $1.50 per gallon per day at the MGD size to approximately 75 cents per gallon per day at the 50 MGD size, and levels off at a price not much below this as one goes to extremely large plants. These prices are representative of the present-day market but would vary with the particular plant efficiency, choice of materials for heat transfer surface, and design philosophy.

The design concepts studied by Oak Ridge National Laboratory[1] result in plant cost estimates significantly below 75 cents per gallon of capacity in large plants. The design concepts which result in these lower plant costs include very long condenser tubing, automated condenser bundle assembly, multiple level evaporator vessels and improved heat transfer coefficients.

## DUAL-PURPOSE OR WATER-ONLY PLANTS?

The foregoing discussion applies whether the water plant is dual-purpose, making both power and water, or single-purpose, making water only. The major difference between the two is that water-only plants are usually designed for higher efficiencies to reduce their heat demand. A review of the recent studies of desalinated water cost leads one to several conclusions concerning the choice between water-only and dual-purpose installations. First, dual-purpose plants produce water more cheaply than water-only plants if the power produced in a dual-purpose plant is sold at the same price as power from a separate power plant of the same size. This method of cost allocation credits the water plant with most of the cost advantages resulting from dual-purpose operation.

One investigation,[2] which compared dual-purpose and water-only plants on this basis, showed estimated cost of desalinated water at 34 cents per thousand gallons dual-purpose, and 43 cents per thousand gallons single-purpose. Both produced 150 MGD, but the dual-purpose plant marketed 508 Mw of electrical power. In this example, water was nine cents per thousand gallons more expensive from a water-only plant than from a dual-purpose plant.

Why is water more expensive from a single-purpose, or water-only, plant? Primarily, because it must pay more for heat. Present-day multistage flash plants use low-pressure steam to supply heat to the brine heaters. In a dual-purpose plant this low-pressure steam is provided at a reduced price as back-pressure steam from the power plant turbine. Since it costs very nearly as much to generate the low-pressure steam needed to run a water-only plant as it costs to generate high-pressure power plant steam, the water-only plant pays a steam cost penalty.

A second reason that water-only plants must pay more for steam is that a water-only installation has a smaller prime steam generator which is not as economical as the larger prime steam generator in a dual-purpose plant producing the same amount of water. Frequently, a water-only plant must pay more for pumping power than a dual-purpose plant which is coupled with a new power plant.

The decision to build a dual-purpose water plant or a water-only plant may be straight-forward. If there is a need for new power generating capacity, if a plant site is available within economical reach of the power and water distribution systems, if the power plant is intended for base-load operation, and if the power company and water agency are interested in a joint undertaking, then the dual-purpose plant is the most economical choice. But, if the power and water demand areas are widely distributed or are not most economically located on a single site, or if long-term base-load operation of the power plant is questionable, or if the demand growth pattern of the two utilities does not permit simultaneous construction of a new facility, then the single-purpose cost penalty is not sufficient to make the choice obvious. When this is the case, it is necessary to compare the alternative costs to choose between dual-purpose and water-only operation.

An example of a combination which led to the selection of a dual-purpose installation as the most economical is the plant being evaluated for the Metropolitan Water District of Southern California.[3] In this case, the growth in power demand in the Los Angeles area justifies the installation of two new nuclear power plants in conjunction with a desalination plant. A man-made island off the Orange County coast provides a site convenient to the power distribution facilities of the utility companies and at the same time is near enough to the established water distribution facilities of the Metropolitan Water District that the product water delivery costs are minimized. Finally, the excellent cooperation between the utility companies, The Southern California Edison Company, San Diego Gas & Electric Company and the City of Los Angeles Department of Water and Power, and the Metropolitan Water District made it possible to develop plans for steam supply arrangements and a plant construction schedule acceptable to all parties.

## WATER-ONLY PLANT DEVELOPMENT

Since the major difference between water-only and dual-purpose plants is how much they pay for steam and how efficiently they use the steam, the development of water-only plants to produce lower cost water will depend on innovations which will reduce the cost of energy as well as improvements in water conversion processes. Much of the water conversion process development work now programmed will be applicable to both dual-purpose and water-only plants. Efforts to improve heat transfer coefficients, condenser design, tubing fabrication and installation methods, vessel design, pumps and auxiliary equipment, are equally applicable to both kinds of plants. Development of saline water conversion processes other than multistage flash, such as vertical tube multiple effect and vapor compression applies to dual-purpose as well as water-only operation. One area of process development which applies specifically to water-only plants is higher temperature operation. This will permit more efficient use of the energy supplied to the brine heaters.

The present multistage flash distillation process is limited to a maximum temperature of 250°F by the formation of calcium sulfate scale. Tests and pilot plant operations on multieffect processes have been successful up to 290°F. If distillation processes such as multistage flash and multieffect evaporation could be operated at still higher temperatures, then more efficient plants could be built. Part of the government desalination program is directed toward achieving this. Scale prevention methods are being developed for operation at temperatures up to 350°F, the corrosion of materials in sea water and the properties of sea water and brines are being measured at elevated temperatures to provide more accurate data for plant design. Whether or not high temperature operation of water-only plants will produce lower cost water depends upon the results of development work now being performed.

## WATER-ONLY PLANT STUDIES

Two studies completed last year approached the problem of reducing the cost of desalination in water-only plants from opposite directions. In the first study, "The Optimum Brine Heater Outlet Temperature in Sea Water Conversion Evaporators," [4] the water plant's efficiency was increased by raising its maximum operating temperature up to 400°F, thereby reducing its energy demand. In the second study, of a "Deep Pool Reactor for Water Desalting," [5] the water plant's efficiency was held at present-day values but a special low-temperature nuclear reactor concept was designed to produce low temperature heat for the water plant.

MAXIMUM BRINE TEMPERATURE STUDY

The maximum brine temperature study was performed, for
the Office of Saline Water, to determine the optimum brine heater
outlet temperature in single-purpose sea water conversion evaporators. The optimum temperature is obtained by balancing the
steam cost savings in the more efficient high temperature plants
against the increased costs for pressure vessels, corrosion protection and scale control. It was first assumed that some method
would be available to prevent the formation of scale in multistage
flash evaporators operating at temperatures up to 400°F. Then,
plant designs were prepared and optimized to determine the minimum cost of converted water with maximum brine temperatures
of 250, 300, 350 and 400°F. A comparison was then made with
known acid pretreatment scale prevention costs to determine how
much a high temperature plant could afford to spend for scale
prevention if a successful process were developed.

In this study, a gas-fired boiler was used to generate medium
pressure steam which drove the water plant pump turbines and
then supplied heat to the brine heaters. Electric power was used
only for minor pumping, plant lighting and control purposes.

The desalination plant designs were based on present multistage flash process experience st 250°F, extrapolated to 400°F.
Four versions of multistage flash were evaluated; ordinary recycle multistage flash, multiple effect multistage flash, a split recycle version which feeds fresh sea water to the hottest stages,
and a variable temperature drop process which uses more stages
at the high temperature end of the plant. The variable temperature drop process looked most promising and was selected for detailed design and cost estimation. In all cases the plant size was
50 MGD.

The most economical plant configuration consisted of six parallel trains of 11-foot diameter cylindrical vessels, each 126 feet
long. The vessel trains were arranged on a sloping site in an in-
verted-U configuration, with the brine heater and recycle pumps
both at the lower end of the U. The brine flashed uphill for the
first 75 stages, being lifted 1.5 inches per stage and then flashed
downhill in the remaining stages. This arrangement allowed the
use of a maximum number of stages over the flashing range. No
high temperature corrosion data was available above 250°F, but
70-30 cupronickel was chosen for condenser tubing and vessel
cladding for cost estimating purposes.

Total plant capital cost estimates were made based on 1965
material prices for all cases. The cost of desalted water was
computed using an annual fixed charge rate of 5.54 per cent, a 30-
year plant life and a 90 per cent load factor. Fossil fuel prices
of 20, 30 and 40 cents per million Btu were used.

The results of this study, for one fuel cost, are summarized in Table I. They indicated that the cost of desalination in water-only plants may be reduced by increasing the maximum operating temperature, up to 350°F, but operation at higher temperatures may not be economical. A 50 MGD water-only plant with fuel available at 30 cents per million Btu would produce water at 39. 3 cents per 1, 000 gallons with a maximum operating temperature of 250°F. With the same site and economic conditions, a plant designed to operate at 350°F would produce water for 6 cents less at 33. 0 cents per 1, 000 gallons if scale could be prevented for the same cost as present-day acid treatment. To achieve this cost reduction it would also be necessary that the plant materials to resist corrosion up to 350°F should cost no more than 70-30 cupronickel cladding and condenser tubing.

## DEEP POOL REACTOR STUDY

The deep pool reactor study, for the Chicago Operations Office of the U. S. Atomic Energy Commission, evaluated the potential of a reactor concept proposed by the Chicago Operations Office to supply heat to water-only desalination plants. This study concentrated on the conceptual design of the reactor while the design and cost estimates of the water plants were based on prevailing multistage flash process experience.

In this concept the reactor core is submerged in a pool of its own coolant, which is demineralized water, in a steel-lined concrete tank extending 100 feet below grade and 50 feet above. The 140 foot head of water in the tank is sufficient to prevent boiling of the coolant at a maximum temperature of 270°F. The coolant circulates down through the core and is heated from 200°F to 270°F. The liquid coolant transmits heat directly to the sea water brine in liquid-to-liquid brine heaters located in a pit adjacent to the reactor tank.

The water plant was designed to absorb heat from the primary reactor coolant in three stages because the reactor design required a coolant range of 200 to 270°F. Three brine heater

TABLE I

High Temperature Water-only Plant Results
Fossil Fuel Price, 30¢/Million Btu

| | | | | |
|---|---|---|---|---|
| Maximum Brine Temperature, °F | 250 | 300 | 350 | 400 |
| Water Production, MGD | 50 | 50 | 50 | 50 |
| Fossil Fuel Boiler Size, MWt (gross) | 326 | 292 | 261 | -- |
| Water Plant Perf. Ratio lb. product/1000 Btu | 17. 5 | 21. 5 | 25. 0 | 28. 0 |
| Total Plant Cost, $ Millions | 39. 3 | 38. 0 | 37. 7 | 38. 2 |
| Cost of Water, Cents/1000 gal. | 39. 3 | 35. 4 | 33. 0 | 33. 3 |

stages were necessary because the temperature rise of brine in the brine heater is limited to about 10 degrees in a plant of normal efficiency. To cool the coolant to 200°F in a single brine heater, it would have been necessary to limit brine temperature to about 200°F, thus reducing the efficiency of the water plant and requiring a larger reactor.

To overcome this, the water plant was designed in three parallel modules, with maximum brine temperatures of 250, 223 and 201°F. The coolant leaving the reactor at 270°F flowed in series through the brine heaters, returning to the reactor pool at 200°F. The performance ratios for the three modules were 14.9, 11.7 and 10 pounds per 1000 Btu averaging 12.7, compared to 17.5 for the 250°F plant in the maximum brine temperature study.

The evaporator plant material specifications include carbon steel vessels with 70-30 cupronickel tubing for brine heater and condenser tubing throughout the water plant modules.

The reactor was fueled with Zircaloy-2 clad $UO_2$ and core parameters typical of current pressurized water-cooled power reactors were assumed. The control rods were actuated by 130-foot long extensions connected to drive mechanisms on the reactor tank lid at the top of the tank. Refueling was performed with the assistance of closed circuit TV cameras by transporting fuel under water to the spent fuel pit, at grade, adjacent to the reactor pit. Reactor auxiliaries, having functions similar to those in conventional nuclear power plants, include the coolant purification system, deaeration system, radioactive waste disposal system, spent fuel pit cooling and purification system, decay heat removal system, component cooling system, emergency poison injection system, ventilation and air cooling system and sea water cooling system. Due to the special reactor conditions, carbon steel was used more extensively than in power reactor systems.

Capital cost estimates based on 1965 material prices for three plant sizes -- 10, 50 and 200 MGD. The 10 and 200 MGD cost estimates were made by adjustments from the 50 MGD base case. The cost of desalted water was computed with an assumed plant life of 30 years and a 90 per cent load factor. For the Chicago Operations Office the fixed charge rate was assumed to be 7 per cent. Fuel cycle cost was taken at 17 cents per million Btu for a 400 MWt reactor based on estimated present-day costs. Electric power was assumed to be available at 6 mills/kwh.

The results of the deep pool reactor study are summarized in Table II, with the fixed charge rate adjusted to 5.54 per cent to permit comparison with the results of the high temperature study.

These results illustrate the reduction in desalted water cost with plant size. There was a 44 per cent reduction between 10 and 50 MGD but only 15 per cent reduction between 50 and 200

TABLE II

Deep Pool Reactor Study Results

| | | | |
|---|---|---|---|
| Water Production, MGD | 10 | 50 | 200 |
| Maximum Brine Temperature, °F | 250 | 250 | 250 |
| Reactor Thermal Rating, MWt | 70 | 400 | 1,600 |
| Total Plant Cost, $ Millions | 22 | 54 | 178 |
| Cost of Heat from Reactor, ¢/Million Btu | 74 | 31 | 23 |
| Cost of Water, Cents/1000 gal. | 81 | 45 | 38 |

TABLE III

Breakdown of Desalted Water Costs

Water Production, 50 MGD
Maximum Brine Temperature, 250°F

| | Maximum Brine Temperature Study | Deep Pool Reactor Study |
|---|---|---|
| Heat or Steam | 18.9 | 20.2 |
| Electric Power | 1.3 | 5.8 |
| Water Plant Capital | 13.2 | 14.6 |
| Water Plant O & M | 5.9 | 4.6 |
| Total Cost of Water | 39.3¢/1000 gal. | 45.2¢/1000 gal. |

MGD. The reduction in the cost of heat from the reactor is more striking with a 58 per cent reduction between 70 and 400 MWt and another 26 per cent between 400 and 1600 MWt. At 1600 MWt the cost of heat at 23 cents per million Btu is within 6 cents of the fuel cycle cost.

## COMPARISON OF RESULTS

It is interesting to compare the results of these two water-only plant studies. The 50 MGD plant from the deep pool reactor study and the 250°F maximum brine temperature plant using 30 cent fossil fuel, are the most nearly comparable. The fossil fueled plant's capital cost is lower by 27 per cent because, 1) the fossil fueled boiler is smaller and costs less than the reactor, 2) it is less expensive to build a multistage flash plant in one module operating with a single maximum brine temperature, and 3) the design basis for the study with the fossil fueled boiler was less conservative, being based on extrapolations of present technology.

A breakdown of the product water cost from these two plants is given in Table III. The majority of the difference in product water cost results from the fact that the reactor plant with a low temperature heat source required purchased power for all in-plant pumping while the fossil fueled plant, using steam turbine pump drives, purchased power only for minor pumping. This is not necessarily an advantage of fossil fuel, but it indicates that for water-only applications the availability of steam for turbine drives is desirable.

## CONCLUSIONS

Desalted water costs are lower from dual-purpose facilities, primarily because they pay less for heat. The cost difference between dual-purpose and water-only operation may be reduced if the single purpose water plant incorporates design features such as turbine driven pumps and a higher maximum brine temperature.

High temperature process development may reduce the cost of water from water-only plants if the cost of the high temperature scale prevention method is within a few cents of the cost of the present acid addition method.

Some attention might profitably be given to redesign of the Deep Pool Reactor which would permit increase in coolant flow to raise the temperature of the coolant returned to the reactor. Such a change would permit an increase in water plant efficiency and a reduction in fuel costs.

Even though most present desalting plants produce water only, there is a worthwhile cost incentive to build dual-purpose installations, if the local water and power demand, utility construction schedules and site location are all favorable.

## NOTES

1. Conceptual design study of a 250 MGD multistage flash distillation plant. ORNL Special Report-3912, Oak Ridge National Laboratory, February 1966.

2. Cost studies of large multistage flash saline water conversion plants, Office of Saline Water Report Number 116, March 1964.

3. Bechtel Corporation report to the Metropolitan Water District of Southern California, Engineering and Economic Feasibility Study for a Combination Nuclear Power and Desalting Plant, December 1965.

4.   Bechtel Corporation report to the Office of Saline Water,
     Study of the Optimum Brine Heater Outlet Temperature in Sea
     Water Conversion Evaporators, October 1965.

5.   Deep Pool Reactor for water desalting, COO-283, VC-80,
     Reactor Technology, TID-4500, 43rd Edition, June 30, 1965.

# 26. Dual-Purpose Nuclear Power and Desalting Plants

William H. Wilson, Bechtel Corporation

You have already read of the Government's interest and participation in the study of a large nuclear power and desalting plant for the Metropolitan Water District. Commissioner Ramey, Mr. Durante, and Assistant Secretary Holum have set the stage, culminating in the contract between MWD and the Government on August 18, 1964, and subsequently the subcontract between MWD and Bechtel on December 15, 1964.

It is my pleasure to present to you the events that have unfolded in Southern California since that time. First of all, just what is MWD?

## METROPOLITAN WATER DISTRICT

The Metropolitan Water District of Southern California (the District) is a public corporation organized for the purpose of supplying water to its member agencies for domestic, industrial, and other beneficial uses. The District supplies water to 13 cities, 12 municipal water districts, and one county water authority within the six southern California counties of Los Angeles, Orange, Riverside, San Bernadino, San Diego, and Ventura. The area served encompasses 4,500 square miles and has a population of 9.5 million.

During the fiscal year ending June 30, 1965, the District delivered over one million acre-feet of Colorado River water to its member agencies. In the early 1970's the District plans to receive imported water from northern California through the California State Water Project Aqueduct now under construction. Under contract with the State of California, the District will ultimately receive 2 million acre-feet of water annually.

Next, let's consider the range of water and power capacities studied.

## WATER AND POWER CAPACITIES

The initial scope of the study was to determine the engineering and economic feasibility of a combination power and desalting plant in the size range of 50 to 150 MGD and 150 to 750 Mw of electric power.

However, early in 1965 the District directed Bechtel to place primary emphasis on producing 150 MGD of desalted water for delivery to the Robert B. Diemer Filtration Plant located near Yorba Linda in Orange County.

Moreover, on April 8, 1965, an Electric Utilities group (the Department of Water & Power of the City of Los Angeles, the Southern California Edison Company, and the San Diego Gas & Electric Company) offered to jointly participate in the proposed dual-purpose plant by furnishing, owning, and operating a two-unit nuclear power plant. The nuclear reactor units would have sufficient capacity to supply the power requirements of the District, plus the steam and the power needs of the District. A back-pressure turbine generator and desalting plant would be owned by the District. Adoption of this concept into the study increased the upper limit of power.capacity considered in the study to a total of 1600 Mw.

## PRINCIPAL FACTORS INVESTIGATED

The principal factors investigated in the course of this study are: Site Selection, Island Design, Comparison of Fossil- and Nuclear-Fueled Desalting Plants, Selection of Power Plant Size, Selection of Desalting Process, Combined Plant Concept, Plant Capital Costs, and Cost of Desalted Water. I'll now go over the highlights of each of these factors.

## SITE SELECTION

The availability of suitable sites along the southern California coast is rapidly diminishing. Using items such as nuclear safety, land cost, and cost of conveying desalted water as considerations, 17 sites for the plant were initially investigated. These sites are located in a region extending from the Oxnard area in the north, through Orange County, to San Diego in the south (See Fig. 1).

Because of its location, which is central to a highly populated area, the Robert B. Diemer Filtration Plant (shown on the accompanying map) was selected as the most beneficial point to blend 150 MGD of desalted water into the District system. Consideration was then confined to those 10 sites along the Orange County coast, in view of the necessity for locating the facility close to the Robert B. Diemer Filtration Plant. Based on an investigation of soil conditions, seismic activity, and economic factors, such as cost of land, water conveyance lines and site preparation, two sites were selected as superior for siting a nuclear combination power and desalting plant: A manmade island, named Bolsa Island, located offshore near Bolsa Chica State Beach in Orange County and connected to the mainland by a 2800-foot causeway, and a shore site, referred to as Pelican Point, located in Orange

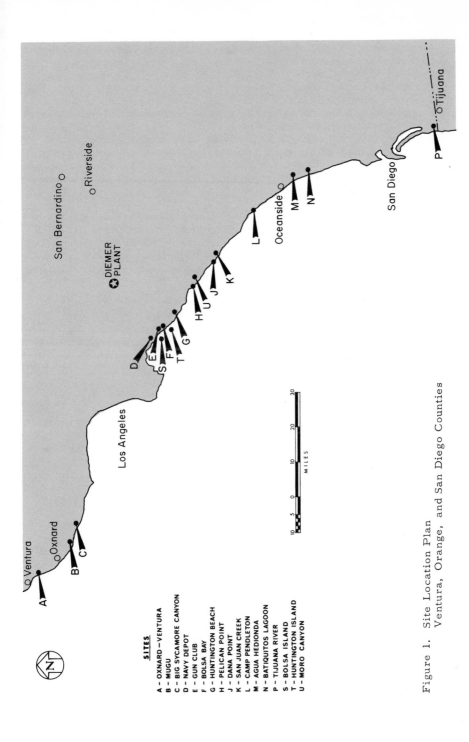

**SITES**

A – OXNARD–VENTURA
B – MUGU
C – BIG SYCAMORE CANYON
D – NAVY DEPOT
E – GUN CLUB
F – BOLSA BAY
G – HUNTINGTON BEACH
H – PELICAN POINT
J – DANA POINT
K – SAN JUAN CREEK
L – CAMP PENDLETON
M – AGUA HEDIONDA
N – BATIQUITOS LAGOON
P – TIJUANA RIVER
S – BOLSA ISLAND
T – HUNTINGTON ISLAND
U – MORO CANYON

Figure 1. Site Location Plan
Ventura, Orange, and San Diego Counties

County on Irvine Company property, adjoining Corona del Mar on the upcoast side and Crystal Cove on the downcoast side.

Detailed engineering analyses were made for each site. In addition, an exploratory drilling program, sonoprobe surveys, and oceanographic investigations were performed to determine the feasibility of the island location. The analyses and investigations are supported by studies by consultants in oceanography, sand transport, marine biology, geology, petroleum geology, aseismic design, soil mechanics, foundations, and coastal engineering, as well as by construction contractors experienced in site excavation and island construction.

Engineering and exploratory studies showed the presence of suitable soil and foundation conditions for the proposed island location, the availability of sufficient borrow material to construct the island, and the absence of active fault lines underlying the proposed location. Acceptable ocean and aseismic criteria were established.

## ISLAND DESIGN

The manmade island is designed to withstand the largest storm wave that can reach close to shore. The island would be constructed with sand fill and with a rock dike around the perimeter. Rock can be brought from quarries on Santa Catalina island and sand can be dredged from the ocean floor. Concrete tribars are being considered for the largest pieces of armor.

These analyses established the technical feasibility of both the Pelican Point and Bolsa Island sites for the location of the dual-purpose nuclear power and desalting facility.

Estimates of the owners' total investment for the dual-purpose plant show that the Bolsa Island site is $7.7 million more favorable than the Pelican Point site. There is an additional saving of $1.9 million for product water conveyance and $0.1 million for pumping and operation and maintenance costs for the water conveyance line in favor of Bolsa Island.

In addition, the Electric Utilities have stated that their capital cost for power transmission to their respective distribution systems from Bolsa Island is at least $20 million more favorable than from Pelican Point. On this basis, the Bolsa Island site is approximately $30 million more favorable than the Pelican Point site.

## COMPARISON OF FOSSIL- AND NUCLEAR-FUELED DESALTING PLANTS

The costs of producing electric power and desalted water in dual-purpose plants using fossil and nuclear fuels have been analyzed and, for the size ranges considered, the nuclear-fueled plants produce the lowest cost desalted water. Based on an annual use of 75 per cent natural gas and 25 per cent fuel oil, at a cost of about 35 cents per million Btu's, desalted water from a fossil-fueled plant would cost 25 per cent more to produce than from a nuclear-fueled plant. The study showed that the price of fossil fuel would have to decrease to 23 cents per million Btu to be competitive with nuclear fuel for desalting.

### SELECTION OF POWER PLANT SIZE

Three dual-purpose plant conceptual designs, providing 150 MGD of desalted water and 100, 750, and 1,600 Mw (net) of power, were considered. Since two products, electric power and water, are involved, the separation of production costs required establishing the value of one of the products. Two power-only concepts were developed to establish reference capital and operating costs for generating power and to allow calculation of the cost of producing water in dual-purpose plants.

The District minimum-power, dual-purpose plant provides for the desalting plant and product water pumping and, in addition, produces 100 Mw for exchange for 800 million kwh per year of power for use by the District in the Colorado River Aqueduct pumping plants. The District maximum-power dual-purpose plant also provides power for the desalting plant and product water pumping, but develops 750 Mw for sale or exchange. The Electric Utilities dual-purpose plant is based on the principles of their proposal and produces 1,500 Mw net for the power companies and 100 Mw for the District. See Table I.

The cost of producing desalted water at the plant were calculated based on economic factors considered appropriate in May 1965, the results are shown in Table II.

TABLE I

Summary of Basic Cases

|  | Water Production MGD | Gross Power Mw | Net Power Mw |
|---|---|---|---|
| District Minimum - Dual Purpose | 150 | 204 | 100 |
| District Maximum - Dual Purpose | 150 | 880 | 750 |
| Electric Utilities - Dual Purpose | 150 | 1800 | 1600 |

TABLE II

Water Costs - May 1965 Basis

| Basic Case | ¢/1,000 Gallons | $ Per Acre-Foot |
|---|---|---|
| District Minimum | 29.8 | 97.1 |
| District Maximum | 23.4 | 76.1 |
| Electric Utilities | 21.4 | 70.0 |

## SELECTION OF DESALTING PROCESS

A fundamental requirement of the desalting plant was that it economically produces 150 MGD of high-quality water, using a process of demonstrated commercial reliability. The process selected as most suitable for the District project was recycle multistage flash distillation.

The conceptual design consists of three parallel 50 MGD trains, based on evaluation of factors, such as scale-up of existing smaller plants and consideration of flexibility, availability, and low cost of water over the plant lifetime. The cost of water was calculated for desalting plants with top brine temperatures between 195 and 250°F. The lowest cost water is produced in a desalting plant having a top brine temperature of 250°F. The flow diagram is shown in Fig. 2 while the principal features are shown in Table III.

## COMBINED PLANT CONCEPT

The dual-purpose plant concept shown in Fig. 3 was investigated sufficiently to establish technical feasibility of combined operation of two nuclear steam supply systems, two condensing and one back-pressure turbine-generator units and the desalting plant during normal operation, startup, shutdown, and emergency conditions.

TABLE III

Features of 150 MGD Multistage Flash
Desalting Plant

| | |
|---|---|
| Total Plant Capacity, MGD | 150 |
| Number of Heat Recovery stages | 49 |
| Number of Heat Rejection stages | 4 |
| Total Number of Stages | 53 |
| Maximum Brine Heater Temperature, deg. F. | 250 |
| Performance Ratio, lb. product water/1000 Btu steam | 10.6 |
| Evaporator Condensing Area, sq. ft. | 10,500,000 |
| Brine Heater Area, sq. ft. | 680,000 |
| Sea Water Flow, gpm | 532,000 |
| Recycle Brine Flow, gpm | 690,000 |

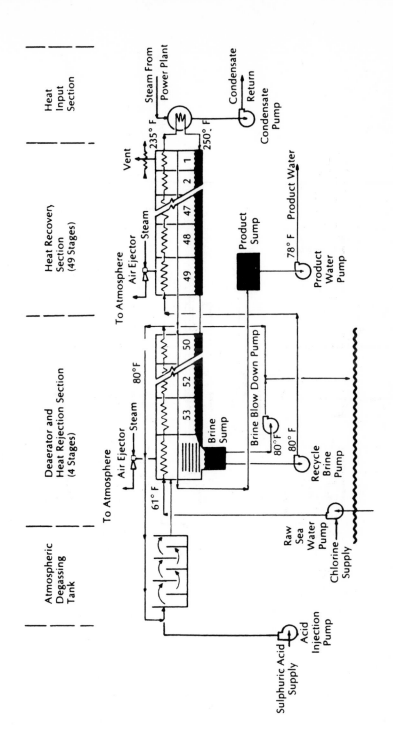

Figure 2.  Desalting Plant Flow Diagram

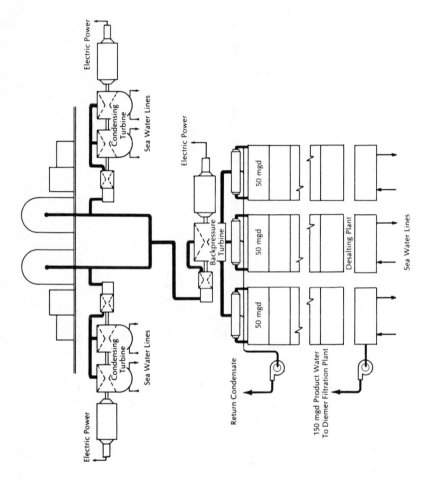

Figure 3.  Dual-Purpose Plant Concept

The dual-purpose plant concept includes (in addition to the 150 MGD multistage flash desalting plant) two reactors, each rated at approximately 3, 000 thermal MWt; one non-condensing turbine, rated at approximately 375 Mw supplying the necessary steam for the desalting plant; and two large condensing turbines rated at approximately 700 Mw each. Total power production would be sufficient to furnish the District with 100 Mw of exchange power for Colorado River aqueduct pumping and the Electric Utilities with their desired 1, 500 Mw.

In addition, a power-only plant, with a net capacity of approximately 1, 500 Mw, was developed for the purpose of establishing a basis for allocation of dual-purpose plant capital costs between the Electric Utilities and the District at each site. A third dual-purpose plant design was developed for comparing the features of the boiling water reactor (BWR) and pressurized water reactor (PWR) nuclear steam supply systems.

## PLANT CAPITAL COSTS

Capital costs (construction and land costs) were estimated for the dual-purpose nuclear power and desalting plant and for the corresponding power-only plant. All estimated costs are based on October 1965 wage and price levels. The difference between these capital cost estimates (before addition of owner's distributable costs) for each site is allocated to the District in accordance with principles of the Electric Utilities proposal. Table IV shows the development of the allocation of capital costs to the District of $133, 100, 000 at Bolsa Island.

Suitable distributable costs to cover the costs of interest during construction, client's engineering and spare parts are added to obtain the total investment required by the Owners as shown in Table V.

TABLE IV

Capital Cost Summary - 1965 Basis
(Millions of Dollars)

|  | Power-Only | Dual-Purpose |
|---|---|---|
| Desalting Plant | $    - | $   94. 0 |
| Power Plant and Other Facilities | 172. 0 | 206. 1 |
| Island and Causeway | 15. 7 | 20. 7 |
| Land and Land Rights | 0. 4 | 0. 4 |
| TOTAL | $ 188. 1 | $ 321. 2 |
| MWD Capital Costs (By Difference) |  | $ 133. 1 |

TABLE V

Total Plant Investment - 1965 Basis
(Millions of Dollars)

| | Bolsa Island | |
| | Power-Only | Dual-Purpose |
|---|---|---|
| Water Production, MGD | - | 150 |
| Power Production, Mw | 1529 | 1629 |
| MWD Investment | $   - | $  144.3 |
| Electric Utilities Investment | 213.7 | 213.1 |
| TOTAL INVESTMENT* | $ 213.7 | $  357.4 |

*Not including product water conveyance or electrical transmission costs.

TABLE VI

| | ¢/1000 Gal. | $/Acre-Foot |
|---|---|---|
| At Desalting Plant | 21.9 | 71.4 |
| Delivered to Diemer | 27.0 | 88.0 |

## COST OF DESALTED WATER

The calculated cost of water to the District was based on the District's dollar investment and the appropriate annual fixed charges, operating and maintenance costs for both the desalting plant and the power plant, desalting plant sulfuric acid costs, nuclear insurance costs, and fuel costs, less credit for the 100 Mw of District power. The resulting average cost of desalted water at the Bolsa Island plant and delivered to the Robert B. Diemer Filtration Plant are shown in Table VI.

The cost of product water to the District over the assumed life in the plant has been calculated and is shown in Fig. 4.

## CONCLUSIONS

The principal conclusions resulting from the work performed in this study are:

— A combination nuclear power and desalting plant to produce 150 MGD of desalted water is technically feasible for operation in 1971.

— A manmade island, shown in Fig. 5, located offshore of the Bolsa Chica State Beach is an acceptable and practicable site for the plant. In addition, the island site offers a lower overall project cost to the participants of approximately $30 million less than the Pelican Point site.

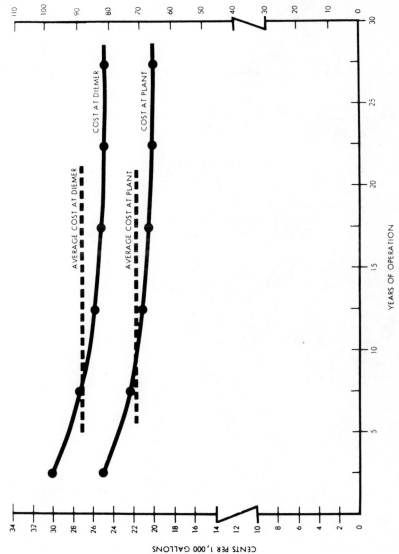

Figure 4.  30-Year Cost of Product Water

Figure 5.  Bolsa Island Dual-Purpose Plant

— The total investment in the proposed dual-purpose plant is $357,400,000 of which $144,300,000 would be District's costs and $213,100,000 the Electric Utilities costs based upon the principles for joint participation offered by the Electric Utilities. In addition, the District's cost for the product water conveyance facilities from the island site to the Diemer Filtration Plant is estimated at $33,500,000.

— The estimated cost of producing desalted water at the island site if 21.9 cents per thousand gallons ($71 per acre-foot) and 27.0 cents per thousand gallons ($88 per acre-foot) delivered to the Diemer Filtration Plant.

— The plant concept based on the Electric Utilities proposal results in the lowest cost desalted water and minimum capital investment to the District and should be pursued.

I would like to clarify a few points that have been raised previously:

1. First and foremost, the study was founded on the specific requirements and conditions existing in southern California, and in particular, the written proposal by the electric power companies. By owning and operating the major power units, the traditional functions of the power companies are maintained. Moreover, MWD is relieved of the need to market power, an enterprise that they are not interested or particularly qualified to perform.

2. The cost of money to MWD of 3.5 per cent was not used on the entire plant, only the MWD investment. In fact, the power companies' investment does not enter into the equation for calculating the cost of water.

3. Even if a higher figure were used for the value of money, it would only improve the position of desalting when compared with the investment in an alternate importation scheme. This is because the capital investment is only about 50 per cent of the cost of desalted water, whereas the capital investment in any importing system is much higher than 50 per cent.

4. Does the demonstration of desalting need to proceed at this time? Yes. Additional supplies of water are required by 1990. Since 12-15 years are required to properly plan, engineer and construct a major aqueduct system, there would be only five or so years of desalting plant operation available by the time a decision on an importation system must be made by the late 1970's.

The initial cost of the desalting plant is only some 2 per cent of the investment which will probably be required by 1990 for water supplied beyond the California State Aqueduct Project now under construction. This 2 per cent might be considered to be a small insurance premium in order to assure a thorough examination of desalting.

5. Moreover, demonstration on the MWD system will permit perfection of MWD corporate management approach to desalting, and of the cooperative arrangements with the public and private power companies, as well as engineering and operating experience on the MWD system.

Such action by leaders in a particular field were previously demonstrated at Dresden and at Yankee, where the construction of nuclear power plants at an early date have contributed heavily to the present healthy state of the nuclear power business.

6. A question was raised concerning the value for the 100 Mw of exchange power at 4.0 mills. MWD is now paying 5-1/8 mills for this power. When the desalting plant is operating, this expense will cease and a suitable worth should be assigned, and MWD selected 4.0 mills. It is not really a major point anyway since even if only 2 mills were assigned to this worth, the calculated cost of water would only rise 3¢/1,000 gallons or less than 15 per cent.

In conclusion, I believe that the study was well founded and properly placed principal efforts on the questions of engineering design and siting of the plant.

# 27. The Texcoco Project

Carlos Graef Fernandez, Director, The Nuclear Center of Mexico

This paper deals with the water problems of Mexico City and with the possibility of solving them with the help of a nuclear reactor.

1. Mexico City has so much water in the rainy season, that the principal preoccupation of the city authorities is to drain all possible water into the sea.

2. Mexico City has such a tremendous scarcity of water in the dry season that this situation has stopped the city from growing and has also stopped industrial development.

3. Mexico City is 7,000 feet above sea level; a fact which at once limits the water supply to the few sources which lie above this tremendous height, or which imposes heavy costs for pumping on water which comes from lower altitudes.

4. Mexico City is drinking its own foundation, with the terrible consequence that it is sinking at a rate of one foot a year. This sinking causes breaking of the water supply lines, and of the sewage pipes; and also causes cracking of the buildings.

How can a nuclear reactor help to solve these problems?

## THE PROBLEM

In the beginning of the sixteenth century the Spaniards conquered Mexico. In 1519 they climbed from the Gulf coast to the Valley of Mexico where they had a most magnificent view from the high mountains. They saw a lake covering 800 square miles, in a high plateau surrounded by mountains; two of which were covered with snow. In the middle of this lake was Mexico City. The city was built on artificial islands in the very shallow lake. Broad canals crossed the town which was one of the most populous in the world; certainly larger than Madrid. Two high stone pyramids rose at the center of the city. At their tops were two fabulous temples: one devoted to the rain god and the other to the war god. On the shores of the lake were several large cities and villages On the northeast shore was the city of Texcoco.

The lake was drained in later centuries.  It had existed for millions of years--since the formation of the volcanoes which enclose the Valley of Mexico.  During these millions of years, the volcanoes threw an incredible mass of volcanic ash and lava into the lake.

A deep well drilled in the Valley of Mexico to a depth of 3,937 feet passes through lake deposits of volcanic ash converted into clay, through lake deposits of gravel and sand carried by rivers into the lake;  it also passes through two lava flows of basalt.  This well, which is the deepest drilled in the Valley until now, does not reach the limestone which underlies certainly most of the lake deposits.

In the geological past the lake was divided into several independent basins by small mountain chains rising in its midst.  At the dawn of history, the lake deposits had erased these divisions. When the Spaniards first saw the lake, the only division which existed was artificial.  The lake was divided in two by a dam designed by Netzahualcoyotl, the Emperor of Texcoco, in the middle of the fifteenth century.

The Valley of Mexico is a high plateau surrounded on all sides by mountains of volcanic origin.  The high plateau is formed by the filled-up basins of the old lake.  Geologists have identified seven separate basins.  The total area of this high plateau is 3,143 square miles.

Modern Mexico City is a town of six-million inhabitants built on the same place as the ancient Indian city.  It lies on the top of one of the marginal basins of the old lake.  The Mexico City basin is the southwest corner of the high plateau.  Its area is 280 square miles, which is 9 per cent of the total area of the Valley.

The water supply for Mexico City comes from five sources. Note that more than one-third of the water comes from 2,000 wells which extract water from underneath the city itself (Figure 1).

The clay which lies under Mexico City is very peculiar.  It was formed by the decomposition of volcanic ash deposited in the old lake.  The void ratio of this clay is $c=7:1$, which means that this material contains one part of solids and seven parts of water by volume.  This clay is, in fact, "reinforced water."  It is a very rich source of water, which in the Mexico City basin happens to be fresh water.  This clay is a wet sponge from which water can be pumped out easily.  In 1936 the intense pumping of this clay started.  Figure 2 shows the proportion of water extracted from below the city compared with the amount of water supplied by other sources.  The explosive growth of the population of the city, also shown in Figure 2, is the reason why the intense pumping had to be so intense.

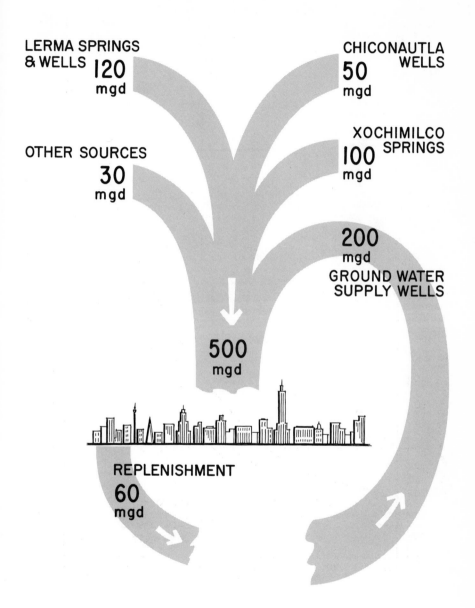

Figure 1.  Mexico City Water Supply

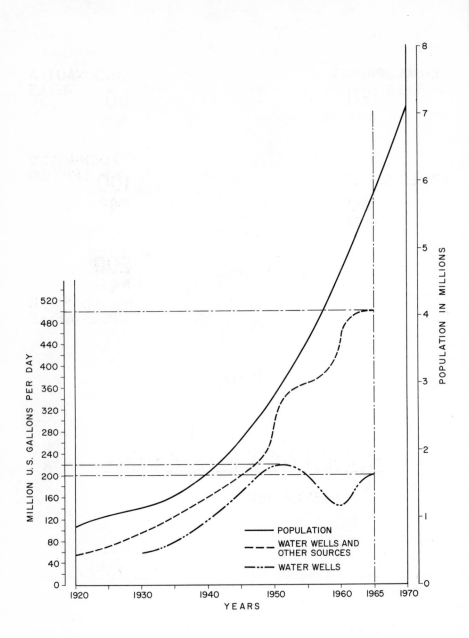

Figure 2.  Mexico City - Population and Water Supply Growth

Because the City of Mexico is 7,000 feet above sea level it is very difficult to find adequate water sources. In the year 1953 a tunnel was finished. This tunnel brings water to the city across the mountains from the high plateau of Toluca, which is even higher than the high plateau of Mexico. All important water sources which lie higher than Mexico City have now been exhausted.

The consequences of squeezing water out of the clay sponge have been fatal to Mexico City. The clay contracts as it loses its water content and causes the sinking of the city, which in some areas has reached the enormous figure of one foot per year. Because the sinking is not uniform, it causes breaking of the water supply lines and the sewage pipes. Some parts of the city are built on the hills bordering the basin and do not participate in the sinking. The sinking is slower in the parts of the basin nearest to the hills.

Mexico City's very fast rate of subsidance poses a very difficult problem for designing foundations for tall buildings. Several solutions have been tried. One of them consists of floating the building. A block of soil is removed which has the same weight as the building which is being placed on that site. The building is set on a concrete box which floats in the mud. This extremely expensive method sounds very nice in theory, but one would have to be able to remove in one instant a hugh block of clay, and in the next instant one would have to substitute it by the concrete box. But the excavation takes time and irreversible changes take place in the clay.

Another cheaper method has been used extensively, and this is setting the buildings on piles. At a depth of about 130 feet a layer of sand interrupts the clay deposits. This sand layer exists everywhere beneath the flat part of the city. To build the foundation of a building, piles are driven down to this layer. Such piles can support buildings as tall as one wants. The piles do not prevent the contraction of the clay. Buildings on piles come out of the soil and increase in height. The same happens to well casings. The piles have to be calculated to stand the combined weight of both building and soil.

The Department of Hydrology of Mexico City (Gobierno del Distrito Federal) has calculated the cost of the sinking of the city at approximately 50-million dollars a year to repair the freshwater and sewage systems, and the public buildings. This figure does not include the damage caused to private buildings by the sinking.

The cost of the water which we extract from the subsoil of Mexico City is the most expensive in the world. To the normal cost of pumping and of distributing one has to add 75 cents (U.S.) per thousand gallons.

Since before Spanish colonial times Mexico City has had the problem of flooding.  To protect the city from floods there are now two tunnels and one cut which drain the Valley of Mexico into the Tula River, and from thence into the Panuco River--and finally into the Gulf of Mexico.  During the months from May to September, the rainy season, the amount of water which falls on the Valley is considerable.  In the southern part of the Valley the average rainfall is of 28 inches a year; in the northern part, 20 inches a year.  The amount of rainwater pouring on the Valley during the showers of the rainy season is quite large.  The two tunnels and the cut are taxed to the limit of their capacities to carry this excess water to the ocean.

The possibility of floods has increased very much with the sinking of the city.  The city is now 30 feet below the level of the bottom of the Texcoco Lake.  The sewage canal which carries the sewage from Mexico City to the tunnels and then into the Tula River, is built on the bottom of the old Texcoco Lake.  The sinking of Mexico City has lowered the sewage-level pipe so that sewage no longer flows by gravity into the sewage canal: it must be pumped up into it.

In the conditions which prevail today there is no possible place for safe water storage in the Valley of Mexico.  Mexico City occupies now the lowest levels in the high plateau.  Storing water in the Valley at any level higher than the City would seriously increase the danger of floods in the city.

### THE SOLUTION

The basin on which Mexico City is built is bordered by mountains on the south and west.  On the north and on the east it is bordered by the basin of the old lake of Texcoco.  This Texcoco basin has an area of 450 (442.5) square miles or 14 per cent of the total area of the Valley.  The Texcoco Lake was a salt lake long before the Spaniards conquered Mexico.  In 1465 the Emperor of Texcoco, Netzahualcoyotl, and the Emperor of Mexico, Montezuma the first, ordered a dam built to separate the salt water of Lake Texcoco from the fresh water of the Lake of Mexico City.  The purpose of this dam was to protect Mexico City from the floods.  This problem is thus 500 years old.

During Spanish colonial times a solution of the problem of floods was attempted by draining the Valley of Mexico into the ocean.  In 1608 a tunnel was finished in Huehuetoca in the north of the Valley; this tunnel drained the high plateau into the Tula River and from there into the Panuco River and finally into the Gulf of Mexico.  The tunnel lasted only 20 years.

In 1709 the cut of Nochistongo, which is still working, was finished.  Since that time the Texcoco Lake became a series of very shallow ponds.

The area of the basin of the old Texcoco Lake, being 442.5 square miles in size, is far larger than the area of the basin of Mexico City which has an extension of 280 square miles. The Texcoco basin is thus larger in area by 60 per cent. The distance of the geographical centers of the two basins is 20 miles. These two basins are probably hydrologically disconnected. In the Texcoco basin there is a water layer at the depth of approximately 100 feet which has a content of dissolved solids of 140,000 parts per million, or four times the salinity of ocean water. The salts of Lake Texcoco are Sodium Carbonate and Sodium Chloride in equal amounts with traces of Lithium and Boron salts. Almost no Calcium is present. A company called "Sosa Texcoco" which is partially state-owned, exploits this water layer to produce soda ash and caustic soda. Underneath Mexico City there is no water layer which is salty or even brackish. (Figure 3.)

The surface water in the Texcoco Lake and the water permeating the clay at depths up to 250 feet have the same composition as that of the water layer of 100 feet. At greater depths the salinity diminishes rapidly. At 300 feet the water is brackish with 2,000 parts of dissolved solids per million. At about 600 feet the salinity is 500 parts per million.

The structure of the clay of the Texcoco basin is even more astonishing than that of the Mexico City basin. In Texcoco the clay has a void ratio of 16:1, an incredibly high water content.

The company "Sosa Texcoco" has about 200 wells scattered over an area of 6,000 extracting water from the water layer of 100 feet depth at a rate of 7.6-million gallons a day. In the last six years the area has sunk at a rate of 1 foot 8 inches per year.

In the Texcoco Basin we have thus a clay with a much higher water content than in Mexico's basin and with a far greater total volume. Why not extract water from the clay of the Texcoco basin and pump it to Mexico City?

The reason why nobody had thought of doing this is the very large salinity of the uppermost water layers in Texcoco. Dr. Nabor Carrillo, First Commissioner of the Mexican National Nuclear Energy Commission, was the first who seriously considered this problem. It may be that his double training, as an expert in both soil mechanics and nuclear energy, was responsible for inspiring such ideas. He was able to envisage the following solution:

1. Extract water from the subsoil of Texcoco in larger quantities than are now being extracted from the subsoil of Mexico City. Thus, more than 180 MGD must be pumped out of the clay of Texcoco.

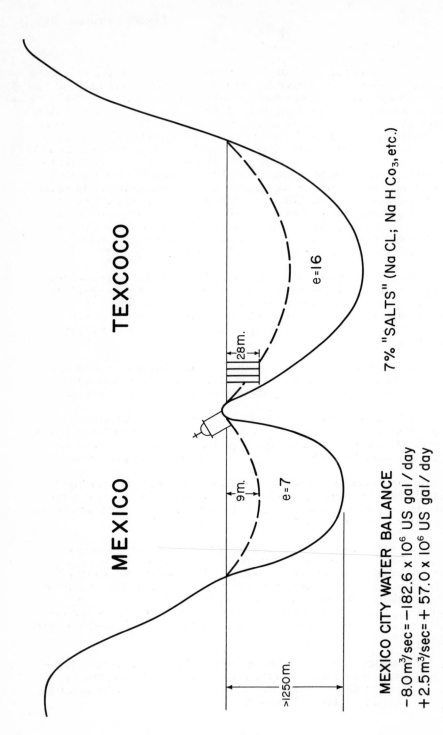

MEXICO    TEXCOCO

9m.    e=7    28m.    e=16

>1250m.

**MEXICO CITY WATER BALANCE**

−8.0m³/sec = −182.6 x 10⁶ US gal / day
+2.5m³/sec = + 57.0 x 10⁶ US gal / day

7% "SALTS" (Na CL; Na H Co₃, etc.)

Figure 3.   Hydrology of Mexico-Texcoco Basins

2. Desalinate this water with the help of a nuclear reactor linked with a multiple-stage flash-evaporator plant.

3. Send this distilled water to Mexico City.

4. Stop extracting water from the subsoil of the City.

The consequences of this would be:

1. Mexico City would stop sinking.

2. Mexico City could continue its natural growth and its industrial development with the availability of larger amounts of water.

3. The bottom of the old Texcoco Lake would sink at a faster rate than that at which Mexico City is sinking now.

As soon as the bottom of the old Texcoco Lake reaches an altitude lower than that of Mexico City, it can be used as a water reservoir for storing the excess water which occurs in the Valley during the rainy season. Instead of draining all the excess water in the rainy season into the ocean, this water could be stored in the Valley for use in the dry season.

If this could be carried out there would be several added advantages. Today the Texcoco Lake dries out almost completely during the dry season. Its surface is the source of dust storms which affect Mexico City every year. The dry bottom surface of the old Lake behaves like a desert, becoming enormously hot.

Whirlwinds originate which raise great quantities of dust into the atmosphere. When the wind blows west or southwest, this dust is blown into the City as a dust storm. Unfortunately these occur several times a year. Sometimes these dust storms are so bad that they completely stop the traffic in downtown Mexico. They are the cause of many diseases of the respiratory system of the inhabitants of our capital.

Rebuilding Lake Texcoco would make these dust storms disappear. Besides that, the area would gain by being enormously beautified by a large lake.

Dr. Nabor Carrillo has explored the possibility of hastening the formation of a lake. With the collaboration of Professors Arthur and Leo Casagrande from Harvard University, he has considered starting the construction of a reservoir immediately.

The void ratio of 16:1 of the clay adds greatly to the feasibility of this project. Explosions can liquify the clay which could be pumped away as liquid. Besides explosives, ultrasonics or electro-osmosis can also be used.

The role of the nuclear reactor in this project is as a source of power for desalination.  The nuclear reactor can thus help to give water to a thirsty city and help to stop the sinking of a city otherwise doomed to collapse.  It can help to stop the dust storms and it will contribute so to the better health of the six-million inhabitants of Mexico City.  It will also help to beautify the surroundings of this city and to humidify its atmosphere.  One can hardly imagine how one can use a reactor to serve more noble purposes.

## THE REALIZATION

The Mexican Government has seen the beauty of the nuclear solution to the water problems of Mexico City.  It has approved a budget to make a feasibility study.

A very capable and experienced civil engineer, Roberto Graue, has been appointed head of the Texcoco Project.  Graue has ordered several wells drilled to find out if the Texcoco basin is really hydrologically independent of the basin of Mexico City. Other wells are being drilled to explore the water layers, to analyze their composition, and to determine the depth of the lake deposits.  Graue is performing tests to find out if the upper layers of clay can be liquified by explosions or by other methods.

In the near future we hope to see the recreation of beautiful Lake Texcoco in its old location.

## REGISTRANTS

R. W. Akerlow, Manager
Special Projects Division
Stearns-Roger Corp.
Denver, Colorado

M. B. Andrew
California Department of
Water Resources
Sacramento, California

Louis V. Avioli, M. D.
New Jersey College of
Medicine
Jersey City, New Jersey

Bruce L. Bailey
Great Lakes Carbon Corp.
Niagara Falls, New York

A. H. F. Barlow
Combustion Engineering,
Inc.
Los Angeles, California

Walter L. Barnes, Jr.
Office of Saline Water
U. S. Department of the
Interior
Wrightsville Beach,
North Carolina

Edward J. Barnett
Massachusetts Institute
of Technology
Nuclear Engineering Dept.
Cambridge, Mass.

Bob Barnhill
Johns-Manville Corp.
Tucson, Arizona

Philip M. Altomarc
NUS Corporation
Los Alamos, New Mexico

Alfred T. Barr
Arizona Power Authority
Tucson, Arizona

Dr. G. V. Beard
A. R. M. U.
Salt Lake City, Utah

Louis G. Boli
Salt River Project
Phoenix, Arizona

John F. Bregar
Arizona State University
Mechanical Engineering
Department
Tempe, Arizona

R. M. Buckwalter
California Department of
Water Resources
Sacramento, California

Elton H. Buell
Arizona Public Service
Company
Phoenix, Arizona

Horace E. Burrier
Southern California
Edison Company
Los Angeles, California

William F. Campbell
UCC - Stellite Division
Kokomo, Indiana

Dr. Nabor Carillo Flores
National Commission of
Nuclear Energy
Mexico, DF

L. K. Cecil
A. I. Ch. E.
Tucson, Arizona

John Cera
Acting Director
Division of Nuclear
Education and Training
U. S. Atomic Energy
Commission
Washington, D. C.

Conard W. Christenson
Los Alamos Scientific
Laboratory
Los Alamos, New Mexico

R. W. Clack
Assistant Professor
Department of Nuclear
Engineering
Kansas State University
Manhattan, Kansas

Richard L. Clark
Scientific Development
Department
Bechtel Corporation
San Francisco, California

Mel Coltharp
Abilene, Texas

Wilfred H. Comtois
Atomic Power Division
Westinghouse Electric
Corporation
Pittsburgh, Pennsylvania

Robert W. Condon
The Boeing Company
Seattle, Washington

Agustin Cortes
Puerto Penasco, Sonora
Mexico

F. E Crever
General Electric Co.
San Jose, California

Paul Cullom
Scottsdale, Arizona

J. K. Cummings
California Department of
Water Resources
Sacramento, California

M. D. Curran
Panhandle Eastern Pipe
Line Company
Garden City, Kansas

P. B. Daitch
Rensselaer Polytechnic
Institute
Troy, New York

Roger F. Detman
C. F. Braun & Company
Alhambra, California

Dr. Richard L. Doan
U. S Atomic Energy
Commission
Washington, D. C.

W. J. Dowis
Richland, Washington

Professor H. E. Dregne
Department of Agronomy
New Mexico State Univ.
University Park
New Mexico

H. R. Drew
Texas Atomic Energy
Research Foundation
Fort Worth, Texas

Jim Dunn
Chicago Bridge & Iron Co.
Oak Brook, Illinois

Richard F. Durning
Salt River Project
Phoenix, Arizona

Mark R. Dusbabek
Fluor Corporation
Los Angeles, California

Octave J. Du Temple
Executive Secretary
American Nuclear Society
Hinsdale, Illinois

Richard B. Egan
University of Colorado
College of Engineering
Engineering Center
Boulder, Colorado

Professor M. El-Wakil
Department of Mechanical
Engineering
University of Wisconsin
Madison, Wisconsin

R. E. Faw
Assistant Professor
Department of Nuclear
Engineering
Kansas State University
Manhattan, Kansas

Joseph W. Ferraro
Board of Public Utility
Commissioners
Dept. of Public Utilities
State of New Jersey
Newark, New Jersey

William C. Finch
Shell Oil Company
Houston, Texas

E. D. Frankhouser
U. S. Army
West Point, New York

Dr. Stephen Gage
The University of Texas
Nuclear Engineering
Program
Austin, Texas

Paul Gast
Laboratory Director's
Office
Argonne National
Laboratory
Argonne, Illinois

Roy E. Gaunt, Manager
Water Province Dept.
Westinghouse Electric
Corporation
Philadelphia, Penn.

John G. Gaydos
Baldwin Lima Hamilton
Corporation
Philadelphia, Penn.

K. R. Geiser
General Electric Company
Phoenix, Arizona

Angelo Giambusso
Desalting Branch
Division of Reactor
Development and
Technology
U. S. Atomic Energy
Commission
Washington, D. C.

Wilfred C. Gilbert
Arizona State Department
of Health
Phoenix, Arizona

Simcha Golan
Technical Specialist
Atomics International
Division of North
American Aviation Inc.
Canoga Park, California

Lionel S. Goldring
American Machine &
Foundry Company
Springdale, Connecticut

Dr. Carlos G. Fernandez
Director
Mexico's Nuclear Center
National Commission of
Nuclear Energy
Mexico, D. F.

Donald V. Graf
Engineering Joint Venture
HWOCR Program Office
Atomics International
Canoga Park, California

John J. Grebe
Consultant
Sun City, Arizona

Dr. Louis Groven
Scientific Counselor
Belgian Embassy
Washington, D. C.

Dr. Reuben H. Gustavson
Department of Chemistry
The University of Arizona
Tucson, Arizona

Roy C. Hageman
U. S. Atomic Energy
Commission
Oak Brook, Illinois

Dr. Philip Hammond,
Director
Nuclear Desalination
Program
National Laboratory
Oak Ridge, Tennessee

James E. Hard
U. S. A. E. C.
Naperville, Illinois

L. G. Hauser
Westinghouse Electric
Corporation
Cheswick, Pennsylvania

L. J. Harris
Chicago Bridge & Iron Co.
Pasadena, California

Thomas A. Hoffman
General Electric
Santa Barbara, California

Kenneth Holum
Assistant Secretary
U. S. Department of the
Interior
Washington, D. C.

Everett D. Howe
University of California
at Berkeley
Orinda, California

Kenneth A. Hub
Argonne National
Laboratory
La Grange, Illinois

Max E. Jackson
U. S. Atomic Energy
Commission
Argonne, Illinois

A. R. Jones
Westinghouse Electric
Corporation
Pittsburgh, Pennsylvania

A. Karel
Westinghouse
International
New York, New York

David D. Kays
Project Engineer
Freeport Demonstration
Plant
The Stearns-Roger Corp.
Denver, Colorado

P. R. Keep
North American Aviation,
Inc.
El Segundo, California

Roland P. Kelly
The Ralph M. Parsons Co.
Los Angeles, California

Geoffrey B. Keyes
Westinghouse Electric
Corporation
Pittsburgh, Pennsylvania

William R. Kimel
Kansas State University
Department of Nuclear
  Engineering
Manhattan, Kansas

Thomas A. Kirkham
Vice President
Equipment Division
Ionics, Incorporated
Watertown, Mass.

Ernest D. Klema
Northwestern University
Willmette, Illinois

Donald F. Koch
Executive Director
Office of Nuclear Energy
  Development
State of Washington
Olympia, Washington

H. R. Kosmata
Douglas United Nuclear
Richland, Washington

W. M. Leaders
Kerr-McGee Corporation
Oklahoma City, Oklahoma

Henry H. Leigh
Phoenix, Arizona

Harry Leon
General Atomics
San Diego, California

James E. MacDonaugh
Bechtel Corporation
Los Angeles, California

William X. Madden
California Department of
  Water Resources
South Pasadena
California

J. E. Maiden
Bechtel Corporation
San Francisco, California

Marvin M. Mann
U. S. A. E. C.
Washington, D. C.

Edward Martin
Federal Water Pollution
  Control Administration
Washington, D. C.

John T. McChesney
Phoenix, Arizona

J. W. McCutchan
U. C. L. A.
Department of
  Engineering
Los Angeles, California

W. F. McIlhenny
Dow Chemical Company
Texas Division
Freeport, Texas

Charles F. Meyer
General Electric Tempo
1141 Cima Linda Lane
Santa Barbara, California

W. Meyer
Department of Nuclear
  Engineering
Kansas State University
Manhattan, Kansas

J. O. Mingle
Department of Nuclear
  Engineering
Kansas State University
Manhattan, Kansas

Professor J. W. Milliman
School of Business
  Administration
University of Indiana
Bloomington, Indiana

Robert B. Minogue
Saline Water Project
General Atomic
Division of General
  Dynamics Corporation
San Diego, California

Clifford K. Monzeglio
Struthers Scientific and
  International Corp.
Canoga Park, California

Philip Mullenbach
Growth Industry Shares
  Incorporated
Chicago, Illinois

E. G. Nielsen
Arizona Power Authority
Phoenix, Arizona

Robert Y. Nelson
Department of Civil
  Engineering
University of Oklahoma
Norman, Oklahoma

H. M. Parker
Staff Consultant
Pacific Northwest
  Laboratories
Richland, Washington

Carlos E. Pena
Universidad de Sonora
Hermosillo, Mexico

Frank K. Pittman
Special Assistant to the
  Vice President
Market Planning
North American
  Aviation, Inc.
El Segundo, California

Hubert R. Platz
Kaiser Engineers
Oakland, California

Joseph L. Plum
Westinghouse Astro-
  nuclear Laboratory
Las Vegas, Nevada

Charles M. Poll
The Ralph M. Parsons Co.
Los Angeles, California

C. Spence Purnell
Westinghouse Electric
  Corporation
Los Angeles, California

A. C. Rand
Assistant Vice President
Marsh & McLennan, Inc.
New York, New York

H. M. Randall
Houston, Texas

Charles Robbins
Executive Manager
Atomic Industrial Forum
New York, New York

C. G. Root
The Kuljian Corporation
Philadelphia, Penn.

David Rose
General Atomic
San Diego, California

Raimundo F. Sales
Aldeota Fortaleza
Ceara, Brazil

Victor A. Salkind
Consulting Engineer
New York, New York

Dr. Frederick G. Sawyer
Pasadena, California

Lou Scheffer
The Ralph M. Parsons Co.
Los Angeles, California

C. M Schillmoller
International Nickel Co.
Los Angeles, California

Vinicio Serment
Comision Nacional de
Energia Nuclear
Mexico, D. F.

Dr. Ronald G. Sowden
UKAEA Liaison Office
British Embassy
Washington, D. C.

James I. Stevens
INFILCO
General American
Transportation Corp.
Tucson, Arizona

Ray L. Stoker
Consulting Engineer
Pittsburgh, Pennsylvania

Glen Steiger
Fluor Corporation
Los Angeles, California

Sidney M. Stoller
S. M. Stoller Associates
New York, New York

Dr. Charles L. Storrs,
Director
HWOCR Program Office
Atomics International
Combustion Engineering
Canoga Park, California

David A. Sundberg, Ed.
Nuclear News
Hinsdale, Illinois

J. B. Thomas
Fort Worth, Texas

Wayne H. Traffas
Gilbert Associates, Inc.
Reading, Pennsylvania

Edward R. Trapnell
The Ralph M. Parsons Co.
Washington, D. C.

Prof. Frank J. Trelease
Dean, College of Law
University of Wyoming
Laramie, Wyoming

William M. Trenholme,
Director
Arizona Atomic Energy
Commission
Phoenix, Arizona

Robert E. Uhrig
University of Florida
Gainesville, Florida

Stan Unitt
Fluor Corporation, Ltd.
Los Angeles, California

Oscar E. Uusima
Gibbs & Hill, Inc.
New York, New York

William R. Walker, Dir.
Water Resources
Research Center
Virginia Polytechnic Inst.
Blacksburg, Virginia

George E. Wearn
Westinghouse
International Co.
New York, New York

Glenn A. Whan
Department of Nuclear
Engineering
University of New Mexico
Albuquerque, New Mexico

William H. Wheeler
Wheeler, Petterson &
Coffeen, Engineers
Tucson, Arizona

J. V. Whipp
C. F. Braun & Company
McLean, Virginia

George White
General Manager
Atomic Power Equipment
Department
General Electric Co.
San Jose, California

W. T. Willey
Arizona Power Authority
Phoenix, Arizona

J. R. Wilson
Professional Engineer
Kaiser Engineers
Oakland, California

William H. Wilson
Bechtel Corporation
Los Angeles, California

Edward C. Wood
Stanford Research Inst.
Portola Valley, Calif.

J. P. Wright
Douglas Aircraft Co., Inc.
Santa Monica, California

J. Louis York
University of Michigan
Department of Chemical
and Metallurgical
Engineering
Ann Arbor, Michigan

Harry Weingarten
Westinghouse Electric
Corporation
Los Angeles, California